The Open University

MS325 Computer algebra, chaos and simulations

Block B

Chaos and modern dynamics

About this course

MS325 Computer algebra, chaos and simulations uses the software package *Maple*™ (copyright Maplesoft™, a division of Waterloo Maple Inc, 2007) which is provided as part of the course. Maple is a computer-assisted algebra package and its usage is the main subject of *Block A Computer algebra*. Advice on such matters as the installation of Maple, the loading and saving of Maple worksheets and other basic 'getting-started' issues is covered in the *Computing Guide*.

Maplesoft™ and Maple™ are trademarks of Waterloo Maple Inc. All other trademarks are the property of their respective owners.

The cover image is composed of a photograph of the Saturnian moon Hyperion (courtesy of NASA) overlaid with a time-T map (in yellow). The view of Hyperion was taken during the close flyby of the spacecraft Cassini on 26 September 2005. Time-T maps are covered in *Block B Chaos and modern dynamics*. This one shows Hyperion's spin rate plotted against its orientation and was generated using Maple from a mathematical model. Regions containing an apparently random scatter of dots indicate chaotic motion in Hyperion's spin angle, the so-called chaotic tumbling.

This publication forms part of an Open University course. Details of this and other Open University courses can be obtained from the Student Registration and Enquiry Service, The Open University, PO Box 197, Milton Keynes, MK7 6BJ, United Kingdom: tel. +44 (0)870 300 6090, e-mail general-enquiries@open.ac.uk

Alternatively, you may visit the Open University website at http://www.open.ac.uk where you can learn more about the wide range of courses and packs offered at all levels by The Open University.

To purchase a selection of Open University course materials, visit http://www.ouw.co.uk, or contact Open University Worldwide, Michael Young Building, Walton Hall, Milton Keynes, MK7 6AA, United Kingdom, for a brochure: tel. +44 (0)1908 858793, fax +44 (0)1908 858787, e-mail ouw-customer-services@open.ac.uk

The Open University, Walton Hall, Milton Keynes, MK7 6AA.

First published 2008.

Edited, designed and typeset by The Open University, using the Open University TEX System.

Printed and bound in the United Kingdom by Hobbs the Printers Limited, Brunel Road, Totton, Hampshire SO40 3WX.

ISBN 978 0 7492 1587 3

1.1

Contents

UNIT 1   Introduction to dynamical systems

Study guide

The main purpose of Section 1.1 is to introduce some basic concepts, so it is relatively short. It contains relatively few exercises.

The purpose of Section 1.2 is to provide introductory background material and historical context. It is also relatively light on exercises, although, as always, you are encouraged to work through them. It should be possible to read through this section quite quickly, depending on your interest in the wider aspects of the subject.

You will probably find that the main workload in this unit is concentrated in Sections 1.3 and 1.4. These sections contain the bulk of the exercises in the unit, particularly Section 1.4, which is by far the largest section, in terms of both pages and workload.

Section 1.5 is partly there to orient you towards concepts that feature more prominently in later units. It contains relatively few exercises, although, again, these should be attempted since they help to consolidate concepts learned in the previous sections, particularly Section 1.4.

Most of this unit can be worked through *without* Maple. Maple is used in Subsection 1.2.3 and, although you can read this subsection without it, your appreciation of the material will be enhanced with Maple on hand. Maple is also used to a small extent in some of the exercises in Section 1.3. Where Maple is used most extensively is in Section 1.5, and, although it is possible to read the section without it, you are encouraged to explore the ideas presented there using Maple.

Introduction

The purpose of this unit is to give an introduction to *dynamical systems* and *chaos*. Dynamical systems can be divided into two types, depending on whether time is treated as a continuous variable or is considered to be discrete. In the case where time is continuous, dynamical systems are formulated in terms of *differential equations*; where time is discrete, *iterative maps* are used. Both of these cases are introduced in Section 1.1, and in Subsection 1.1.1, the term *orbit* is defined and the distinction between *autonomous* and *nonautonomous* differential equations and maps will be explained. An informal introduction to the notion of chaos is given in Subsection 1.1.2.

Section 1.2 then gives an overview of some of the more important examples of chaotic phenomena occurring in the real world, and provides some historical context behind the subject. The purpose of this is to motivate the study of dynamical systems and chaos. Much of this section is descriptive, with few mathematical details and exercises, although Subsection 1.2.3 provides an opportunity to explore the famous *Lorenz system* using Maple.

Most of the material of this block will concentrate on dynamical systems formulated as iterative maps. For this reason, Section 1.3 is included to provide some motivating examples of maps as they occur in various applications of mathematics. Examples included are: *population dynamics* in Subsection 1.3.1; the *Newton–Raphson method* in Subsection 1.3.2; *finite-difference approximation* to differential equations in Subsection 1.3.3; and *time-T maps* and *Poincaré return maps* in Subsection 1.3.4. This last subsection is important because it shows how maps can be generated from differential equations, thus connecting the two formulations of dynamical systems, and this is a very useful device in the exploration of chaos.

Section 1.4 is devoted to autonomous differential equations. The emphasis is on how to understand the behaviour of their solutions without explicitly solving them in closed form. In particular, a picture is developed based on the *flow* generated by orbits in *phase space*, which will be defined along with a diagram giving an overall picture of possible flows called a *phase portrait*. Subsection 1.4.1 is concerned with one-dimensional differential equations, and Subsection 1.4.2 with two-dimensional differential equations, both *linear* and *nonlinear*. An important feature of phase portraits is the existence of *fixed points* along with their *stability*, and this will be discussed extensively in Subsections 1.4.1 and 1.4.2. Another important feature, occurring only in nonlinear systems, is the presence, or otherwise, of isolated periodic solutions called *limit cycles*, and this will be the subject of Subsection 1.4.3. This section closes with a discussion, in Subsection 1.4.4, of an important theorem, the *Poincaré–Bendixson theorem*, the proof of which is beyond the scope of this course. The theorem places restrictions on the type of orbits allowed in two-dimensional autonomous systems and, in particular, shows that chaos is not possible in such systems. It has nothing to say about higher-dimensional systems where chaos is found.

The unit concludes in Section 1.5 with a study of a version of *Duffing's equation*. Here it will be shown how the inclusion of a simple nonlinear term in an otherwise well-understood linear nonautonomous differential equation can lead to some rich and complicated behaviour, including chaos. This will mainly be studied numerically, using Maple, but it will be shown how the use of time-T maps can elucidate the very complicated-looking chaotic orbits generated by the differential equation. This serves as a useful motivating example for the later units of this block, and, in particular, shows again the importance of maps in the study of differential equations.

1.1 A brief look at dynamical systems and chaos

1.1.1 Introduction to dynamical systems

Dynamics is concerned with how quantities evolve in time. The subject has a long history, with the first important breakthroughs occurring in the seventeenth century, particularly with the work of Sir Isaac Newton (1642–1727), in the mid-1660s, who wanted to understand the motion of mechanical objects such as planets. The type of question being asked is this: given the value of some quantity at a given instant in time, how does it vary and what values does it take at later times? A **dynamical system** is a fixed rule which determines how the quantity varies in time.

Let us look at some examples. Consider the real variable $x(t)$ as a function of continuous time, $t \geq 0$. Then the first-order differential equation

$$\dot{x} = f(x), \quad x(0) = x_0, \tag{1.1}$$

for some suitable function $f : \mathbb{R} \longrightarrow \mathbb{R}$, is a simple example of a dynamical system. Here, and throughout this block, $\dot{x}$ denotes the time derivative dx/dt, and $\ddot{x}$ denotes the second derivative d^2x/dt^2. The function $f(x)$ on the right-hand side of Equation (1.1) is called the **phase velocity**. If Equation (1.1) can be solved for the given initial condition, then we know the value of $x(t)$ for a range of subsequent times, $t > 0$. An example of such a solution is shown in Figure 1.1. The trajectory $x(t)$ for $t > 0$, from the initial value x_0, is called the **orbit** of x_0. The differential equation gives us a rule for determining the evolution of x in time, and because time is continuous, this is an example of a **continuous-time dynamical system**. It is actually an example of a **one-dimensional** dynamical system, since it describes the evolution of a single scalar variable, x. Note that the phase velocity $f(x)$ is a function of x *only*; it is *not* an *explicit* function of time, t. Such a system, where the phase velocity is independent of time, is called **autonomous**.

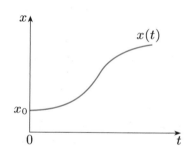

Figure 1.1 Plot of $x(t)$ as a function of t after starting at $x(0) = x_0$

Exercise 1.1

Show that the orbit $x = x(t)$ of Equation (1.1) can be expressed using the integral

$$t = \int_{x_0}^{x} \frac{du}{f(u)}.$$

You need to assume that $x = x(t)$ can be inverted to $t = t(x)$.

We can generalize to higher dimensions. An example of a **two-dimensional** continuous-time dynamical system is the following. Let the two real variables $x(t)$ and $y(t)$ be functions of time $t \geq 0$, so that we can think of $(x(t), y(t))$ as being a point in the xy-plane. Then the **two-dimensional system of differential equations** is the pair of first-order differential equations

$$\begin{aligned} \dot{x} &= f(x, y), \\ \dot{y} &= g(x, y), \end{aligned} \tag{1.2}$$

with initial condition $(x(0), y(0)) = (x_0, y_0)$. The velocity functions

$f, g : \mathbb{R}^2 \longrightarrow \mathbb{R}$ are assumed to be sufficiently well behaved, and the system has a two-component phase velocity, (f, g). In this case, the system will generate a trajectory $(x(t), y(t))$, $t \geq 0$, in the xy-plane starting at the initial point (x_0, y_0); this is called the orbit of (x_0, y_0). An example of this is shown in Figure 1.2. Note that this is again an autonomous system since time, t, does not *explicitly* appear in the velocity functions f and g. Of course, we could go on to define systems of differential equations in an arbitrary number of dimensions. An important property of these systems is that, provided that the velocity functions (components of the phase velocity) f, g, etc. are sufficiently well behaved, one can establish the existence and uniqueness of orbits for a range of subsequent times given the initial conditions. This will be discussed further in Section 1.4.

The functions $f(x, y)$ and $g(x, y)$ are well behaved if certain conditions such as continuity and continuous differentiability with respect to x and y are satisfied.

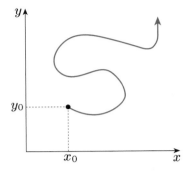

Figure 1.2 Example of an orbit of a two-dimensional continuous-time dynamical system, starting at (x_0, y_0)

So far, all the differential equations have been expressed in terms of first-order derivatives only. But a higher-order differential equation can always be re-expressed as a system of first-order differential equations. To see this, consider the following second-order differential equation (for $t \geq 0$):

$$\ddot{x} = g(x, \dot{x}), \quad x(0) = x_0, \quad \dot{x}(0) = y_0.$$

We now introduce a new dependent variable, $y(t)$, defined by $y = \dot{x}$, which implies that $\dot{y} = \ddot{x}$. The second-order differential equation can now be rewritten as

$$\begin{aligned} \dot{x} &= y, & x(0) &= x_0, \\ \dot{y} &= g(x, y), & y(0) &= y_0. \end{aligned} \tag{1.3}$$

Note that this is just a special case of the two-dimensional system of differential equations given in Equations (1.2), with $f(x, y) = y$. So a study of general systems of *first-order* differential equations, in arbitrary dimension, will also incorporate *higher-order* differential equations.

Exercise 1.2

Express the equation for damped simple harmonic motion,

$$\ddot{x} + c\dot{x} + \omega^2 x = 0,$$

as a system of first-order differential equations.

One also encounters **nonautonomous** differential equations, where the phase velocity depends *explicitly* on time. An example of a nonautonomous one-dimensional differential equation is

$$\dot{x} = f(x, t), \quad x(0) = x_0,$$

where $f(x, t)$ is now a function of both x *and* t. However, we can transform this one-dimensional nonautonomous system into a two-dimensional autonomous system in the following way. Introduce a new dependent variable $\theta(t)$, with the property $\dot{\theta} = 1$ and $\theta(0) = 0$. We are always free to do this. This implies that $\theta(t) = t$ (by integrating $\dot{\theta} = 1$ with constant of integration 0 since $\theta(0) = 0$), and the one-dimensional equation can be rewritten as

$$\dot{x} = f(x, \theta),$$
$$\dot{\theta} = 1$$

(with initial condition $(x(0), \theta(0)) = (x_0, 0)$), which is a two-dimensional *autonomous* system of differential equations, since t does not now explicitly appear on the right-hand side.

Exercise 1.3

Show that the two-dimensional nonautonomous system

$$\dot{x} = f(x, y, t), \quad x(0) = x_0,$$
$$\dot{y} = g(x, y, t), \quad y(0) = y_0,$$

can be re-expressed as a three-dimensional autonomous system.

In general, we can transform a nonautonomous system of differential equations into an autonomous system by increasing the dimension by one. So the study of general autonomous systems in arbitrary dimension will also encompass nonautonomous systems.

The dynamical systems discussed so far treat time as a continuous variable. We can also consider systems where time is taken to be a discrete variable, denoted by n, say, which takes non-negative integer values $n = 0, 1, 2, 3, \ldots$. Then if the real variable x_n is the value of some quantity at time n, the equation

$$x_{n+1} = f(x_n),$$

with $f \colon \mathbb{R} \longrightarrow \mathbb{R}$, determines how x_n develops in time, with x_0 being its initial value. This is a **discrete-time dynamical system**, usually referred to as a **map**. In this case, the map is **one-dimensional**; such maps will be the subject of the second unit of this block. Note that if x_0 is given, then x_n for all $n \geq 1$ can be determined by successive iterations of the map. However, as will become evident in the next unit, even the simplest nonlinear map can generate extremely rich and complicated behaviour.

A *linear* map is one where $f(x)$ has the form $f(x) = ax + b$ with constant a and b. Any map not of this form is *nonlinear*.

As with differential equations, we can go on to define higher-dimensional maps. So, for example, if we have two real variables, x_n and y_n, at each discrete time point $n = 0, 1, 2, \ldots$, then the set of equations

$$x_{n+1} = f(x_n, y_n),$$
$$y_{n+1} = g(x_n, y_n),$$

with $f, g \colon \mathbb{R}^2 \longrightarrow \mathbb{R}$, determines the evolution of (x_n, y_n) for all $n \geq 1$, given the initial point (x_0, y_0). This is a **two-dimensional map**; the properties of such dynamical systems will be explored in some detail in the final two units of this block. We can think of this map as generating points (x_n, y_n), $n = 0, 1, 2, \ldots$, in the xy-plane, as illustrated in Figure 1.3.

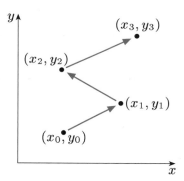

Figure 1.3 Points generated under a two-dimensional map starting at (x_0, y_0)

Exercise 1.4

The maps considered so far are **autonomous maps**, which means that the mapping functions are independent of the discrete time n. The maps considered in this block will generally be of this type. However, one can also consider **nonautonomous maps** such as

$$x_{n+1} = f(x_n, n).$$

Show that this is equivalent to the autonomous two-dimensional map

$$x_{n+1} = f(x_n, y_n),$$
$$y_{n+1} = g(y_n),$$

where $g(y) = 1 + y$ and $y_0 = 0$.

1.1.2 Introduction to chaos

The dynamical systems of the previous section have the following important property: given the initial conditions, a unique trajectory is known to exist; that is, provided that the initial values of the dynamical variables are known, in principle the subsequent values are also known. Such dynamical systems are said to be **deterministic**.

Orbits for these systems can be classified in a variety of ways: in this course we are mainly concerned with orbits that remain bounded for all time, and these can be classified as being stable or unstable. During the two centuries following Newton's work, it was implicitly assumed that planetary orbits are stable, and it was only in 1889 that the French mathematician Jules Henri Poincaré (1854–1912) was to prove that this is *not* necessarily the case.

The notion of stability and chaos is intimately connected with the relative separation of orbits that are initially very close. General statements about this behaviour are fraught with difficulties because there are many exceptions, but as a general rule if $\Delta(t)$ is the distance between two orbits at time t, such that $\Delta(0)$ is very small, then, for small t, $\Delta(t)$ is proportional to t for stable orbits, and $\Delta(t)$ increases exponentially with t for **chaotic** orbits. This exponential growth means that there is an **extreme sensitivity** to the initial conditions, which is a characteristic feature of chaotic motion. Such behaviour is illustrated in Figure 1.4 for a differential system with dimension greater than one, where only the x-coordinate is plotted and in this case $\Delta(t) \simeq e^{ht}\delta x_0$ with $h > 0$. It should be emphasized that this is not a precise definition of chaos, which will be given in later units, but it serves to give a rough idea of the notion.

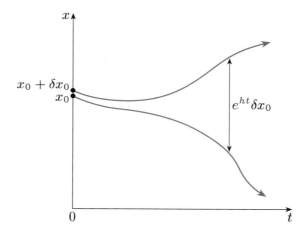

Figure 1.4   Comparison of trajectories with slightly different initial values for chaotic motion. The x-axis refers to the x-component of a system of differential equations of sufficiently high dimension. The initial separation, δx_0, is extremely small.

The extreme sensitivity to initial conditions makes the evolution of a chaotic dynamical system appear erratic and random although, of course, strictly speaking, the system is deterministic and, in principle, the evolution can always be determined from the initial conditions *provided* that one knows the *exact* initial values. Unfortunately, in typical real-world applications of dynamical systems, one can never know the exact initial values because no measuring instrument can record data to arbitrary accuracy; there will always be some error, however small (we could regard δx_0 in Figure 1.4 as such an error). The error will grow exponentially fast for a chaotic orbit, causing the system rapidly to lose 'memory' of its initial data, so eventually two or more distinct orbits may appear to come from the same initial point (look at Figure 1.4 while squinting your eyes). It is this which makes chaotic orbits appear random, and the presence of chaos places severe limitations on our ability to predict the behaviour of dynamical systems over long periods of time.

1.2 Chaotic phenomena in the real world

Since chaos theory has a rather remarkable history, we are going to begin this section with a brief historical overview before describing in greater detail specific examples of chaotic phenomena in the real world.

The story properly starts with Newton and his work in the 1660s, which culminated in 1687 with the publication of his magnum opus, *Principia*, in which he formulated his laws of mechanics and his law of universal gravitation. The *Principia* is fiercely difficult – it was written in the language of geometry rather than the calculus – and it took some time for the wealth of ideas in it to be fully accepted. However, by the middle of the eighteenth century it had been translated into the language of the calculus, and mathematicians had become secure in the belief that the motion of all bodies in the universe could be completely determined by Newton's laws. Famously, this belief in a predictable deterministic universe found full expression in the words of French mathematician Pierre-Simon Laplace (1749–1827), first articulated in 1773:

> The present state of the system of nature is evidently a consequence of what it was in the preceding moment, and if we conceive of an intelligence that at a given instant comprehends all the relations of the entities of this universe, it could state the respective position, motions, and general affects of all these entities at any time in the past or future.

It was a compelling vision, and it led to the expectation that the universe, or more specifically the solar system, could be understood as a clockwork machine (see Figure 1.5). One specifies all the initial conditions, such as the positions and velocities of the planets, and all subsequent motions can then be determined for all time, which means that the future positions of the planets can be calculated. The differential equations may become complicated, but it was believed that, with sufficient ingenuity and application, they could eventually be solved to the required degree of accuracy. But, thanks to Poincaré, this ambition came crashing down at the end of the nineteenth century. More will be said about this in Subsection 1.2.1, but suffice to say that Poincaré discovered that for certain dynamical problems, there exists extreme sensitivity to initial conditions. However, little further progress was made until the second half of the twentieth century, when the advent of electronic computers made both rapid computation and (later) the graphical representation of results possible.

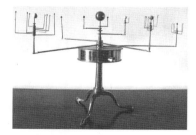

Figure 1.5 A mechanical orrery: a clockwork model of the solar system (named after Charles Boyle, 4th Earl of Orrery).
Image courtesy of Dr. Miruna Daniela Popescu, Armagh Observatory.

The next breakthrough came in 1963 when the American meteorologist Edward Lorenz (1917–) used a computer to solve the equations of a simplified convective-fluid model of the atmosphere. Lorenz's model, which will be described in more detail in Subsection 1.2.3, consisted of a three-dimensional system of differential equations. Much to Lorenz's surprise, he found that his numerical computations gave completely different results depending on whether his initial data were specified to 6-digit or 3-digit accuracy. He had accidentally hit upon a chaotic system with extreme sensitivity to initial conditions. He came to the view that weather prediction over long periods of time was impossible, regardless of the available computing power. In 1972 he presented a paper entitled 'Predictability: does the flap of a butterfly's wings in Brazil set off a tornado in Texas?', from which the epithet 'the butterfly effect', which today is popularly used to describe extreme sensitivity to initial conditions, was born. Of course, as Lorenz was careful to point out, Amazonian butterflies do not cause tornadoes anywhere, let alone north of the Rio Grande, but it was a striking analogy and one that later caught the public imagination.

However, it was a number of years before Lorenz's work made much of an impact, not least because it was published in a meteorological journal rather than a mathematical one. But by the mid-1970s the word 'chaos' had entered into the scientific lexicon, and chaotic phenomena were being investigated in a wide range of applications, some of which are described in the remainder of this section.

The term 'chaos' was introduced into mathematics in 1975 in the now famous paper entitled 'Period three implies chaos' by Tien Yien Li and James Yorke of the University of Maryland, USA.

1.2.1 The solar system

In the *Principia* Newton showed how his laws of mechanics and his law of universal gravitation predicted that the planets orbit the Sun in ellipses, consistent with Kepler's laws. Newton's calculations involved the approximation that each planet independently interacts with the Sun whilst ignoring all other bodies in the solar system, but since the Sun accounts for more than 99.8% of the mass of the solar system, this is a very good approximation. Thus Newton solved what we now call the two-body problem. However, to gain a more accurate description of how bodies move in the solar system, it is necessary to take account of further interactions, such as those between individual planets, for example the interactions between the Sun and Mercury, given the presence of Jupiter. While certain efforts to solve this type of problem led to the development of what today is known as perturbation theory, others led to attempts to solve the three-body problem *per se*. Indeed Newton, in the course of his work on lunar theory (the motion of the Moon), had tried to tackle the three-body problem but with little success, and it engaged the attention of many leading mathematicians of the eighteenth and nineteenth centuries.

More formally, the two-body problem can be stated as follows: if two bodies interact gravitationally, given their initial conditions, determine their subsequent motion. The problem can be generalized for any number of bodies.

Jupiter is the largest planet in the solar system and exerts a measurable influence on the orbits of other planets in the solar system. The precession of the perihelion of Mercury is mostly caused by the presence of Jupiter.

One of the attractions of the three-body problem is its close relationship with the question of the stability of the solar system. This is the question of deciding whether the planets in the distant future will continue to move in the way that they do now or whether in the long term something catastrophic, such as a collision or an escape, will eventually occur. Or, put another way, if we know the present positions and velocities of the planets, can we predict their motions for all future time (and deduce them for all past time)? If we ignore all other forces, such as tidal or relativistic effects, and take only gravitational forces into account, the solar system can be modelled by the n-body problem, where n is a whole number, and investigated accordingly. In 1884 King Oscar II of Sweden sponsored a prize competition in mathematics to commemorate his 60th birthday, which was taking place in 1889, in which one of the questions asked for a solution to the n-body problem. Poincaré took up the challenge, focusing his efforts on the three-body problem from which he hoped to be able to generalize. Although Poincaré did not solve the three-body problem – which gives an indication of its difficulty! – his memoir contained so much in the way of new mathematics that he was awarded the prize. But while Poincaré was preparing the memoir for publication he discovered an important mistake, and it was in correcting the mistake that he discovered, to his surprise and consternation, trajectories that exhibited what we would now call chaotic behaviour. There are now believed to be many instances of chaos in the solar system, some of which are discussed below.

The orbit of Pluto

Extensive numerical simulations of the planet Pluto, using a special-purpose computer called the Digital Orrery (Figure 1.6), have indicated that Pluto's orbit is sensitive to initial conditions and is likely to be chaotic. In particular, it has been predicted that a 1 km uncertainty in the measured position of Pluto would grow to an astronomical unit (the mean distance from the Sun to the Earth, denoted AU, which is approximately 93 million miles) in about 100 million years. This may sound like a long time but is relatively short when compared to the age of the solar system, which is over four billion years old. Moreover, it suggests that there are serious limitations in the capacity of celestial mechanics either to predict events far into the future or to deduce events in the distant past.

Figure 1.6   The Digital Orrery, a special-purpose computer built at Caltech in 1984 by Gerald Sussman.
Image courtesy of Professor Gerald Sussman.

The tumbling of Hyperion

Hyperion is one of Saturn's more distant moons and, with equatorial radii of $180 \times 140 \times 112.5$ km, is the *largest irregularly shaped* natural satellite ever observed. A recent image of Hyperion is shown in the left panel of Figure 1.7. Partly as a result of Hyperion's highly aspherical shape, the satellite tumbles in a chaotic way as it orbits Saturn. This tumbling of Hyperion is a particularly dramatic physical example of chaotic behaviour. Indeed, the effect can be seen from terrestrial observatories, and one finds that the relative brightness of Hyperion appears to vary erratically in time.

Hyperion taken from the Cassini flyby of 26 September 2005.
Image courtesy of NASA Jet Propulsion Laboratory (NASA-JPL).

Phobos taken from ESA's Mars Express spacecraft on 22 August 2004.
Image courtesy of ESA/DLR/FU Berlin (G. Neukum).

Figure 1.7   The satellites Hyperion and Phobos

There are many other examples of chaotic tumbling of aspherical satellites in the solar system. Much closer to home are the satellites of Mars, in particular the satellite Phobos. With equatorial radii of $13.4 \times 11.2 \times 9.2$ km, Phobos is much smaller than Hyperion but almost as aspherical (although its orbit is less eccentric) and therefore subject to similar chaotic tumbling phenomena. A recent image of Phobos is shown in the right panel of Figure 1.7.

Let us describe Hyperion's tumbling motion more precisely. Figure 1.8(a) illustrates schematically the orbit of Hyperion (H) around Saturn (S). The eccentricity of the orbit (which should be about 0.1) is exaggerated for clarity (in reality it would appear closer to being circular), but it is important to note that the orbit is an ellipse, with Saturn at a focus, and not a circle. The location of Hyperion in its orbit, as specified by its distance from Saturn, r, and the angle f (the true anomaly, given by the angle PSH in Figure 1.8(a), P being the point in the orbit closest to Saturn), progresses according to Kepler's laws. The chaotic motion, the so-called tumbling, shows in its orientation as it goes around Saturn, as quantified by its spin angle. As Hyperion orbits Saturn, it spins about an axis perpendicular to its orbital plane, with Hyperion's longest axis (axis of smallest principal moment of inertia) in the plane. The spin angle, θ, is the angle between Hyperion's longest axis and the line SP in Figure 1.8(a). The dynamics of θ is chaotic.

The true anomaly is the angle between the periapsis (the point in an orbit when two objects are closest together) of an orbit and the object's current orbital position, measured from the body being orbited and in the direction of orbital motion.

Kepler's laws are usually stated in terms of planetary motion about the Sun, but the same laws also apply to satellites orbiting planets.

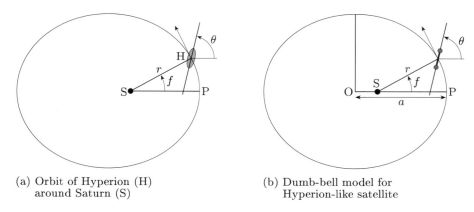

(a) Orbit of Hyperion (H) around Saturn (S)

(b) Dumb-bell model for Hyperion-like satellite

Figure 1.8 Schematic illustration of the orbit of Hyperion together with the dumb-bell model

Some insight into this is gained through the following model, illustrated in Figure 1.8(b), which treats Hyperion as a dumb-bell connecting two point masses. By taking the length of the dumb-bell to be much smaller than r, one can show that the orbit of its centre of mass is an ellipse, with semi-major axis of length a, and that $r = r(t)$ and $f = f(t)$ evolve according to Kepler's laws. Moreover, the spin angle θ satisfies the second-order differential equation

$$\ddot{\theta} = -\frac{3}{2}\omega^2 \left(\frac{a}{r(t)}\right)^3 \sin\left(2\left(\theta - f(t)\right)\right), \tag{1.4}$$

where ω is the orbital frequency, i.e. $\omega = 2\pi/T$, with T being the orbital period. Now, if the orbit is circular, r is constant ($r = a$) and $f = \omega t$. In this case, as will become apparent in Exercise 1.7 below, Equation (1.4) can be rearranged to give a simple expression relating $\theta - f$ and $\dot{\theta}$, with no explicit time dependence, and there will be *no* chaos. However, for an elliptical orbit like Hyperion's, r and f will be relatively complicated functions of t, thus preventing us from relating θ and $\dot{\theta}$ in the simple way mentioned earlier, and the dynamics of θ can then become chaotic. So two ingredients contribute to Hyperion's chaotic tumbling: (i) it has an irregular shape, and (ii) the orbit of its centre of mass is an ellipse and strictly non-circular. Both of these conditions need to be met for chaotic tumbling.

Asteroids and meteorites

Between the orbits of Mars and Jupiter is a band of millions of rocky objects, each orbiting the Sun, called the asteroids (see Figure 1.9). These range in size from 940 km (Ceres) to less than 1 km in diameter. An interesting feature of the asteroid belt is seen when the distribution of asteroids (i.e. the number of asteroids found in a narrow band) is plotted as a function of mean distance from the Sun. Such a plot is shown in Figure 1.10.

The orbits of planets and asteroids are ellipses. For an object whose orbit has a sufficiently low eccentricity, as is typical of planets and main-belt asteroids, its mean distance from the Sun is very close to its semi-major axis.

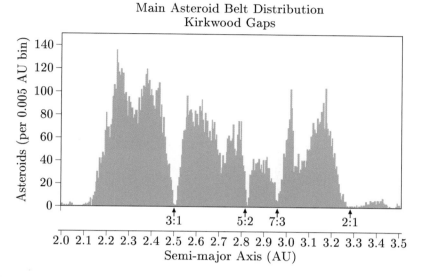

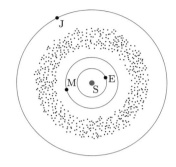

Figure 1.9 Schematic illustration showing the orbits of Earth (E), Mars (M) and Jupiter (J) around the Sun (S), with the asteroid belt being the band of points between the orbits of Mars and Jupiter

Figure 1.10 Distribution of asteroids: the vertical axis gives the number of asteroids found in a relatively narrow band (referred to as the bin) of width 0.005 AU at a distance from the Sun indicated by the horizontal axis

One sees that the distribution is far from uniform and contains gaps, the so-called Kirkwood gaps, where very few asteroids are found. The gaps tend to occur at points where the orbital period of the asteroid has a simple integer relationship with that of Jupiter. For example, the 3:1 Kirkwood gap, indicated in Figure 1.10, occurs where the asteroids make three revolutions around the Sun for every one that Jupiter makes; the 5:2 gap is where asteroids orbit the Sun five times for every two revolutions of Jupiter, etc. For many years it was not fully understood why the asteroid belt was depleted at these particular resonances with Jupiter. But now, thanks to the work of Jack Wisdom in the 1980s, an explanation which includes chaotic dynamics has been found. Wisdom showed that at these resonances (particularly 3:1) an asteroid can suddenly (in astronomical timescales) and, since chaos is involved, unpredictably change its course in such a way that it departs from the main asteroid belt and crosses over into the region of the solar system occupied by the inner planets. Furthermore, when such an event happens, near approaches and collisions with the inner planets become possible. These near collisions are responsible for meteor showers; indeed, it is now widely believed that most meteorites falling on the Earth originate from asteroidal fragments emerging from the Kirkwood gaps with chaos playing a role. An asteroid, possibly originating from a Kirkwood gap, may have collided with the Earth about 65 million years ago leading to the great extinction of species which included the dinosaurs. This raises the tantalising notion that chaotic dynamics was, in a sense, responsible for the demise of the dinosaurs and the consequential ascent of our own species. Of course, it also raises the rather more alarming prospect that our own extinction could come about as the result of a future similar impact.

The gaps were first noticed in 1857 by the American astronomer Daniel Kirkwood (1814–1895).

Exercise 1.5

Recall that the planets and asteroids orbit the Sun in ellipses (with the Sun at a focus). Kepler's third law states that for a given orbiting object, the square of its orbital period is proportional to the cube of its semi-major axis. Given that Jupiter's semi-major axis is 5.2034 AU, use Kepler's third law to determine the location (in AU) of the following Kirkwood gaps: (a) 3:1, (b) 5:2, (c) 7:3, (d) 2:1. Compare your results with Figure 1.10.

1.2.2 Mechanical experiments

It is possible to find chaotic motion in simple mechanical devices. You may have encountered desktop executive toys capable of exhibiting complicated motion (see Figure 1.11). It turns out that this motion is often chaotic. Below, we describe a few simple mechanical systems where chaos occurs. For some of these, the equations of motion are given, and the key ingredient in these equations is the presence of nonlinearity.

Figure 1.11 Chaotic toy

Driven pendulum

Consider the pendulum, illustrated in Figure 1.12, consisting of a light rod (modelled as massless) of length l with a bob of mass m at its end. Of interest is the evolution of the angle, θ, that the pendulum makes with the vertical. The equation of motion for θ can be obtained by applying Newton's second law and resolving in the direction of the vector $\mathbf{e}_\theta$ (see Figure 1.12), perpendicular to the rod. This gives

$$ml\ddot{\theta} = -mg\sin\theta. \qquad (1.5)$$

If θ is kept small, the approximation $\sin\theta \simeq \theta$ can be made, leading to the linear equation $\ddot{\theta} = -g\theta/l$. This is the equation for **simple harmonic motion**, which you may be familiar with, describing small oscillations of the pendulum about its equilibrium position. In order to produce chaos, though, one needs to keep Equation (1.5) *nonlinear*. However, more needs to be added to get chaos, in particular a driving term. (Equation (1.5) leads to a simple relationship between θ and $\dot{\theta}$, just as with Equation (1.4) for circular orbits; see Exercise 1.6 below.) We now add a damping term proportional to $\dot{\theta}$ to Equation (1.5), coming from friction at the pivot, and a driving force proportional to $\sin(\Omega t)$, which accelerates the bob first clockwise then anticlockwise in a sinusoidal way. With these additions, Equation (1.5) becomes

$$\ddot{\theta} + c\dot{\theta} + \frac{g}{l}\sin\theta = \Gamma\sin(\Omega t), \qquad (1.6)$$

with $c > 0$, describing a damped *driven* pendulum. Equation (1.6) can be solved numerically (using Maple), and it can be shown that chaos occurs for certain values of the parameters (e.g. when $c = 0.05$, $g = l = 1$, $\Gamma = 0.6$ and $\Omega = 0.7$). It should be stressed that although the driving term, $\sin(\Omega t)$, is needed to get chaos, this is *not* true for the damping term, $c\dot{\theta}$, which is included here for completeness and for use later on in the unit.

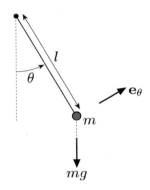

Figure 1.12 Pendulum of length l with m being the mass of the bob and g the acceleration due to gravity

The driving force has constant angular frequency Ω and constant amplitude $ml\Gamma$, so Γ is a measure of its strength.

The constant c is a parameter encompassing the frictional forces of the system.

Exercise 1.6

Show that Equation (1.5) gives the following relationship between θ and $\dot{\theta}$:

$$\tfrac{1}{2}\dot{\theta}^2 - \frac{g}{l}\cos\theta = \text{constant}.$$

This is known as the *constant of motion* (or first integral) of the differential equation. [*Hint*: Multiply both sides of Equation (1.5) by $\dot{\theta}$, and note that $\frac{d}{dt}(\dot{\theta}^2) = 2\dot{\theta}\ddot{\theta}$ and $\frac{d}{dt}f(\theta) = \dot{\theta}f'(\theta)$ for any function $f(\theta)$.]

Exercise 1.7

Consider the equation describing Hyperion's spin, Equation (1.4), when the orbit is *circular*, so that $r = a$ (constant) and $f = \omega t$. Using methods similar to those of Exercise 1.6, show that in this case the equation has the following constant of motion:

$$(\dot{\theta} - \omega)^2 - 3\omega^2\cos^2(\theta - \omega t) = \text{constant}.$$

Double pendulum

A double pendulum is formed by taking the pendulum of the previous subsection and joining a second rod at a pivot on the bob of the first, as shown in Figure 1.13. Here, a light rod of length l_1 hangs from a fixed pivot at one end, with a bob of mass m_1 at the other; from the latter a second (lower) light rod, with length l_2 and bob mass m_2, is pivoted. Whereas with the single pendulum a driving force is required to produce chaos, in this case no such force is required provided that the pivots are sufficiently *frictionless*, so no damping is included in the model equations. If damping were included then, in the absence of a driving force, the system would eventually grind to a halt with no interesting dynamics. We now have two evolving variables, θ_1 and θ_2. The equations of motion for these variables are rather complicated, involving two coupled nonlinear second-order differential equations, and nothing is gained by presenting them here. However, as θ_1 and θ_2 are set in motion, the system can become chaotic. The fact that the *non-driven* single pendulum can never be chaotic, unlike the non-driven *double* pendulum, is an instance of an important theorem to be discussed in Subsection 1.4.4.

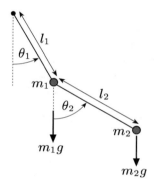

Figure 1.13 Double pendulum consisting of two light rods articulated at a pivot at m_1

Chaotic waterwheel

Figure 1.14 shows schematically the idea behind the chaotic waterwheel. Cups are attached to the rim of a wheel which is held vertically. Water passes steadily through a nozzle above the wheel, directed towards filling the top cup and also other cups in its near vicinity at equal rates on either side (i.e. the system has left–right symmetry). But the cups have holes in their bottoms causing water to leak out. If the flow rate through the nozzle is too slow, the top cup will never get sufficiently heavy for the wheel to overcome friction at its bearing. The wheel then stays stationary. As the flow rate increases above a certain threshold, the top cup becomes heavy enough to set the wheel in motion. Eventually, upon increasing the flow rate further, the wheel will start rotating steadily, either clockwise or, equally likely due to symmetry, anticlockwise, at a constant angular velocity ω.

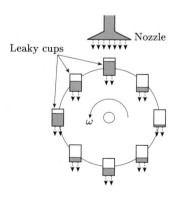

Figure 1.14 Chaotic waterwheel. This is a schematic depiction; actual realizations have many more cups.

19

However, on increasing the flow rate still further, this steady rotation can become unstable. This happens when the lower cups are unable to leak out enough water, making the wheel too heavy to maintain its steady rotation so that it slows down or even reverses direction. To see how this can happen, recall that some of the water from the nozzle also passes into the cups neighbouring the top cup so that upward-moving cups begin to fill with water as they approach the top. One then observes the wheel making a few turns in one direction with varying ω, then suddenly reversing direction and making a few turns in that direction before switching directions yet again, and so on, in a rather erratic fashion. This motion is, in fact, chaotic. What is interesting about the chaotic waterwheel is that the equations describing its motion are identical to those Lorenz wrote down in his model of atmospheric convection (to be described in the next subsection). The physical situations are quite different but the chaotic waterwheel is an experimental realization of the Lorenz system, and an actual working model was first built by Willem Malkus and Lou Howard at the Massachusetts Institute of Technology in the 1970s.

1.2.3 The Lorenz system

Edward Lorenz wished to understand convective currents in the atmosphere when it is heated from below. Convection is a consequence of the fact that fluids generally get less dense as they heat up. Thus, when a portion of fluid under gravity is heated, it flows upwards due to its lower density, displacing cooler fluid as it rises. The resulting flow is referrred to as a convection current. In the atmosphere, as the hotter fluid (in this case air) rises, it starts to cool down so that it becomes more dense again and therefore flows back down due to gravity. This sets up a circulatory convection current, and the presence of these in the atmosphere has important implications in determining weather patterns.

Lorenz considered a simplified model of this convective process as illustrated in Figure 1.15. Here, viscous fluid is confined to a rectangular cell with its lower side maintained at a temperature T_l, through the application of heat, and the cooler upper side kept at temperature $T_u < T_l$. This fixed temperature difference ($\Delta T = T_l - T_u$) drives a circulating convection current as shown in the figure. Lorenz was able to describe this system mathematically with the following three-dimensional system of differential equations:

$$\dot{x} = \sigma(y - x),$$
$$\dot{y} = rx - y - xz, \tag{1.7}$$
$$\dot{z} = xy - bz.$$

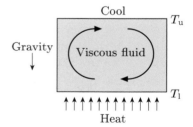

Figure 1.15 Convection cell containing a viscuous fluid under gravity

The details are not important here, but roughly speaking the variable x is related to the fluid velocity and proportional to the circulatory fluid flow so that when $x > 0$ the fluid circulates clockwise and when $x < 0$ it circulates anticlockwise; the variable y is proportional to the temperature difference between ascending and descending fluid elements; and z is proportional to the distortion of the vertical temperature profile from its equilibrium shape. The parameter σ is called the Prandtl number and is related to the viscous and thermal properties of the fluid; r is called the Rayleigh number and is a measure of the imposed temperature difference, ΔT, across the rectangle; and b is a geometrical parameter related to the shape of the rectangular cell.

Recall from the previous subsection that the Lorenz system of differential equations, Equations (1.7), also describes the motion of the chaotic waterwheel shown in Figure 1.14. In modelling the waterwheel in this way, one assumes that there is a sufficiently large number of cups around the rim of the wheel so that a continuum approximation can be made. In the case of the waterwheel, x is directly proportional to the angular velocity, ω, of the wheel. The other two variables, y and z, are related to the leading coefficients in the Fourier series for the distribution of the mass of water in the cups as a function of the angle around the wheel. Finally, the parameters, σ, r and b are given by combinations of various waterwheel parameters such as the radius of the wheel, the cup leakage rate, the rotational damping rate and the moment of inertia of the wheel.

It is important to note the presence of nonlinear terms in the Lorenz system (1.7). These are the terms $-xz$ and xy in the equations for $\dot{y}$ and $\dot{z}$, respectively. It is these terms which give rise to chaos. One can use Maple to examine the chaotic nature of the Lorenz system. Start a new Maple worksheet and input the following (the package DEtools will be needed):

```
>   restart:  with(DEtools):
>   eqn1 := diff(x(t),t)=sigma*(y(t)-x(t)):
>   eqn2 := diff(y(t),t)=r*x(t)-y(t)-x(t)*z(t):
>   eqn3 := diff(z(t),t)=x(t)*y(t)-b*z(t):
>   Lorenz := eqn1,eqn2,eqn3;
```

The package DEtools contains commands useful in the treatment of differential equations. These include DEplot and DEplot3d, which plot solutions of systems of first-order differential equations.

$$Lorenz := \frac{d}{dt}\,\mathrm{x}(t) = \sigma\,(\mathrm{y}(t) - \mathrm{x}(t)),$$
$$\frac{d}{dt}\,\mathrm{y}(t) = r\,\mathrm{x}(t) - \mathrm{y}(t) - \mathrm{x}(t)\,\mathrm{z}(t),\ \frac{d}{dt}\,\mathrm{z}(t) = \mathrm{x}(t)\,\mathrm{y}(t) - b\,\mathrm{z}(t)$$

where the Lorenz sytem of differential equations has been assigned to Lorenz. Now enter the following to assign values to sigma, r and b:

```
>   sigma:=10;  r:=28;  b:=8/3;
```
$$\sigma := 10$$
$$r := 28$$
$$b := \frac{8}{3}$$

These are exactly the same values that Lorenz himself took for σ, r and b in 1963. Now, to solve numerically the Lorenz system for time, t, from 0 to 20, with $(x(0), y(0), z(0)) = (5, 5, 5)$, and then to plot the orbit of this initial value, the DEplot3d command can be used as follows:

```
>   DEplot3d({Lorenz},{x(t),y(t),z(t)},t=0..20,
    [[x(0)=5,y(0)=5,z(0)=5]],scene=[x(t),y(t),z(t)],
    stepsize=0.01,method=rkf45,linecolor=black,thickness=1,
    orientation=[-99,63]);
```

The resulting three-dimensional plot of the orbit is shown in Figure 1.16(a), overleaf. Remember, you can vary the orientation of the plot by placing the mouse cursor over it and then moving the mouse whilst pressing down its left button. However, some clarity may be gained by plotting a two-dimensional projection of the orbit in, say, the xz-plane, from typing the following:

```
>   DEplot({Lorenz},{x(t),y(t),z(t)},t=0..20,
    [[x(0)=5,y(0)=5,z(0)=5]],scene=[x(t),z(t)],stepsize=0.01,
    method=rkf45,linecolor=black,thickness=1);
```

Note that the method chosen in DEplot3d/DEplot is rkf45, which is specified since the default method used by DEplot3d/DEplot is often not accurate enough for dealing with chaotic orbits. The method rkf45, which is the default method used by dsolve, is of Runge–Kutta type.

The result is shown in Figure 1.16(b); the shape of the orbit has the appearance of an owl's face, characteristic of the Lorenz system. The orbit spends time spiralling around one 'eye' then suddenly jumps to the other eye, spirals a few turns, then jumps back again, and so on, in an apparently random way that never exactly repeats itself.

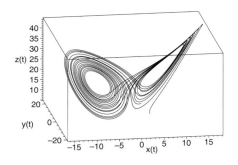

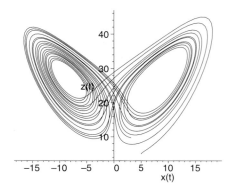

(a) Three-dimensional plot of the orbit

(b) Two-dimensional projection of the orbit in the xz-plane

Figure 1.16   Orbit of a Lorenz system, for parameters $\sigma = 10$, $r = 28$ and $b = 8/3$, starting at $(x, y, z) = (5, 5, 5)$

Further insight is gained by plotting x (or one of the other variables) against time, t. This is done with the Maple command

```
>   DEplot({Lorenz},{x(t),y(t),z(t)},t=0..20,
      [[x(0)=5,y(0)=5,z(0)=5]],scene=[t,x(t)],stepsize=0.01,
      method=rkf45,linecolor=black,thickness=1);
```

and the result is shown in Figure 1.17. Recall that $x(t)$ signifies the strength and direction of fluid circulation in the convection cell or the angular velocity of the waterwheel. So, from Figure 1.17, one sees that the system rotates clockwise up to about $t \simeq 0.5$, then suddenly switches to anticlockwise and rotates in that direction until about $t \simeq 6$, then switches direction again, and so on, the process appearing erratic. In the case of the waterwheel, it has been known for people to place bets as to which direction the wheel turns next! You should try experimenting with all this in Maple; for example, try repeating the above commands for different initial conditions.

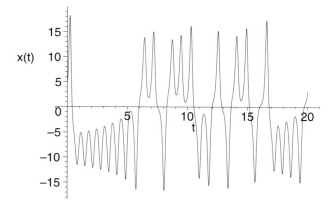

Figure 1.17   The x-component of the orbit as a function of time t

However, the essence of chaos is the extreme sensitivity to initial conditions. To see this in the Lorenz system, we shall compare two orbits starting from two very nearby points, namely one starting from $(5.00, 5.00, 5.00)$ (to be plotted in black), as before, and the other from $(5.01, 5.00, 5.00)$ (to be plotted in red). The required Maple command for this is

```
>  DEplot3d({Lorenz},{x(t),y(t),z(t)},t=0..20,
   [[x(0)=5,y(0)=5,z(0)=5],[x(0)=5.01,y(0)=5,z(0)=5]],
   scene=[x(t),y(t),z(t)],stepsize=0.01,method=rkf45,
   linecolor=[black,red],thickness=1,orientation=[-99,63]);
```

which compares three-dimensional plots of the two orbits and is shown in
Figure 1.18(a). A more transparent way of seeing how the two orbits
eventually differ is to compare plots of one of the components, x say, as
functions of t. This is obtained from the Maple command

```
>  DEplot({Lorenz},{x(t),y(t),z(t)},t=0..20,
   [[x(0)=5,y(0)=5,z(0)=5],[x(0)=5.01,y(0)=5,z(0)=5]],
   scene=[t,x(t)],stepsize=0.01,method=rkf45,
   linecolor=[black,red],thickness=1);
```

and is shown in Figure 1.18(b).

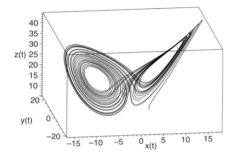

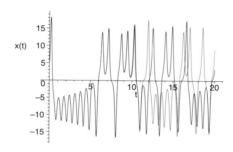

(a) Three-dimensional plots of the
two orbits

(b) The x-component of the orbits
as functions of t

Figure 1.18   Comparing two orbits of the Lorenz system, for parameters $\sigma = 10$,
$r = 28$ and $b = 8/3$, one starting at $(x, y, z) = (5.00, 5.00, 5.00)$ (black), the other
starting at $(x, y, z) = (5.01, 5.00, 5.00)$ (red)

Now you can see the situation which so surprised Edward Lorenz; even
though the two orbits start off very close to one another, they eventually
move apart, as shown clearly in Figure 1.18(b), with each orbit visiting the
'eyes' at different times.

1.3   Maps

The subsequent units of this block are mainly concerned with discrete-time
dynamical systems, i.e. iterative maps. This is because maps are usually
simpler to analyse than continuous-time dynamical systems, i.e. differential
equations, and yet a study of them will uncover many of the essential
properties common to both discrete-time and continuous-time dynamics.
As a way of motivating the study of maps, as well as introducing them as
interesting systems in their own right, we present in this section a medley
of common instances where maps can be usefully employed.

1.3.1 Population dynamics in biology

Here we shall show how the dynamics of a biological population can be modelled as a discrete-time dynamical system.

Consider a population of some animal species in a closed environment, such as a species of insect kept in a jar. Suppose we know that the insect continuously reproduces and we count the number of insects in the jar once a week. Let this number after week $n = 0, 1, 2, \ldots$ be denoted by N_n, with N_0 being the initial population.

We wish to determine the rule under which the population number N_n evolves as the weeks progress. If the jar is infinitely big and there are no restrictions on the food supply then, providing the birth rate exceeds the death rate, the number of insects will continue to increase. Moreover, the number of insects in any given week will be proportional to the number in the previous week. Thus we have

$$N_{n+1} = rN_n, \tag{1.8}$$

where the constant $r > 1$ is the rate at which the population is growing, called the **growth rate**. Thus we have arrived at a map (in this case a linear map, which will be described in more detail in the next unit). Because $r > 1$, the map in Equation (1.8) describes an insect population that increases exponentially. This would be fine if the environment really were of infinite extent, with an infinite food supply, but would be quite unreasonable if the insects were kept in a finite jar with a restricted food supply. They would eventually run out of food and space. Therefore we need to modify (1.8) so that the population starts to decrease before it gets too large. One way of doing this is to assume that the growth rate r itself depends on the population number N_n, rather than just being a constant. There will then exist a number $C > 0$, called the **carrying capacity**, such that when the population number exceeds the number C, the insects start to die off more rapidly due to overcrowding. In other words, we require r to have the property that $r > 1$ (population increases) for $N_n < C$, whereas $r < 1$ (population decreases) whenever $N_n > C$. The simplest way of doing this is to assume a linear relationship between r and N_n,

$$r = a - bN_n, \quad a > 1, \quad b = (a-1)/C$$

(a being a constant), so that Equation (1.8) becomes

$$N_{n+1} = aN_n - bN_n^2. \tag{1.9}$$

This leads to the map

$$N_{n+1} = f(N_n),$$

where $f(N) = aN - bN^2$.

Exercise 1.8

Show that by introducing the new variable $x_n = kN_n$, one can find a k for which Equation (1.9) reduces to

$$x_{n+1} = ax_n(1 - x_n). \tag{1.10}$$

The map in Equation (1.10) is called the **logistic map** and will be studied extensively in the next unit.

For a system involving several different competing species, for example, species competing for the same food supply and/or preying off one another, the resulting population dynamics would be modelled by a higher-dimensional map describing the evolution of the populations of the different species. Such models, and more complicated ones, are useful in mathematical ecology.

1.3.2   The Newton–Raphson method

Suppose that we wish to find a solution of the equation $f(x) = 0$, for some function $f(x)$, and that this solution lies at $x = x_s$. The Newton–Raphson method gives an iterative map which under certain conditions provides successively improved estimates of x_s at each iterate starting from an initial guess x_0.

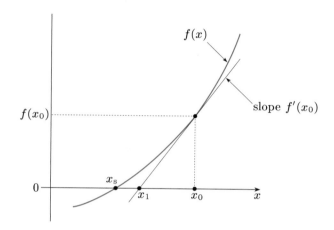

Figure 1.19   The Newton–Raphson method. The zero of $f(x)$ at x_s is required, with x_0 its first estimate and x_1 the next improved one.

The method is illustrated in Figure 1.19; x_0 is a first estimate for the solution x_s. The next improved estimate, x_1, is taken to be the point where the tangent to $f(x)$ at x_0 crosses the x-axis, as indicated in the figure. The point x_1 is related to x_0, $f(x_0)$ and $f'(x_0)$ by

$$f'(x_0) = \frac{f(x_0)}{x_0 - x_1},$$

which can be rearranged to yield

$$x_1 = x_0 - \frac{f(x_0)}{f'(x_0)}.$$

We can then repeat the above process by letting x_1 play the role of x_0 to obtain x_2, etc., leading to a series of successively improved estimates of x_s. This process can be expressed as the following *iterative map*:

$$x_{n+1} = F(x_n), \quad F(x) = x - \frac{f(x)}{f'(x)}. \tag{1.11}$$

We require that $f'(x_n) \neq 0$ for all $n = 0, 1, 2, \ldots$.

Exercise 1.9

The square root of a is the (positive) zero of the function $f(x) = x^2 - a$. Use this to construct an iterative map which gives successively improved estimates of $\sqrt{a}$. Write a Maple program to test it for $a = 5$.

The zero of the function $e^x - a$ is $\ln(a)$. Construct an iterative map giving improved estimates of $\ln(a)$, and test it using Maple for $a = 2$.

Exercise 1.11

Repeat the approach of Exercise 1.9, but this time to find the iterative map determining $a^{1/p}$ for general p. Test it using Maple for $p = 7$ and $a = 3$.

1.3.3 Finite-difference approximation to differential equations

A direct way of relating a differential equation to an iterative map is by applying a finite-difference approximation to it. Consider the one-dimensional differential equation for $x(t)$ (with $t \geq 0$)

$$\dot{x} = f(x), \quad x(0) = x_0. \tag{1.12}$$

Divide time into small discrete increments of duration h, i.e. $t = nh$, with $n = 0, 1, 2, \ldots$, and let $x_n = x(nh)$. Now approximate the time derivative $\dot{x}(nh)$ by the Euler forward difference $(x_{n+1} - x_n)/h$, so that the differential equation (1.12) is approximated by

$$\frac{x_{n+1} - x_n}{h} = f(x_n),$$

which can be rearranged as

$$x_{n+1} = x_n + hf(x_n). \tag{1.13}$$

In this context, Equation (1.13) is sometimes referred to as a *difference equation*, but for our purposes it is just another example of a map. Clearly, finite-difference approximations to higher-dimensional differential equations yield higher-dimensional maps. It is worth emphasizing that approximating differential equations by maps is how digital computers solve ordinary differential equations numerically, though the maps used tend to be considerably more sophisticated and accurate than that of the Euler method, Equation (1.13), presented here.

Exercise 1.12

Another approach to modelling population dynamics in biology is to keep time, $t \geq 0$, continuous and describe population growth using differential equations. An example of such an equation for the population size $x(t)$ is the *logistic differential equation*

$$\dot{x} = Ax - Bx^2, \quad x(0) = x_0. \tag{1.14}$$

(a) With $B = 0$, show that x grows exponentially for $A > 0$ and diminishes exponentially for $A < 0$.

(b) By dividing time into small increments, $t = nh$, with $x(nh) = x_n$, $n = 0, 1, 2, \ldots$, and applying Euler's method, show that the logistic differential equation is approximated by a map

$$x_{n+1} = ax_n - bx_n^2,$$

and give expressions for a and b.

Exercise 1.13

Consider the following second-order differential equation for $x(t)$, $t \geq 0$:

$$\ddot{x} + g(x)\dot{x} + f(x) = 0, \quad x(0) = x_0, \quad \dot{x}(0) = y_0.$$

By first rewriting this equation as a two-dimensional system of first-order differential equations, show that the Euler approximation, with discrete time $t = nh$, $n = 0, 1, 2, \ldots$, gives the two-dimensional map

$$x_{n+1} = x_n + hy_n,$$
$$y_{n+1} = y_n - h\left(g(x_n)y_n + f(x_n)\right),$$

where $x_n = x(nh)$ and $y_n = y(nh)$.

1.3.4   The time-*T* map and the Poincaré return map

Subsection 1.3.3 provided a link between differential equations and maps, although the approach involved an approximation, namely a finite-difference approximation. There is another type of map which can be extracted from differential equations that does *not* involve an approximation; these maps turn out to be very useful in elucidating the very convoluted paths that orbits can sometimes take, particularly when chaotic. Indeed, such maps are especially useful in the study of chaos, and they come in two (sometimes related) types, time-*T* and Poincaré return maps, to be described below. At this stage, it is worth emphasizing that these maps are usually easier to analyse than the differential equations from which they derive, and the orbits of the maps are, in general, much simpler to visualize. Moreover, maps can be approximated (in ways not usually applicable to differential equations), and useful insights can be gained by replacing exact maps by simpler 'model' maps which encapsulate the essential features of the dynamical system under study. Maps often exhibit behaviour generic to a wide class of systems, which justifies the study of these simplified maps.

The stroboscopic time-*T* map

The idea behind a **time-*T* map** is to generate a discrete set of points from a differential equation by taking 'snapshots' of its orbit at regular intervals (of duration T) in time, much like a stroboscope. For example, suppose we are given the following autonomous one-dimensional differential equation for $x(t)$, $t \geq 0$:

$$\dot{x} = f(x), \quad x(0) = x_0. \tag{1.15}$$

The discrete set of points are then $x_n = x(nT)$, $n = 0, 1, 2, \ldots$, and, since the differential equation is autonomous, x_{n+1} can be obtained by setting x_n as the initial condition in Equation (1.15) (instead of x_0) and then solving for $x(t)$ at $t = T$, calling the solution x_{n+1}. This process can be generalized for higher-dimensional autonomous differential equations, which will generate correspondingly higher-dimensional maps. For example, consider the differential equation

$$\dot{x} = Ax, \quad x(0) = x_0. \tag{1.16}$$

where A is a constant. Its solution is easily found to be (see Exercise 1.12)

$$x(t) = x_0 e^{At},$$

and therefore the time-T map is

$$x_{n+1} = e^{AT} x_n,$$

which can be obtained by setting $x(0)$ to x_n and evaluating $x(t)$ at $t = T$ to obtain x_{n+1}. So we have arrived at the map $x_{n+1} = F(x_n)$, where $F(x) = e^{AT} x$. This is an example of a **linear map** since $F(x)$ is a linear function of x.

However, time-T maps are more usefully applied to *nonautonomous* differential equations with a phase velocity which is *periodic* in time, i.e. differential equations where the explicit time dependence is periodic. You have already met such equations in this unit, for example the equation governing the motion of Hyperion, Equation (1.4), and the equation for a damped *driven* pendulum, Equation (1.6). In such cases the time step for the stroboscopic snapshots, T, is taken to be the periodicity of the system. Consider a one-dimensional example of such a system:

$$\dot{x} = f(x, t), \quad x(0) = x_0, \quad \text{and} \quad f(x, t + T) = f(x, t), \tag{1.17}$$

i.e. where the phase velocity $f(x, t)$ is periodic in t with period T. As before, identify the discrete set of points $x_n = x(nT)$, $n = 0, 1, 2, \ldots$, as the snapshots, and determine from the differential equation (1.17) the map $x_{n+1} = F(x_n)$. Now, since $f(x, t)$ repeats itself in time across each snapshot, the map function $F(x)$ does not depend on n, and the same function maps x_0 to x_1, and x_1 to x_2, etc., just as with the autonomous case discussed above. Thus the function $F(x)$ is obtained by solving Equation (1.17) for $x(t)$, given $x(0) = x_0$, determining $x_1 = x(T)$ and identifying the function $F(x)$ via $x_1 = F(x_0)$.

These ideas can be applied to higher-dimensional nonautonomous differential equations, and this will be discussed below. First we shall consider a particular instance of Equation (1.17),

$$\dot{x} = g(t)x, \quad x(0) = x_0, \quad \text{and} \quad g(t + T) = g(t), \tag{1.18}$$

which can be solved via the method of separation of variables. Putting

$$\int \frac{dx}{x} = \int g(t)\, dt,$$

and applying the initial condition, we obtain

$$\int_{x_0}^{x(t)} \frac{du}{u} = \ln \left| \frac{x(t)}{x_0} \right| = \int_0^t g(s)\, ds,$$

so

$$x(t) = x_0 \exp \left(\int_0^t g(s)\, ds \right), \tag{1.19}$$

from which the time-T map immediately follows via $x(T) = x_1 = F(x_0)$, where

$$F(x) = bx, \quad b = \exp \left(\int_0^T g(t)\, dt \right),$$

which is also a linear map. Note that Equation (1.19) confirms that x_n maps to x_{n+1} with the same map function $F(x)$ (independent of n) since

$$\frac{x_{n+1}}{x_n} = \exp \left(\int_{nT}^{(n+1)T} g(t)\, dt \right) = \exp \left(\int_0^T g(s)\, ds \right) = b, \tag{1.20}$$

and so $x_{n+1} = F(x_n)$, where the penultimate equality in (1.20) follows from a change of integration variable, $s = t - nT$, and the periodicity of g,

$$g(s + nT) = g(s).$$

Exercise 1.14

Find the time-T map for the differential equation

$$\dot{x} = (1 - \cos t)\, x, \quad x(0) = x_0,$$

where $T = 2\pi$.

In Section 1.2, you encountered higher-dimensional examples of nonautonomous differential equations containing terms periodic in time. Recall the equation for the driven pendulum (Equation (1.6)) on page 18. The equation is nonautonomous because of the presence of the periodic forcing term $\Gamma \sin(\Omega t)$, having period $T = 2\pi/\Omega$. The discrete-time states of the system can be identified as the values of $\theta(t)$ and $\dot{\theta}(t)$ at increments of the forcing period $T = 2\pi/\Omega$. So these states are

$$\begin{pmatrix} \theta_n \\ \dot{\theta}_n \end{pmatrix} = \begin{pmatrix} \theta(nT) \\ \dot{\theta}(nT) \end{pmatrix}, \tag{1.21}$$

and a two-dimensional map takes $\begin{pmatrix} \theta_n \\ \dot{\theta}_n \end{pmatrix}$ to $\begin{pmatrix} \theta_{n+1} \\ \dot{\theta}_{n+1} \end{pmatrix}$. It is possible to define a map in this way because an initial condition on $(\theta, \dot{\theta})$ *uniquely* determines the subsequent evolution. So $(\theta_n, \dot{\theta}_n)$ can be taken as the initial condition which uniquely determines $(\theta_{n+1}, \dot{\theta}_{n+1})$. Unfortunately, the resulting map cannot be expressed in simple mathematical terms, as in the above examples; instead the iterates are determined by solving the differential equation numerically across a single period T.

Another example of a differential equation containing periodic nonautonomous terms is that which describes the tumbling of Hyperion (Equation (1.4)), on page 16. Recall that Hyperion orbits Saturn with a fixed orbital period T. The variable which specifies Hyperion's distance from Saturn, $r(t)$, is periodic with period T, and the orbital angular variable, $f(t)$, appears in the equation within a periodic term, also of period T. Thus discrete-time states can be formed by recording values of $\theta(t)$ and $\dot{\theta}(t)$ at increments of the orbital period T, as in Equation (1.21). This would be equivalent to recording $\theta(t)$ and $\dot{\theta}(t)$ each time Hyperion crosses a given point in its orbit such as, say, the point P in Figure 1.8, so that θ_n and $\dot{\theta}_n$ would be the values of these variables at the nth passage across this point. A map then takes $\begin{pmatrix} \theta_n \\ \dot{\theta}_n \end{pmatrix}$ to $\begin{pmatrix} \theta_{n+1} \\ \dot{\theta}_{n+1} \end{pmatrix}$.

Exercise 1.15

Consider the equation for forced harmonic motion:

$$\ddot{x} + \omega^2 x = \Gamma \sin(\Omega t), \quad \text{where} \quad \Omega \neq \omega, \tag{1.22}$$

with $x(0) = x_0$ and $\dot{x}(0) = y_0$. Define $y(t) = \dot{x}$, $T = 2\pi/\Omega$, and let $\mathbf{x}(t) = \begin{pmatrix} x(t) \\ y(t)/\omega \end{pmatrix}$ and $\mathbf{x}_n = \mathbf{x}(nT)$, for $n = 0, 1, 2, \ldots$.

Show that the time-T map for $\mathbf{x}_n$ is given by

$$\mathbf{x}_{n+1} = \begin{pmatrix} c & s \\ -s & c \end{pmatrix} \mathbf{x}_n + \begin{pmatrix} -s \\ 1-c \end{pmatrix} R\Omega/\omega, \tag{1.23}$$

where $s = \sin(\omega T)$, $c = \cos(\omega T)$ and $R = \Gamma/(\omega^2 - \Omega^2)$. Note that the matrix multiplying $\mathbf{x}_n$ in Equation (1.23) is the rotation matrix for angle $-\omega T$.

The Poincaré return map

The orbits of differential equations can often appear very convoluted, as exemplified by those of the Lorenz system shown in Figure 1.16. Here, the orbit is complicated but stays bounded. Poincaré devised a way of distilling such complicated behaviour into something more digestible (though not, of course, for the Lorenz system). His idea is illustrated in Figure 1.20, which depicts the orbit of an autonomous three-dimensional system of differential equations.

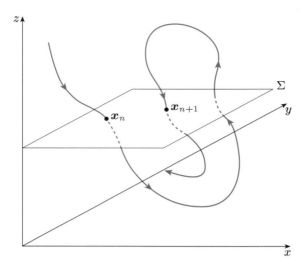

Figure 1.20   An orbit piercing the Poincaré section Σ in a downward direction at points $\mathbf{x}_n$, $n = 0, 1, 2, \ldots$, with $\mathbf{x}_n$ being the nth such intersection

Imagine a surface Σ, embedded in $\mathbb{R}^3$; in the example illustrated, Σ is a plane of constant z. The points in Σ are denoted by the vector $\mathbf{x}$; in the example, $\mathbf{x}$ specifies the (x, y)-coordinates on the constant-z surface. The surface Σ is called the **surface of section** or the **Poincaré section**. Now, each time the orbit pierces the surface Σ in the same sense, the downward direction in the case illustrated, the point of intersection is recorded, the nth such intersection being denoted by $\mathbf{x}_n$. The map $\mathbf{P} \colon \Sigma \longrightarrow \Sigma$ defined by

$$\mathbf{x}_{n+1} = \mathbf{P}(\mathbf{x}_n)$$

is called the **Poincaré return map**. Again, as with time-T maps, it is possible to define a map in this way because an initial condition for the differential equations uniquely determines all subsequent evolution. Thus $\mathbf{x}_n$ can be taken as an initial condition which uniquely determines subsequent points including $\mathbf{x}_{n+1}$. Hence the problem of understanding the (possibly) complicated behaviour of the continuous-time three-dimensional dynamical system has been simplified to the study of the two-dimensional map $\mathbf{P}(\mathbf{x})$. These ideas can be applied to general dimensions, so that two-dimensional differential equations give rise to one-dimensional Poincaré return maps, and more generally d-dimensional differential equations give $(d - 1)$-dimensional return maps. Also, Σ need not be a plane but can be generalized to other smooth surfaces as appropriate for the system under consideration. The main difference between time-T maps and Poincaré return maps is that the iterates in time-T maps are *equally spaced in time*, whereas this is not necessarily the case for the surface piercings in Σ which are the iterates of Poincaré return maps.

1.4   Differential equations: flows in phase space

This section is concerned with continuous-time dynamical systems applied to a d-dimensional vector $\mathbf{x}(t)$. The dynamical system, formulated as a d-dimensional system of first-order differential equations, is expressed in vector terms as

$$\dot{\mathbf{x}} = \mathbf{f}(\mathbf{x}), \quad \mathbf{x}(0) = \mathbf{x}_0, \tag{1.24}$$

with phase velocity $\mathbf{f} \colon \mathbb{R}^d \longrightarrow \mathbb{R}^d$. For example, when $d = 1$, $\mathbf{x}(t) = x(t)$ (a scalar), $\mathbf{x}_0 = x_0$, $\mathbf{f}(\mathbf{x}) = f(x)$, and Equation (1.24) reduces to Equation (1.1). Similarly, for $d = 2$, we write

$$\mathbf{x} = \begin{pmatrix} x \\ y \end{pmatrix}, \quad \mathbf{x}_0 = \begin{pmatrix} x_0 \\ y_0 \end{pmatrix} \quad \text{and} \quad \mathbf{f}(\mathbf{x}) = \begin{pmatrix} f(x, y) \\ g(x, y) \end{pmatrix},$$

so that Equation (1.24) becomes Equations (1.2). For $d = 3$, we could have $\mathbf{x} = (x, y, z)^T$ and $\mathbf{f}(\mathbf{x}) = (f, g, h)^T$ where f, g and h are all functions of x, y and z. An example of a three-dimensional system of this type is the Lorenz system, Equations (1.7) on page 20, where in this case $f = \sigma(y - x)$, $g = rx - y - xz$ and $h = xy - bz$. However, in most of what follows, only cases where $d < 3$ will be considered.

The superscript T notation denotes the *transpose* operation on a vector or matrix. So $(x, y)^T = \begin{pmatrix} x \\ y \end{pmatrix}$.

Note that Equation (1.24) is *autonomous*. In this section only autonomous systems will be considered. However, as you may recall from the discussion on page 11, this entails no loss of generality, since nonautonomous systems can be transformed to higher-dimensional *autonomous* systems. Furthermore, as also discussed in Subsection 1.1.1, Equation (1.24) also incorporates higher-order differential equations, again by going to a high enough dimension.

For nonlinear systems it is usually very difficult, or indeed impossible, to find the exact solution of Equation (1.24) in closed form. However, by taking a geometrical approach, it is possible to develop a qualitative understanding of the behaviour of its solutions. One can visualize the orbit of some initial vector $\mathbf{x}_0$ by tracking its path in the $\mathbf{x}$-space. This space is called the **phase space**, and the path is called the **phase path**. Figure 1.21 shows a two-dimensional example of this. In two dimensions, the phase space is sometimes referred to as the **phase plane**, in this case the xy-plane. From Equation (1.24), we can see that the phase velocity $\mathbf{f}(\mathbf{x})$ is a vector field which determines the velocity, $\dot{\mathbf{x}}$, of an orbit as it passes through the point $\mathbf{x}$ in phase space. One can also think of this velocity field as the **flow** of orbits (starting from various initial points) in phase space; at any given point in phase space, it gives the direction in which an orbit progresses as time increases. The term 'flow' will often be used in this way as if one were visualizing a fluid.

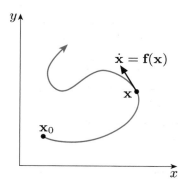

Figure 1.21   Path of the orbit of $\mathbf{x}_0$ in two dimensions

Some understanding of the range of behaviour of orbits for a system of differential equations can be obtained by constructing a diagram showing a range of possible flows in phase space. A collection of phase paths is referred to as a **phase flow**, and a diagram showing the phase flow is called a **phase portrait**; a schematic planar example is shown in Figure 1.22.

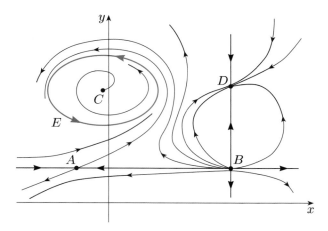

Figure 1.22   Schematic example of a phase portrait, with fixed points at A, B, C and D, and a limit cycle (shown in red) at E

Phase portraits can often be quite complicated, and in order to understand them it is necessary to identify their salient features, the most important being **fixed points** and **closed orbits**. Fixed points, also called **equilibrium points**, are points where the velocity $\dot{\mathbf{x}}$, or flow, is zero. From Equation (1.24), we can see that these points occur at the zeros of $\mathbf{f}(\mathbf{x})$. Four fixed points are shown in Figure 1.22, located at A, B, C and D. These fixed points could be **stable** (D), whereby all nearby orbits flow into them, or **unstable** (B and C), whereby all nearby orbits flow away from them. One can also find fixed points called **saddles** (A), which are also unstable in that almost all orbits eventually flow away from them, although there are exceptional orbits that flow into them. The other salient features, closed orbits, correspond to periodic solutions. An example is shown in Figure 1.22, marked out as the oval labelled E. Other orbits may asymptotically approach this closed path, as shown; in this case, such a structure is called a **limit cycle**. So an overall picture of the phase portrait can be developed by first identifying fixed points, closed orbits and limit cycles.

The discussion so far has tacitly assumed that the autonomous system of differential equations, given in Equation (1.24), actually *has* a solution. In fact, the following theorem, the proof of which will not be given here, resolves this issue in that, under certain reasonable assumptions on the vector field $\mathbf{f}(\mathbf{x})$, it establishes not only the **existence** of a solution but also its **uniqueness**. The theorem holds for general dimension.

Theorem 1.1

Consider the d-dimensional autonomous system $\dot{\mathbf{x}} = \mathbf{f}(\mathbf{x})$, with $\mathbf{x}(0) = \mathbf{x}_0$. If $\mathbf{f}(\mathbf{x})$ is continuous and the partial derivatives of all its components, with respect to each coordinate component, are continuous for $\mathbf{x}$ in some open connected set $D \subset \mathbb{R}^d$, then for $\mathbf{x}_0 \in D$, the system has a solution $\mathbf{x}(t)$ on an open time interval $-t_1 < t < t_1$, and this solution is *unique*.

In other words, if $\mathbf{f}(\mathbf{x})$ is continuously differentiable, then the existence and uniqueness of its solutions are guaranteed. The uniqueness of an orbit at a given point in phase space has an important consequence because it implies that orbits can *never* intersect; that is, no two phase paths can *pass* through the *same* point. If this were to happen, the uniqueness property would be violated because then there would exist initial points in phase space from which at least two different solutions could emerge. Note, however, that two or more orbits could meet at a fixed point, where they would come to a stop, and not proceed further, since at a fixed point $\dot{\mathbf{x}} = \mathbf{0}$, so they would not pass through the point.

In the remainder of this section, we first discuss flows in one-dimensional systems (Subsection 1.4.1), followed by fixed points in two-dimensional flows (Subsection 1.4.2), and then move on to a discussion on limit cycles (Subsection 1.4.3), mainly with reference to planar flows. Finally, we give an account of an important theorem which places restrictions on the flow properties of two-dimensional autonomous systems (Subsection 1.4.4).

1.4.1   One-dimensional flows

The one-dimensional version of Equation (1.24) is

$$\dot{x} = f(x), \quad x(0) = x_0.$$

We can solve this formally in terms of an integral as in Exercise 1.1. It may be possible to evaluate the integral to obtain a convenient closed-form expression for $x(t)$, but often it is not possible. Nevertheless, we can, with relative ease, obtain an understanding of the nature of the solutions by examining their flow properties in the one-dimensional phase space for x. As a starting point, consider the equation for $f(x) = ax$:

$$\dot{x} = ax, \quad x(0) = x_0, \quad a \neq 0.$$

The solution to this is

$$x(t) = x_0 e^{at}$$

(see Exercise 1.12(a)), which shows that, with increasing time, orbits move away from $x = 0$ if $a > 0$ and approach $x = 0$ if $a < 0$. In other words, $x = 0$ is an unstable fixed point when $a > 0$, and a stable fixed point when $a < 0$. But this behaviour could have been deduced without seeing the explicit solution. This follows by considering the dependence of the function $f(x) = ax$ on x. Any fixed point $x = x_{\mathrm{f}}$ must satisfy $f(x_{\mathrm{f}}) = 0$, and the only solution for this is $x_{\mathrm{f}} = 0$. Now, since $\dot{x} = f(x)$, when $f(x) > 0$ the orbits must flow in the positive x-direction, whereas when $f(x) < 0$ the flow must go in the negative x-direction. Figure 1.23 shows how to represent this graphically, where $f(x)$ is plotted as a function of x, and the large arrows indicate the direction of the flows in the one-dimensional phase space for x.

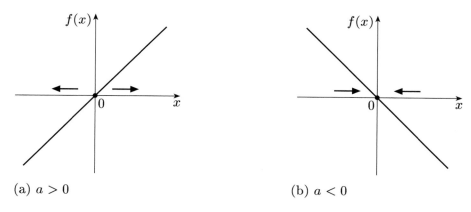

(a) $a > 0$ (b) $a < 0$

Figure 1.23   Flows for $f(x) = ax$; large arrows indicate direction of flow

Figure 1.23(a) shows that for $a > 0$, the orbits flow away from the fixed point at the origin because, for positive a, flows must point towards positive x when $x > 0$ and negative x when $x < 0$. Thus for $a > 0$ the fixed point is unstable. Figure 1.23(b) shows that for $a < 0$, the orbits flow towards the fixed point because in this case flows must point towards negative x when $x > 0$ and positive x when $x < 0$. Thus for $a < 0$ the origin is a stable fixed point. We stress that all this was deduced from the zero and the sign of $f(x)$ for various x; an explicit solution was not required.

A more complicated situation, for $\dot{x} = f(x)$, is shown in Figure 1.24. In this case, $f(x)$ has three zeros, the locations of which are the fixed points of the flow. Arrows representing the one-dimensional flow are drawn along the x-axis, with directions corresponding to the sign of $f(x)$: positive where $f(x) > 0$ and negative where $f(x) < 0$. Hence we find that one of the fixed points (x_2 in the figure) is unstable (because flow arrows point away from it), whilst the other two are stable (since flow arrows point towards them).

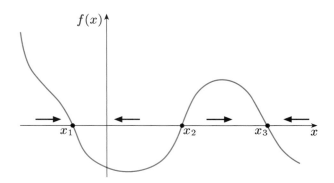

Figure 1.24   Flows for the differential equation $\dot{x} = f(x)$. Flows in x are indicated by large arrows. There are three fixed points: stable at x_1 and x_3, and unstable at x_2.

Note that, in general, if x_f is a fixed point of the flow $\dot{x} = f(x)$, so that $f(x_f) = 0$, then, provided $f'(x_f) \neq 0$, the following rule can simplify the determination of the stability of the fixed point: the fixed point is unstable if $f'(x_f) > 0$ and stable if $f'(x_f) < 0$.

Exercise 1.16

For the one-dimensional differential equation $\dot{x} = f(x)$, determine the fixed points and their stability, and sketch the one-dimensional phase flow on the real line for each of the following cases.

(a) $f(x) = x(1 - x^2)$ (b) $f(x) = -x^3$

(c) $f(x) = x^2(1 - x)$ (d) $f(x) = \sin x$

Exercise 1.17

For the logistic differential equation in Exercise 1.12 (page 26, Equation (1.14)), determine its fixed points and sketch the one-dimensional phase flow on the real line, taking care to consider all possible values of A and B, but assuming that $B \neq 0$.

1.4.2   Fixed points in two-dimensional flows

Here we consider fixed points in two-dimensional systems of differential equations, studying flow properties in their vicinities and their stability. As with the one-dimensional flows in the previous subsection, we consider only *autonomous* systems. First we look at the simpler case of linear systems of differential equations, and then we move on to nonlinear systems. It is important to study flows in linear systems because the methods developed in so doing can be applied to nonlinear systems near their fixed points, essentially by taking a linear approximation about these points.

Linear differential equations

A planar linear system of differential equations, for the variable $\mathbf{x}(t) \in \mathbb{R}^2$, can be expressed in terms of a constant 2×2 matrix $\mathbf{A}$ as

$$\dot{\mathbf{x}} = \mathbf{Ax}, \quad \mathbf{x}(0) = \mathbf{x}_0, \tag{1.25}$$

where the matrix of constants $\mathbf{A}$ is given by

$$\mathbf{A} = \begin{pmatrix} a & b \\ c & d \end{pmatrix}, \tag{1.26}$$

and $\mathbf{x} = (x, y)^T$. Throughout, $\mathbf{A}$ is taken to be *nonsingular*. This system always has a fixed point at $\mathbf{x} = \mathbf{0}$, for any $\mathbf{A}$, since here $\dot{\mathbf{x}} = \mathbf{A0} = \mathbf{0}$.

Exercise 1.18

For the more general inhomogeneous linear system

$$\dot{\mathbf{x}} = \mathbf{Ax} + \mathbf{h}, \tag{1.27}$$

where $\mathbf{h}$ is some constant planar vector, show that a change of variable

$$\mathbf{x} = \mathbf{v} - \mathbf{A}^{-1}\mathbf{h}, \tag{1.28}$$

where $\mathbf{A}^{-1}$ is the inverse of $\mathbf{A}$, leads to the homogeneous system $\dot{\mathbf{v}} = \mathbf{Av}$.

We now wish to determine the stability of the fixed point at $\mathbf{0}$ and the nature of the phase flow in its vicinity. This is done by examining the eigenvalues and eigenvectors of the matrix $\mathbf{A}$.

An eigenvector $\mathbf{u}$ of $\mathbf{A}$, with corresponding eigenvalue λ, satisfies the equation

$$\mathbf{Au} = \lambda\mathbf{u}. \tag{1.29}$$

Recall that the equation determining the eigenvalue λ is

$$\det(\mathbf{A} - \lambda\mathbf{I}) = 0, \tag{1.30}$$

where $\mathbf{I}$ is the identity matrix. Equation (1.30) can be expressed as a polynomial in λ, called the **characteristic polynomial**, the roots of which determine the values of the eigenvalues. Since $\mathbf{A}$ is the 2×2 matrix given in Equation (1.26), Equation (1.30) becomes

$$\begin{vmatrix} a - \lambda & b \\ c & d - \lambda \end{vmatrix} = 0, \tag{1.31}$$

giving a *quadratic* characteristic polynomial. In general, quadratics have two distinct roots, giving two distinct eigenvalues, λ_1 and λ_2, with respective eigenvectors $\mathbf{u}_1$ and $\mathbf{u}_2$.

Exercise 1.19

Show that for a 2×2 matrix $\mathbf{A}$, the characteristic polynomial can be expressed as

$$\lambda^2 - (\operatorname{tr} \mathbf{A})\lambda + \det \mathbf{A} = 0, \tag{1.32}$$

where $\operatorname{tr} \mathbf{A}$ denotes the trace of the matrix $\mathbf{A}$.

Exercise 1.20

Use the result of Exercise 1.19 to show that for a 2×2 matrix $\mathbf{A}$ with eigenvalues λ_1 and λ_2, the following relations hold:

$$\det \mathbf{A} = \lambda_1 \lambda_2, \quad \operatorname{tr} \mathbf{A} = \lambda_1 + \lambda_2.$$

So, by solving the quadratic in Equation (1.32), the eigenvalues are given by

$$2\lambda = \operatorname{tr} \mathbf{A} \pm \sqrt{(\operatorname{tr} \mathbf{A})^2 - 4 \det \mathbf{A}}. \tag{1.33}$$

Since we are assuming that $\mathbf{A}$ is nonsingular, this means that both of its eigenvalues are *non-zero*.

Let us now return to the planar linear system, Equation (1.25). Suppose that the initial vector $\mathbf{x}_0$ is parallel to an eigenvector $\mathbf{u}$ of $\mathbf{A}$, with corresponding eigenvalue λ. For the time being, the eigenvalues of $\mathbf{A}$ are assumed to be real. So, writing $\mathbf{x}_0 = c\mathbf{u}$, where c is a real constant, it follows that the solution of Equation (1.25) is

$$\mathbf{x}(t) = ce^{\lambda t}\mathbf{u}. \tag{1.34}$$

To see why this is so, first substitute Equation (1.34) into the left-hand side of Equation (1.25):

$$\dot{\mathbf{x}} = c\frac{d}{dt}\left(e^{\lambda t}\right)\mathbf{u} = c\lambda e^{\lambda t}\mathbf{u}.$$

Now substitute Equation (1.34) into the right-hand side of Equation (1.25):

$$\mathbf{A}\mathbf{x} = ce^{\lambda t}\mathbf{A}\mathbf{u} = ce^{\lambda t}\lambda\mathbf{u},$$

the last equality following from the definition of an eigenvalue. Therefore the left-hand and right-hand sides give identical results, showing that Equation (1.34) solves Equation (1.25). It has the correct initial value, since $\mathbf{x}(0) = c\mathbf{u} = \mathbf{x}_0$. Thus the *orbit* of $\mathbf{x}_0$ follows a straight-line path along the (eigen)direction $\mathbf{u}$, either away from the origin if $\lambda > 0$ or towards the origin if $\lambda < 0$.

Now, let us consider a general initial vector $\mathbf{x}_0$, not necessarily in an eigendirection. In general, the matrix $\mathbf{A}$ will have two distinct eigenvalues λ_1 and λ_2, again assumed to be real, with corresponding linearly independent eigenvectors $\mathbf{u}_1$ and $\mathbf{u}_2$. Since these two eigenvectors are linearly independent, any vector in the plane, including $\mathbf{x}_0$, can be expressed as a linear combination of them. Therefore we can write

$$\mathbf{x}_0 = c_1\mathbf{u}_1 + c_2\mathbf{u}_2, \tag{1.35}$$

where c_1 and c_2 are real constants, and, following reasoning similar to the above, the solution of Equation (1.25), with this initial vector, can be expressed as

$$\mathbf{x}(t) = c_1 e^{\lambda_1 t}\mathbf{u}_1 + c_2 e^{\lambda_2 t}\mathbf{u}_2. \tag{1.36}$$

Exercise 1.21

Show that Equation (1.36) solves the linear system of Equation (1.25).

From the solution given by Equation (1.36), we can now make the following observations. If $\lambda_1 > \lambda_2 > 0$, then all orbits (except at $\mathbf{0}$) flow away from the fixed point at the origin. Such a fixed point is unstable and is referred to as an **unstable node**. The phase flow for this case is shown in Figure 1.25(a). Note the role played by the two eigenvectors (or eigendirections) which are along the straight-line paths in the figure. In the case where $\lambda_1 < \lambda_2 < 0$, all orbits will eventually flow into the origin. The fixed point at the origin is then stable and is referred to as a **stable node**. The phase flow for this is shown in Figure 1.25(b).

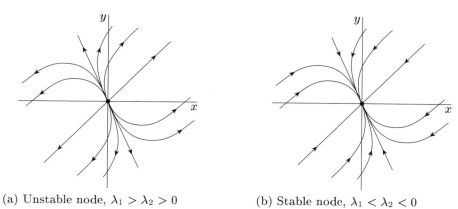

(a) Unstable node, $\lambda_1 > \lambda_2 > 0$ (b) Stable node, $\lambda_1 < \lambda_2 < 0$

Figure 1.25   *Nodal* phase flow with a fixed point at the origin. The straight-line paths are the eigendirections.

If $\lambda_1 > 0 > \lambda_2$, the orbits approach the fixed point towards the eigendirection $\mathbf{u}_2$ (with negative eigenvalue) but are eventually deflected away from it towards the other eigendirection $\mathbf{u}_1$ (with positive eigenvalue). The fixed point is therefore unstable but with properties different from an unstable node. Such a fixed point is called a **saddle point** and has the property that all orbits eventually flow away from it except those starting at $c\mathbf{u}_2$, which flow into it. The phase flow for a saddle point is shown in Figure 1.26.

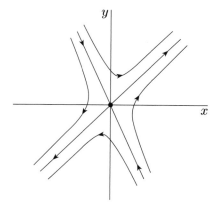

Figure 1.26   Phase flow with a *saddle point* at the origin, $\lambda_1 > 0 > \lambda_2$

So far, we have only considered matrices $\mathbf{A}$ which have two distinct real eigenvalues, $\lambda_1 \neq \lambda_2$. We now wish to describe the situation where the eigenvalues are real and repeated, i.e. $\lambda_1 = \lambda_2 = \lambda$. From Equation (1.33), this occurs when $(\mathrm{tr}\,\mathbf{A})^2 = 4 \det \mathbf{A}$. This situation occurs in the following two cases: (i) **A** is *diagonal*, for which one can show there are two linearly independent eigenvectors, and (ii) **A** is *non-diagonal*, where one can show that there is only *one* linearly independent eigenvector.

Let us start by considering the first case, **A** diagonal. Here, **A** takes the form

$$\mathbf{A} = \begin{pmatrix} \lambda & 0 \\ 0 & \lambda \end{pmatrix},$$

so the linear system, Equation (1.25), decouples to give

$$\dot{x} = \lambda x, \quad x(0) = x_0,$$
$$\dot{y} = \lambda y, \quad y(0) = y_0.$$

The solution of equations of this type should, by now, be familiar and is

$$x(t) = x_0 e^{\lambda t}, \quad y(t) = y_0 e^{\lambda t},$$

which can be expressed in vector form as

$$\mathbf{x}(t) = e^{\lambda t} \mathbf{x}_0.$$

The orbit then flows in a straight-line path in the direction of the initial vector $\mathbf{x}_0$, away from the origin for $\lambda > 0$ (unstable fixed point) and towards the origin for $\lambda < 0$ (stable fixed point). Therefore the phase flow for such a fixed point consists of straight lines radiating from it, and such a fixed point is called an **unstable star** in the case where it is unstable and a **stable star** where it is stable. The phase flows for unstable and stable stars are illustrated in Figure 1.27.

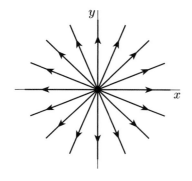

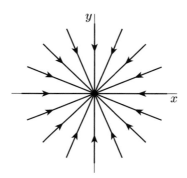

(a) Unstable star, $\lambda_1 = \lambda_2 > 0$ and **A** diagonal

(b) Stable star, $\lambda_1 = \lambda_2 < 0$ and **A** diagonal

Figure 1.27 *Star* phase flow with a fixed point at the origin

Let us now consider the other case of repeated eigenvalues, where **A** is non-diagonal. In this case there is only one independent eigenvector. A way to understand the phase flow for such a fixed point is to consider the flow at nodes, as shown in Figure 1.25, and to imagine bringing the two eigendirections together into a single line. The resulting phase flow is shown in Figure 1.28, and such a fixed point is called an **unstable improper node** when it is unstable ($\lambda > 0$) and a **stable improper node** when it is stable ($\lambda < 0$).

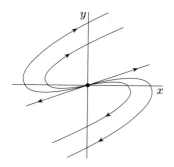
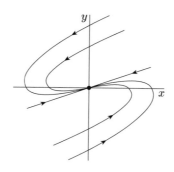

(a) Unstable improper node,
   $\lambda_1 = \lambda_2 > 0$ and $\mathbf{A}$ non-diagonal

(b) Stable improper node,
   $\lambda_1 = \lambda_2 < 0$ and $\mathbf{A}$ non-diagonal

Figure 1.28   *Improper nodal* phase flow with a fixed point at the origin

Up to now, we have assumed that the eigenvalues of $\mathbf{A}$ are real. Of course, complex-valued eigenvalues are possible, since they are roots of a quadratic, in which case they appear as a complex conjugate pair

$$\lambda_1 = \nu + i\omega, \quad \lambda_2 = \nu - i\omega, \quad \omega \neq 0,$$

with ν and ω being real. The arguments leading to Equations (1.35) and (1.36) remain valid for complex eigenvalues. The eigenvectors $\mathbf{u}_1$ and $\mathbf{u}_2$ can be expressed as a complex conjugate pair, $\bar{\mathbf{u}}_2 = \mathbf{u}_1 = \mathbf{u}$. Then, since $\mathbf{x}_0$ must be real, the constants c_1 and c_2 must also be complex conjugates, $\bar{c}_2 = c_1 = c$, and $\mathbf{x}_0$ can be written as $\mathbf{x}_0 = 2\,\mathrm{Re}(c\mathbf{u})$. From Equation (1.36) we then have

The notation $\bar{z}$ denotes the complex conjugate of z.

Recall that $z + \bar{z} = 2\,\mathrm{Re}(z)$.

$$\mathbf{x}(t) = e^{\nu t}\left(ce^{i\omega t}\mathbf{u} + \bar{c}e^{-i\omega t}\bar{\mathbf{u}}\right) = 2e^{\nu t}\,\mathrm{Re}(ce^{i\omega t}\mathbf{u}). \tag{1.37}$$

The important thing to note from Equation (1.37) is that the components of $\mathbf{x}(t)$ consist of linear combinations of $\cos(\omega t)$ and $\sin(\omega t)$ multiplied by a factor of $e^{\nu t}$; other details are not important here. Thus the orbits oscillate about the fixed point, and spiral away from it for $\nu > 0$ (fixed point is unstable) or spiral into it when $\nu < 0$ (fixed point is stable). So, for $\nu \neq 0$, the phase paths have spiral shapes, and the fixed point is called an **unstable spiral** for $\nu > 0$ or a **stable spiral** for $\nu < 0$. Typical spiral phase flows are shown in Figure 1.29.

Recall that $e^{\pm i\omega t} = \cos(\omega t) \pm i\sin(\omega t)$.

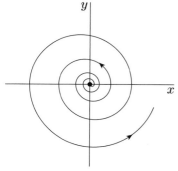
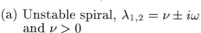
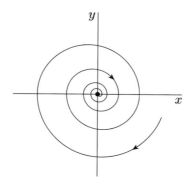

(a) Unstable spiral, $\lambda_{1,2} = \nu \pm i\omega$
   and $\nu > 0$

(b) Stable spiral, $\lambda_{1,2} = \nu \pm i\omega$
   and $\nu < 0$

Figure 1.29   *Spiral* phase flows with a fixed point at the origin

If $\nu = 0$, i.e. the eigenvalues of $\mathbf{A}$ are purely imaginary, then the orbits are periodic, with period $T = 2\pi/\omega$, and the phase paths are closed *elliptical* paths centred on the origin, as shown in Figure 1.30. The major and minor axes of the ellipses are not necessarily parallel to the coordinate axes. Such a fixed point is called a **centre**.

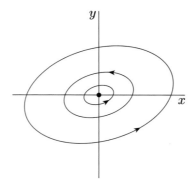

Figure 1.30   Phase flow about a *centre* at the origin, $\lambda_{1,2} = \pm i\omega$

In conclusion, the stability of a fixed point, and its classification (i.e. node, spiral etc.), is determined from the eigenvalues of **A**. The following table summarizes how a fixed point is classified from the eigenvalues of **A**.

Eigenvalues real $\lambda_1, \lambda_2 \in \mathbb{R}$	$\lambda_1 > \lambda_2 > 0$	unstable node
	$\lambda_1 < \lambda_2 < 0$	stable node
	$\lambda_1 > 0 > \lambda_2$	saddle point
	$\lambda_1 = \lambda_2 > 0$ and **A** diagonal	unstable star
	$\lambda_1 = \lambda_2 < 0$ and **A** diagonal	stable star
	$\lambda_1 = \lambda_2 > 0$ and **A** non-diagonal	unstable improper node
	$\lambda_1 = \lambda_2 < 0$ and **A** non-diagonal	stable improper node
Eigenvalues complex $\lambda_{1,2} = \nu \pm i\omega$ $\nu, \omega \in \mathbb{R},\ \omega \neq 0$	$\nu > 0$	unstable spiral
	$\nu < 0$	stable spiral
	$\nu = 0$	centre

Let us now consider an example.

Example 1.1

Classify the fixed point of the linear system

$$\dot{x} = 2x - 2y, \quad \dot{y} = 2x - 3y.$$

Solution

When expressing this system in vector form, $\dot{\mathbf{x}} = \mathbf{A}\mathbf{x}$, the matrix **A** is

$$\mathbf{A} = \begin{pmatrix} 2 & -2 \\ 2 & -3 \end{pmatrix},$$

so $\operatorname{tr} \mathbf{A} = -1$ and $\det \mathbf{A} = -2$. Thus, from Equation (1.33) on page 36, the eigenvalues of **A** are given by

$$2\lambda = -1 \pm \sqrt{1 + 8},$$

and therefore take values $\lambda_1 = 1$ and $\lambda_2 = -2$. So $\lambda_1 > 0 > \lambda_2$, and hence the fixed point is a *saddle point*. ◆

Exercise 1.22

Classify the fixed points of the following linear systems.

(a) $\dot{x} = 2x + 2y, \quad \dot{y} = -2x - y$

(b) $\dot{x} = -2x + y, \quad \dot{y} = x - 2y$

(c) $\dot{x} = 3x - y, \quad \dot{y} = x + y$

(d) $\dot{x} = 2x - 3y, \quad \dot{y} = 2x - 2y$

Exercise 1.23

The equation for damped (and undamped) simple harmonic motion is

$$\ddot{x} + c\dot{x} + \omega^2 x = 0,$$

where $c \geq 0$ ($c = 0$ being the undamped case) and $\omega > 0$. Use the results of Exercise 1.2 to represent this equation in matrix form, $\dot{\mathbf{x}} = \mathbf{A}\mathbf{x}$. Hence classify the fixed point at $\mathbf{x} = \mathbf{0}$, taking care to distinguish all possible cases as c varies within the range $0 \leq c < \infty$.

Nonlinear differential equations

Now consider the general *nonlinear* two-dimensional flow, Equation (1.24) for $d = 2$, which we now express in component form as

$$\dot{x} = f(x, y), \quad \dot{y} = g(x, y), \tag{1.38}$$

with initial values $(x(0), y(0)) = (x_0, y_0)$. Suppose that the system has a fixed point at $\mathbf{x}_f = (x_f, y_f)^T$. This satisfies $\mathbf{f}(\mathbf{x}_f) = 0$, so

$$f(x_f, y_f) = 0, \quad g(x_f, y_f) = 0.$$

As with linear systems, we wish to determine the stability of this fixed point and classify it. This is done by expanding Equations (1.38) about $\mathbf{x} = \mathbf{x}_f$ using Taylor's theorem for functions of two variables. So, writing

$$u = x - x_f, \quad v = y - y_f,$$

then substituting into Equations (1.38) and applying Taylor's expansion, we obtain

$$\begin{aligned}
\dot{u} &= u f_x(x_f, y_f) + v f_y(x_f, y_f) + \cdots, \\
\dot{v} &= u g_x(x_f, y_f) + v g_y(x_f, y_f) + \cdots,
\end{aligned} \tag{1.39}$$

keeping only terms linear in u and v (the ellipsis indicates higher-order terms such as u^2, v^2, uv, etc.), and where we have used the notation

$$f_x = \frac{\partial f}{\partial x}, \quad f_y = \frac{\partial f}{\partial y}, \quad \text{etc.}$$

We now define the vector $\mathbf{v}$ and the **Jacobian matrix J** by

$$\mathbf{v} = \mathbf{x} - \mathbf{x}_f = \begin{pmatrix} u \\ v \end{pmatrix}, \quad \mathbf{J}(\mathbf{x}) = \begin{pmatrix} f_x(x, y) & f_y(x, y) \\ g_x(x, y) & g_y(x, y) \end{pmatrix},$$

so that Equations (1.39) can be expressed as

$$\dot{\mathbf{v}} = \mathbf{J}(\mathbf{x}_f)\mathbf{v} + \cdots. \tag{1.40}$$

Throughout, it is assumed that $\mathbf{J}$ is *nonsingular*. Recall that we wish to classify the fixed point, and therefore we are only interested in the phase flow in the immediate vicinity of $\mathbf{x}_f$. In this region, terms nonlinear in u and v are small compared to linear terms, so we might expect that the

The term Jacobian (to describe the determinant of what is now known as the Jacobian matrix) was coined by James Joseph Sylvester (1814–97) in 1852. It was named for Carl Gustav Jacob Jacobi (1804–51), who first introduced the notion in 1841.

nature of the fixed point can be deduced from the linearized system $\dot{\mathbf{v}} = \mathbf{A}\mathbf{v}$ where $\mathbf{A} = \mathbf{J}(\mathbf{x}_f)$. The classification of the fixed point at $\mathbf{v} = \mathbf{0}$ can then be determined from the eigenvalues of $\mathbf{A}$, as explained previously.

Let us now look at an example.

Example 1.2

Find and classify the fixed points of the nonlinear system

$$\dot{x} = x - y, \quad \dot{y} = x(1 - x) + y.$$

Solution

Defining $f(x, y) = x - y$ and $g(x, y) = x(1 - x) + y$, the fixed points must satisfy $f(x, y) = g(x, y) = 0$. Now, $f(x, y) = 0$ implies that $x = y$ at the fixed points. Substituting this into the equation for $g(x, y)$ implies that at the fixed points,

$$x(1 - x) + x = x(2 - x) = 0,$$

implying that $x = 0$ or $x = 2$, so the fixed points are at $(0, 0)$ and $(2, 2)$. Now, $f_x = 1$, $f_y = -1$, $g_x = 1 - 2x$ and $g_y = 1$, so the Jacobian for this system is

$$\mathbf{J}(x, y) = \begin{pmatrix} 1 & -1 \\ 1 - 2x & 1 \end{pmatrix}.$$

For the fixed point at $(0, 0)$,

$$\mathbf{J}(0, 0) = \begin{pmatrix} 1 & -1 \\ 1 & 1 \end{pmatrix},$$

so $\operatorname{tr} \mathbf{J} = 2$ and $\det \mathbf{J} = 2$, from which, by applying Equation (1.33), the eigenvalues of $\mathbf{J}(0, 0)$ are given by

$$2\lambda = 2 \pm \sqrt{4 - 8},$$

which gives the complex conjugate pair $\lambda = 1 \pm i$, having positive real part. Therefore $(0, 0)$ is an *unstable spiral*.

For the fixed point at $(2, 2)$,

$$\mathbf{J}(2, 2) = \begin{pmatrix} 1 & -1 \\ -3 & 1 \end{pmatrix},$$

so $\operatorname{tr} \mathbf{J} = 2$ and $\det \mathbf{J} = -2$, from which, by applying Equation (1.33), the eigenvalues of $\mathbf{J}(2, 2)$ are given by

$$2\lambda = 2 \pm \sqrt{4 + 8},$$

so $\lambda_1 = 1 + \sqrt{3}$ and $\lambda_2 = 1 - \sqrt{3}$. Hence, since $\lambda_1 > 0 > \lambda_2$, $(2, 2)$ is a *saddle point*. ◆

A question now arises. Is it safe to neglect higher-order terms and assume the equivalence of the nonlinear system with its linearized counterpart? The answer is provided by a theorem (a proof of which will not be given here) which states that the phase flow of the linearized system is qualitatively equivalent to that of the nonlinear system in a region sufficiently close to the fixed point *provided* that the fixed point of the linearized system is *not* one of the special borderline cases, that is, *not* a *centre*, *star* or *improper node*. So if the linearized system predicts a node, saddle point or spiral, the fixed point of the nonlinear system will also be a node, saddle point, or spiral, respectively, and with the same stability. This is not necessarily the case for a centre, star or improper node.

However, in the case of a star or improper node, the *stability* of the fixed point is still correctly predicted by the linearized system. So if the linearized system predicts a stable star or stable improper node, the fixed point of the nonlinear system may instead be a stable node but it will still be *stable*. Similarly, if the linearized system predicts an unstable star or an unstable improper node, the fixed point in the nonlinear system will be unstable too. The theorem has more important implications for a centre, because here the stability could change when taking into account higher-order terms. A centre in the linearized system may be an *unstable* or *stable* spiral in the nonlinear system.

Exercise 1.24

Find and classify the fixed points of the following nonlinear systems.

(a) $\dot{x} = y, \quad \dot{y} = x^2 - 3x + y + 2$

(b) $\dot{x} = -2x + y, \quad \dot{y} = x^2 + y^2 - 5$

1.4.3 Limit cycles

A **limit cycle** is an *isolated* closed orbit, i.e. closed in phase space and therefore periodic in time. It is isolated in the sense that neighbouring orbits (that is, all orbits in some neighbourhood of the limit cycle) are not closed but either approach the limit cycle asymptotically, as in the case of a **stable limit cycle**, or move further away from it, as for an **unstable limit cycle**. A phase portrait showing a stable limit cycle is given in Figure 1.31(a), and another showing an unstable limit cycle is given in Figure 1.31(b). One may also find a **half-stable limit cycle** – an example is given in Figure 1.31(c) – where neighbouring orbits on one side approach the limit cycle but neighbouring orbits on the other side move further away.

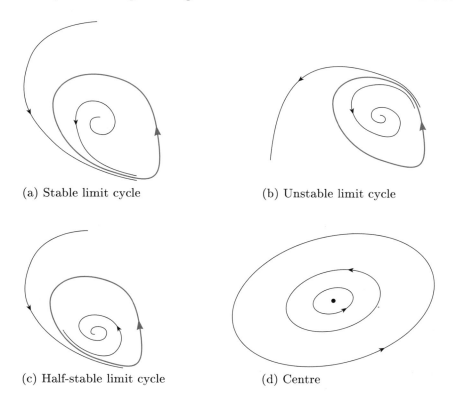

(a) Stable limit cycle

(b) Unstable limit cycle

(c) Half-stable limit cycle

(d) Centre

Figure 1.31 Schematic phase portraits showing periodic orbits, with (a) to (c) being limit cycles (shown in red) and (d) being a centre

Limit cycles emerge spontaneously from some differential equations without the need of a periodic forcing term. In this sense they are self-sustaining, and the amplitude and periodicity of their oscillations are inherent in the differential equation and do not depend on initial conditions. Some examples will be given below, but it is important to note that limit cycles can *only* be found in *nonlinear* systems; they do *not* occur in linear systems. Of course, closed periodic orbits do occur in linear systems. These are the closed elliptical orbits that surround *centres*, as discussed above in Subsection 1.4.2 and shown schematically in Figure 1.31(d). But for centres, the closed orbits are *not* isolated; each closed orbit is flanked by neighbouring closed orbits. This feature is characteristic of linearity: if the periodic orbit $\mathbf{x}(t)$ is a solution of the linear system $\dot{\mathbf{x}} = \mathbf{A}\mathbf{x}$, then so too is $c\mathbf{x}(t)$, for any constant c, and the amplitude of the periodic orbit is fixed by the initial conditions.

The closed-curve solution in phase space found for the van der Pol oscillator in Section 4.6 of Block A is an example of a limit cycle.

Limit cycles are very important in the real world. The beating of a heart is a nonlinear oscillation which, when naively modelled by a system of nonlinear differential equations, is an example of a stable limit cycle. This is important for the function of the heart; if the heart is perturbed in some way, made to beat faster, say, then after removing the perturbation the heartbeat (usually) reverts back to its normal spontaneous amplitude and periodicity. A linear oscillation would not achieve this. Other examples of limit cycles are the self-sustaining oscillations in certain electronic circuits; spontaneously oscillating chemical reactions; and the very dangerous spontaneous oscillations which can emerge in vibrating structures such as some bridges and aircraft wings.

Let us now turn to an example of a two-dimensional differential system with a limit cycle. Perhaps the simplest example to analyse is one expressed in terms of polar coordinates $(r(t), \theta(t))$, where

$$x(t) = r(t)\cos\theta(t), \quad y(t) = r(t)\sin\theta(t).$$

Exercise 1.25

Show that the two-dimensional system expressed in Cartesian coordinates in Equations (1.38), on page 41, has the following form when expressed in polar coordinates:

$$\dot{r} = f(r\cos\theta, r\sin\theta)\cos\theta + g(r\cos\theta, r\sin\theta)\sin\theta,$$
$$\dot{\theta} = \left(g(r\cos\theta, r\sin\theta)\cos\theta - f(r\cos\theta, r\sin\theta)\sin\theta\right)/r.$$

So, as seen in Exercise 1.25, it is possible to express a two-dimensional system in polar form. Consider now the following two-dimensional system written in polar form:

$$\begin{aligned} \dot{r} &= r(1 - r^2), \\ \dot{\theta} &= 1, \end{aligned} \tag{1.41}$$

with initial condition $(r(0), \theta(0)) = (r_0, \theta_0)$. In this system, the radial coordinate $r(t)$ and the angular coordinate $\theta(t)$ are decoupled, which makes analysis easier. Indeed, the solution of the equation for θ is easy to find, being just $\theta(t) = t + \theta_0$ for the given initial condition. For the equation for r, we can use the methods expounded in Subsection 1.4.1 for one-dimensional flows to determine the flow properties of $r(t)$. Thus, plotting $\dot{r} = r(1 - r^2)$ against r, as in Figure 1.32(a), we see that the flow of r proceeds in the positive r-direction for $0 < r < 1$, and in the negative r-direction for $r > 1$, with an unstable fixed point on the r-line at $r = 0$, and a stable 'fixed point' on the r-line at $r = 1$. This translates in the $r\theta$-plane to there being an *unstable spiral* at the origin and a *stable limit cycle* on the circle $r = 1$. The phase portrait is shown in Figure 1.32(b).

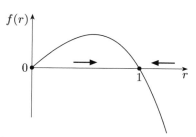

(a) Flow of the radial coordinate $r(t)$, for $\dot{r} = f(r) = r(1 - r^2)$

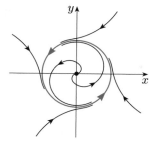

(b) Phase portrait showing the unstable spiral at the origin and the limit cycle at $r = 1$

Figure 1.32   Flow of the radial component and phase portrait for the system $\dot{r} = r(1 - r^2),\ \dot{\theta} = 1$

Exercise 1.26

Show that Equations (1.41) can be expressed in Cartesian coordinates as

$$\dot{x} = x\left(1 - x^2 - y^2\right) - y,$$
$$\dot{y} = y\left(1 - x^2 - y^2\right) + x. \tag{1.42}$$

Hence confirm, by linearizing and using the methods of Subsection 1.4.2, that the origin is an unstable spiral.

Exercise 1.27

Describe the phase portrait of the following system, pointing out the location and stability of any fixed points or limit cycles:

$$\dot{x} = x\left(1 - x^2 - y^2\right)\left(x^2 + y^2 - 4\right) - y,$$
$$\dot{y} = y\left(1 - x^2 - y^2\right)\left(x^2 + y^2 - 4\right) + x.$$

[*Hint*: Express the system in polar form first.]

Exercise 1.28

Describe the phase portrait of the following system expressed in polar form,

$$\dot{r} = -r\left(1 - r^2\right)^2,\quad \dot{\theta} = 1,$$

taking care to locate any fixed points or limit cycles and determining their stability if found.

1.4.4   The Poincaré–Bendixson theorem

Here we state, without a proof, an important theorem concerned with autonomous two-dimensional flows. Recall that, as a consequence of Theorem 1.1, different phase paths of some autonomous system $\dot{\mathbf{x}} = \mathbf{f}(\mathbf{x})$, with continuously differentiable $\mathbf{f}$, cannot pass through the same point in phase space. This constraint has particular potency in two dimensions. For example, suppose a system has a closed orbit in phase space, i.e. a periodic solution. Then any other orbit whose initial point $\mathbf{x}_0$ was inside this closed orbit could *never* reach points outside it because this would require two orbits passing through the same point. The orbit initially inside the closed orbit would stay inside it for all time. So for two dimensions (but not three or higher), geometrical constraints coupled with uniqueness place special limitations on the nature of the phase flow. We now state the **Poincaré–Bendixson theorem**.

Theorem 1.2

Consider the two-dimensional *autonomous* system $\dot{\mathbf{x}} = \mathbf{f}(\mathbf{x})$, with $\mathbf{x}(0) = \mathbf{x}_0$ and $\mathbf{f}$ continuously differentiable. Let D be a closed bounded region in $\mathbb{R}^2$. If a solution of the system $\mathbf{x}(t)$ is such that $\mathbf{x}(t) \in D$ for all $t \geq 0$ (i.e. the solution stays bounded), then this orbit must (i) be a closed path (i.e. a periodic orbit); or (ii) approach a closed path (i.e. a limit cycle) as $t \to \infty$; or (iii) approach a fixed point as $t \to \infty$.

This theorem, whose proof is beyond the scope of this course, implies that chaos is not possible in autonomous two-dimensional flows, since chaotic orbits are bounded but clearly their long-term behaviour does not come under any of the categories listed in Theorem 1.2. *A fortiori*, chaos cannot occur in one-dimensional flows. An example of this theorem in action is when considering chaos in the pendulums discussed in Subsection 1.2.2. For the single nonlinear pendulum, illustrated in Figure 1.12, chaos was possible only with the inclusion of the forcing term $\Gamma \sin(\Omega t)$. This is because Equation (1.6) without this term can be expressed as an autonomous two-dimensional flow and, from the Poincaré–Bendixson theorem, this cannot give chaotic solutions. Therefore one needs to make it nonautonomous, hence the forcing term. However, this is not the case for the double pendulum shown in Figure 1.13. In this case, the equation of motion has two displacement variables, θ_1 and θ_2, and two velocities, $\dot{\theta}_1$ and $\dot{\theta}_2$, giving rise to a four-dimensional system of differential equations, and the Poincaré–Bendixson theorem does not apply to such systems.

1.5   Duffing's equation

In the previous section, only autonomous differential equations were considered, and usually in just one or two dimensions, where, as a result of the Poincaré–Bendixson theorem, chaos is not possible. We now consider some *nonautonomous* differential equations in two dimensions. In this case chaos cannot be ruled out by Theorem 1.2; in any case, two-dimensional nonautonomous systems are equivalent to three-dimensional autonomous systems, where chaos is possible. We start with a brief discussion of forced damped simple harmonic motion and, in particular, its long-term steady-state behaviour. This is, of course, a linear equation, but it will lead on to a consideration of a similar equation, differing mainly through the inclusion of a nonlinear (cubic) term. It will be demonstrated that such a modification leads to radically different behaviour, including chaotic motion. This last section of this introductory unit will serve to acquaint you with some of the concepts discussed later in the block, and it will also emphasize the value of maps as a way of distilling information from the much more complicated orbits coming from differential equations.

1.5.1 The simple harmonic oscillator revisited

Recall the equation describing the driven damped pendulum, Equation (1.6) on page 18. If the angle of the pendulum, $\theta(t)$, is always kept small, by appropriate choice of initial conditions, then the equation of motion is well approximated by a linear equation, which we now express with $x(t)$ replacing $\theta(t)$:

$$\ddot{x} + c\dot{x} + \omega^2 x = \Gamma \sin(\Omega t). \tag{1.43}$$

This is the equation for forced damped simple harmonic motion, with natural angular frequency ω (where $\omega = \sqrt{g/l}$ for the pendulum). In the absence of the sinusoidal force $\Gamma \sin(\Omega t)$, the system has a fixed point at $x = \dot{x} = 0$, the phase flow properties of which were deduced in Exercise 1.23, where it was found that, for $c > 0$, all orbits tend to the fixed point at the origin. With the inclusion of the forcing term, the solution of Equation (1.43) consists of two terms, the **transient** term, which is the solution of the homogeneous form of Equation (1.43), and the **steady-state** solution, which is the *particular integral* for Equation (1.43). For $c > 0$ (positive damping), the transient term gets vanishingly small as time progresses, eventually leaving only the steady-state term as the solution. This steady-state solution has the form

$$x(t) = R\cos(\Omega t + \phi), \tag{1.44}$$

where R and ϕ are constants, so its periodicity is identical to that of the forcing term. Thus, with $y = \dot{x}$, the steady-state phase curve is the ellipse centred on the fixed point at the origin,

$$x^2 + \frac{y^2}{\Omega^2} = R^2,$$

which is illustrated in Figure 1.33.

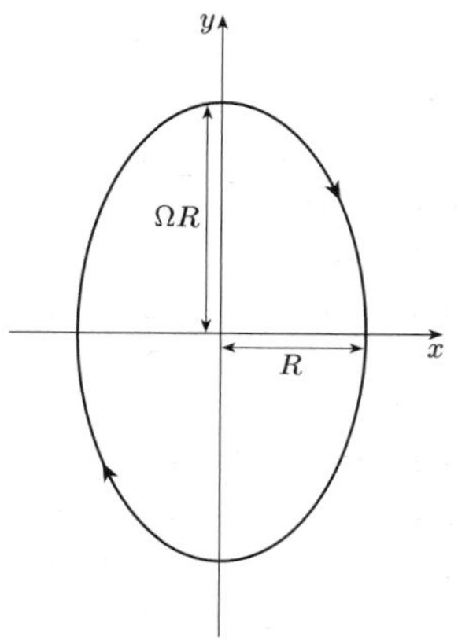

Figure 1.33 Steady-state phase curve for forced damped simple harmonic motion

Exercise 1.29

Show that for the forced damped simple harmonic system in Equation (1.43), the amplitude R of the steady-state solution is given by

$$R = \frac{\Gamma}{\sqrt{\left(\Omega^2 - \omega^2\right)^2 + c^2\Omega^2}}.$$

1.5.2 Duffing's double-well oscillator

Consider the experimental set-up illustrated in Figure 1.34. A flexible steel beam is fixed at one end with its free end placed near two permanent magnets, as shown. Because the beam is made of steel (and is ferromagnetic), its free end is attracted to the magnets in such a way that it tends to bend towards one or the other. A sinusoidal force $\Gamma \sin(\Omega t)$ is applied to the whole apparatus, but in the absence of this force the beam will settle into one of two equilibrium positions, located according to which magnet the beam bends towards.

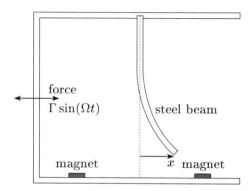

Figure 1.34 Apparatus of the magneto-elastic system consisting of a (ferromagnetic) steel beam oscillating between two permanent magnets

The horizontal displacement of the free end is denoted by $x(t)$ (see the figure), and it is the dynamics of this variable which is of interest here. The motion of x can be shown to be well described by the equation

$$\ddot{x} + c\dot{x} - x + x^3 = \Gamma \sin(\Omega t), \tag{1.45}$$

where $c > 0$ is a damping constant. This equation is sometimes called the **double-well Duffing equation**, a particular version of Duffing's equation. Note that it differs from the equation for forced damped simple harmonic motion in that the *sign* of the x term is reversed, and there is a *cubic* term, x^3; the resulting dynamics are very different.

The 'double-well' refers to the shape of the potential energy graph, which has two minima of equal depth located at the two equilibrium positions of the beam.

Exercise 1.30

Express Equation (1.45) as a two-dimensional system of first-order differential equations. In the case where $\Gamma = 0$, locate all the fixed points and classify them, considering all cases where $c \geq 0$.

On completing Exercise 1.30, you will have found two stable fixed points in phase space at $(-1, 0)$ and $(1, 0)$, these being the two stable equilibrium positions of the beam, and an unstable fixed point at $(0, 0)$, corresponding to the unstable equilibrium position of the beam where it is unbent (straight) and equidistant from the two magnets.

As a result of the nonlinear term x^3, the prospect of finding analytical solutions of Equation (1.45) in the presence of the forcing term is pretty hopeless, so Maple will now be used to numerically investigate this equation. We start by plotting orbits on the (x, y) phase plane, with $y = \dot{x}$, and for t sufficiently large to allow transients to vanish, just as we did for the harmonic oscillator: Figure 1.33 shows only the *steady-state* phase curve. This is done by using the Maple procedure `dufforbit` which takes as input the parameters Γ, Ω and c, together with $x_{\min}$, $x_{\max}$, $y_{\min}$ and $y_{\max}$ (written as `xmin` etc. in the Maple code), and plots the orbit for $100 \leq t \leq 500$, displayed in the delimited plane $x_{\min} < x < x_{\max}$ and $y_{\min} < y < y_{\max}$. The initial condition is set to be $x(0) = 1$ and $y(0) = 0.5$.

```
>   restart:  with(DEtools):
>   dufforbit := proc(Gamma,Omega,c,xmin,xmax,ymin,ymax)
>     local eqn,x,y,t,ttl;
>     eqn := diff(x(t),t)=y(t),
       diff(y(t),t)=x(t)-c*y(t)-(x(t))^3+Gamma*sin(Omega*t);
>     ttl := cat("Gamma=",convert(Gamma,string),", Omega=",
       convert(Omega,string),", c=",convert(c,string));
>     DEplot([eqn],[x(t),y(t)],t=100..500,[[x(0)=1,y(0)=0.5]],
       x=xmin..xmax,y=ymin..ymax,stepsize=0.01,method=rkf45,
       thickness=1,linecolor=black,font=[TIMES,ITALIC,24],
       axesfont=[TIMES,ROMAN,18],titlefont=[TIMES,ROMAN,18],
       title=ttl);
>   end proc:
```

Note how the title is constructed using the `cat` and `convert` commands so as to display varying parameter values. This was explained in *Unit A4*, Subsection 4.6.1 – see page 183 of *Block A*.

After typing in the above procedure, the following command will generate the orbit with the required parameter values (in this case with $\Gamma = 0.1$, $\Omega = 1.25$ and $c = 0.3$, the result of which is shown in Figure 1.35(a), overleaf):

```
>   dufforbit(0.10,1.25,0.30,-2,2,-2,2);
```

As with the Lorenz system, the method `rkf45` is specified in `DEplot` since the default method, being insufficiently accurate, can give wrong results when chaos is involved.

Let us start by setting $\Omega = 1.25$ and $c = 0.3$ and vary the strength of the force Γ, from 0.1 upwards. For Γ below about 0.28, the orbit stays relatively close to one of the stable fixed points, in this case $(1, 0)$, because the initial condition is closer to this one, and rotates about it in a simple closed curve, as shown in parts (a) and (b) of Figure 1.35. As Γ increases above 0.28, the shape of the orbit starts getting more complicated, as shown in parts (c) and (d) for $\Gamma = 0.3$ and 0.317, respectively, although for these values, the orbit still stays close to just one of the stable fixed points. Then, for Γ above about 0.32, the orbit appears *chaotic*, as shown for $\Gamma = 0.332$ in Figure 1.35(e). Note that in this case, the orbit strays close to both stable fixed points but has a very complicated form, as is typical of a chaotic orbit. Increasing Γ further, chaos disappears, leading to orbits like that shown in Figure 1.35(f) for $\Gamma = 0.37$. This orbit appears to be periodic but is quite convoluted and passes close to both stable fixed points. Another chaotic orbit is shown in Figure 1.35(g), for $\Gamma = 0.7$, and a simple periodic orbit is shown for the relatively strong force strength $\Gamma = 2.0$ in Figure 1.35(h). Two more chaotic orbits are shown in Figure 1.36, this time for the same values of Γ and Ω ($\Gamma = 3.0$, $\Omega = 1.0$) but for different values of c ($c = 0.1$ and $c = 0.02$).

In order to obtain Figure 1.35(h) and both panels of Figure 1.36, different values of `xmin`, `xmax`, `ymin` and `ymax` need to be put into `dufforbit`.

(a) Gamma=.10, Omega=1.25, c=.30

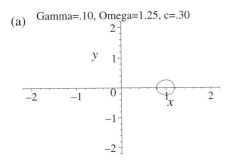

(b) Gamma=.20, Omega=1.25, c=.30

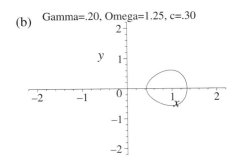

(c) Gamma=.30, Omega=1.25, c=.30

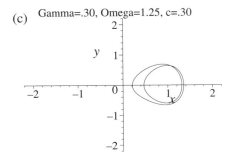

(d) Gamma=.317, Omega=1.25, c=.30

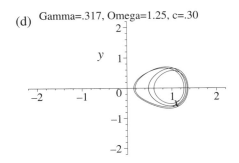

(e) Gamma=.332, Omega=1.25, c=.30

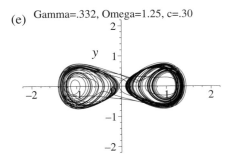

(f) Gamma=.37, Omega=1.25, c=.30

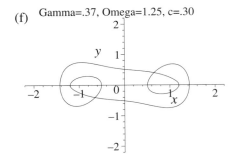

(g) Gamma=.70, Omega=1.25, c=.30

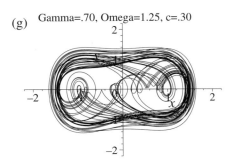

(h) Gamma=2.00, Omega=1.25, c=.30

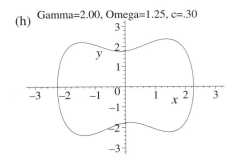

Figure 1.35   Orbits of the double-well Duffing equation with $\Omega = 1.25$, $c = 0.30$, and Γ ranging from 0.10 to 2.0

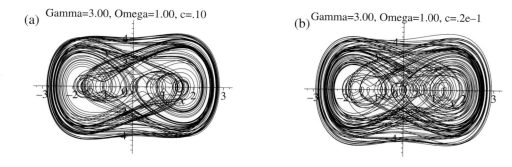

Figure 1.36   Orbits of the double-well Duffing equation for $\Gamma = 3.0$, $\Omega = 1.0$, and two different values of c: (a) $c = 0.10$, (b) $c = 0.02$

Exercise 1.31

Show that if the solution of Equation (1.45) always stays sufficiently close to the fixed point at $(1, 0)$, its phase curve is given by the ellipse

$$(x - 1)^2 + \frac{y^2}{\Omega^2} = R^2, \quad \text{where} \quad R = \frac{\Gamma}{\sqrt{\left(\Omega^2 - 2\right)^2 + c^2 \Omega^2}}.$$

So the addition of the nonlinear term x^3 in Equation (1.45) leads to surprisingly rich and complicated behaviour. However, it is difficult to make much sense of this behaviour when displayed as in Figures 1.35 and 1.36, particularly for chaotic orbits with their spaghetti-like phase paths. One of the purposes of this section is to show how much more insight is gained from examining the time-T maps for this system. The nonautonomous term in Equation (1.45) is periodic with period $T = 2\pi/\Omega$, which is therefore chosen as the time step in the time-T map. The iterates of this map, (x_n, y_n), are the values of $(x(t), y(t))$ at $t = nT$ for $n = 0, 1, 2, \ldots$. The set $\{(x_n, y_n), n = 0, 1, 2, \ldots\}$ will be referred to as the orbit of the time-T map. So as to remove transients, the orbit of the map will only be displayed for a sufficiently large n, and $n \geq 10$ will suffice here. The Maple procedure `Tmap` will plot the orbit of the time-T map for $10 \leq n \leq N$, where N is the last argument of `Tmap`; the other arguments are the same as those of `dufforbit`.

```
>   restart:
>   Tmap := proc(Gamma,Omega,c,xmin,xmax,ymin,ymax,N::posint)
>       local eqn,x,y,t,ttl,orb,L;
>       eqn := diff(x(t),t)=y(t),
          diff(y(t),t)=x(t)-c*y(t)-(x(t))^3+Gamma*sin(Omega*t);
>       ttl := cat("Gamma=",convert(Gamma,string),", Omega=",
          convert(Omega,string),", c=",convert(c,string)):
>       orb :=
          dsolve({eqn,x(0)=1,y(0)=0.5},{x(t),y(t)},type=numeric):
>       L := [seq(eval([x(t),y(t)],orb(i*2*Pi/Omega)),i=10..N)];
>       plot(L,x=xmin..xmax,y=ymin..ymax,style=point,
          symbol=point,color=black,font=[TIMES,ITALIC,24],
          axesfont=[TIMES,ROMAN,18],axes=BOXED,title=ttl,
          titlefont=[TIMES,ROMAN,18]);
>   end proc:
```

Recall that the default method used by `dsolve` is `rkf45`.

To generate a time-T map orbit, the following command is entered:

```
>   Tmap(0.332,1.25,0.3,-2,2,-1,1,10000);
```

In this case $N = 10\,000$ is quite high because, for these parameter values, the orbit is chaotic. Much lower values of N can be tried for simpler orbits. Figure 1.37 shows the time-T map orbits for all the cases displayed in Figure 1.35, with Figure 1.37(a) corresponding to Figure 1.35(a), etc. Figure 1.38 shows the time-T map orbits corresponding to Figure 1.36. For cases where the orbits are *non-chaotic*, the iterates of the map quickly approach limiting values at one or a finite number of points on the xy-plane. These are the **fixed points** of the map and will be a major topic in the next and subsequent units of this block. The significance of these fixed points is that they indicate that the continuous orbit $x(t)$ is *periodic*. So, in parts (a), (b) and (h) of Figure 1.37, the map orbit settles into a single point, indicating that the long-term behaviour of $x(t)$ is periodic with period T. However, in Figure 1.37(c), the map orbit alternates between two points, and this is called a **period-2 orbit**; it indicates that here $x(t)$ has period $2T$. In Figure 1.37(d), the map orbit is period-4 (you should be able to pick out four points although two are very close together), so $x(t)$ has settled into an orbit with periodicity $4T$; in part (f) one finds a period-5 orbit, so $x(t)$ has periodicity $5T$. The periodicities of $x(t)$ (particularly the period-4 and period-5 cases) are not at all obvious from looking at the trajectories displayed in Figure 1.35, but are much clearer from looking at the map orbits. Period-k fixed points in maps, and transitions between periodicities (period doubling), will be discussed at length in the next unit.

When only a few points appear in the time-T orbit, they are plotted as crosses, for clarity, rather than points. This is done by writing `symbol=cross` instead of `symbol=point` in the `plot` option in the procedure.

In the case of chaotic orbits, the orbit of the time-T map does not settle onto a finite number of points but falls onto an intricate and curiously shaped set as shown in parts (e) and (g) of Figure 1.37, and in Figure 1.38. These sets are called **strange attractors** or sometimes **chaotic attractors**, and have interesting geometrical properties associated with self-similarity. They are examples of objects called **fractals**, which will be the subject of *Unit 4*. Strange attractors like those illustrated in Figures 1.37 and 1.38 have actually been *observed* in magneto-elastic experiments similar to that depicted in Figure 1.34. It is possible to characterize the nature of these sets in terms of calculable numbers. Thus, with the help of maps, some quantifiable sense can be made of chaotic orbits after all, even though, at first sight, this seemed a rather daunting prospect from looking at the trajectories in Figures 1.35 and 1.36.

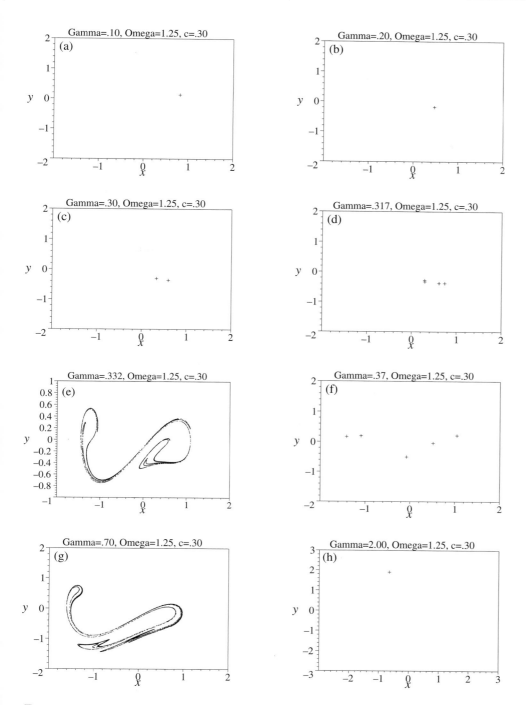

Figure 1.37 Time-T maps of the double-well Duffing equation for values of Γ, Ω and c corresponding to Figure 1.35

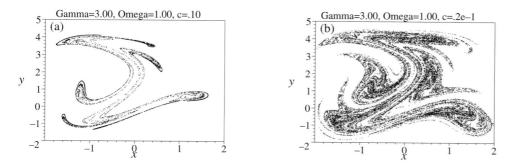

Figure 1.38 Time-T maps of the double-well Duffing equation for values of Γ, Ω and c corresponding to Figure 1.36

1.6   End of unit exercises

These exercises are a little more challenging than others in the text, but will test your deeper understanding of the material in this unit.

Exercise 1.32

For $T = 2\pi/\Omega$, find the time-T map $x_{n+1} = F(x_n)$ for the one-dimensional *nonautonomous* system

$$\dot{x} = -cx + A\cos(\Omega t).$$

[*Hint*: You may assume the identity

$$\int_0^t ds\, e^{as}\cos(bs) = \frac{e^{at}(a\cos(bt) + b\sin(bt)) - a}{a^2 + b^2}.\,]$$

Exercise 1.33

Consider the planar system expressed in polar coordinates

$$\dot{r} = r\left(1 - r^2\right), \quad \dot{\theta} = 1.$$

By taking the positive x-axis as the Poincaré section Σ, show that the Poincaré return map for the radial coordinate $r_{n+1} = P(r_n)$ is given by

$$P(r) = \left(1 + e^{-4\pi}(r^{-2} - 1)\right)^{-1/2}.$$

[*Hint*: You may assume the integral

$$\int \frac{dx}{x(1 - x^2)} = -\tfrac{1}{2}\ln\left|1 - x^{-2}\right|.\,]$$

Exercise 1.34

Consider the Lorenz system of equations, Equations (1.7) on page 20, and assume that $b > 0$, $\sigma > 0$ and $r > 0$.

(a) Find all the fixed points of the system for (i) $0 < r < 1$ and (ii) $r > 1$.

(b) By extending the arguments of Subsection 1.4.2 to three dimensions, determine the stability of the fixed point at $(0, 0, 0)$ for (i) $0 < r < 1$ and (ii) $r > 1$.

Learning outcomes

After studying this unit you should be able to:

- understand in basic terms what dynamical systems are when formulated in both continuous and discrete time;

- understand roughly what chaos is and be familiar with examples of its occurrence in the real world;

- understand maps as they arise from population dynamics, the Newton–Raphson method and finite-difference approximations to differential equations;

- understand Poincaré return maps and how to construct time-T maps from differential equations;

- describe qualitative properties of the solutions of differential equations in terms of their flow in phase space;

- determine fixed points and their stability for one-dimensional flows;

- find and classify fixed points in both linear and nonlinear two-dimensional flows;

- locate limit cycles in simple two-dimensional systems;

- appreciate that chaos cannot occur for autonomous two-dimensional differential equations;

- understand how time-T maps can elucidate complicated or chaotic orbits coming from differential equations.

Solutions to Exercises

Solution 1.1

Re-expressing Equation (1.1) using separation of variables gives

$$\int \frac{dx}{f(x)} = \int dt,$$

and by integrating we obtain

$$\int_a^x \frac{du}{f(u)} = t,$$

where the constant of integration has been absorbed into the integral's lower limit, a. Applying the initial condition $x(0) = x_0$ gives $\int_a^{x_0} \frac{du}{f(u)} = 0$, implying that $a = x_0$, and yielding the result expressed in the question.

Solution 1.2

Introduce the new variable $y(t)$, and let $y = \dot{x}$ so that $\ddot{x} = \dot{y}$. Then the equation in question can be written as

$$\dot{x} = y,$$
$$\dot{y} = -cy - \omega^2 x.$$

Solution 1.3

This follows by direct analogy to the one-dimensional case given in the text. So, introducing an additional dependent variable $\theta(t)$, with the properties $\dot{\theta} = 1$ and $\theta(0) = 0$, implying $\theta(t) = t$, gives rise to the three-dimensional autonomous system

$$\dot{x} = f(x, y, \theta),$$
$$\dot{y} = g(x, y, \theta),$$
$$\dot{\theta} = 1,$$

with initial condition $(x(0), y(0), \theta(0)) = (x_0, y_0, 0)$.

Solution 1.4

Given that $g(y) = 1 + y$, we have $y_{n+1} = 1 + y_n$, so

$$y_n = y_{n-1} + 1$$
$$= y_{n-2} + 2$$
$$\vdots$$
$$= y_0 + n,$$

and since $y_0 = 0$, we have $n = y_n$. Substituting this into the original nonautonomous map gives

$$x_{n+1} = f(x_n, n) = f(x_n, y_n),$$

and this together with $y_{n+1} = g(y_n)$ gives the two-dimensional autonomous map given in the question.

Solution 1.5

If T is the orbital period and a the semi-major axis, Kepler's third law states that a^3/T^2 is constant. So if T_J and T_A are the orbital periods of Jupiter and

an asteroid, respectively, and a_J and a_A their corresponding semi-major axes, then Kepler's third law implies $a_J^3/T_J^2 = a_A^3/T_A^2$, which implies $a_A = a_J(T_A/T_J)^{2/3} = 5.2034(T_A/T_J)^{2/3}$. This is now applied to each of the given cases.

(a) For the 3:1 gap, $T_J = 3T_A$, so the above formula gives $a_A = 2.502$ AU.

(b) For the 5:2 gap, $2T_J = 5T_A$, giving $a_A = 2.825$ AU.

(c) For the 7:3 gap, $3T_J = 7T_A$, giving $a_A = 2.958$ AU.

(d) For the 2:1 gap, $T_J = 2T_A$, giving $a_A = 3.278$ AU.

These results compare very well with Figure 1.10.

Solution 1.6

Following the hint, multiplying Equation (1.5) by $\dot{\theta}$ gives

$$\dot{\theta}\ddot{\theta} = -\frac{g}{l}\dot{\theta}\sin\theta. \tag{1.46}$$

But the left-hand side of (1.46) is equal to

$$\frac{1}{2}\frac{d}{dt}\dot{\theta}^2,$$

and the right-hand side of (1.46) is equal to

$$\frac{g}{l}\frac{d}{dt}\cos\theta.$$

Thus (1.46) can be re-expressed as

$$\frac{d}{dt}\left(\frac{1}{2}\dot{\theta}^2 - \frac{g}{l}\cos\theta\right) = 0,$$

from which follows the answer.

Solution 1.7

With $r = a$ and $f = \omega t$, Equation (1.4) becomes

$$\ddot{\theta} = -\frac{3}{2}\omega^2\sin\left(2(\theta - \omega t)\right). \tag{1.47}$$

Introduce a change of variable $\varphi = \theta - \omega t$, so that $\dot{\varphi} = \dot{\theta} - \omega$ and $\ddot{\varphi} = \ddot{\theta}$. Substituting into Equation (1.47) gives

$$\ddot{\varphi} = -\frac{3}{2}\omega^2\sin(2\varphi).$$

Multiplying this equation by $\dot{\varphi}$, and using $\sin(2\varphi) = 2\sin\varphi\cos\varphi$, leads to

$$\dot{\varphi}\ddot{\varphi} = -3\omega^2\dot{\varphi}\sin\varphi\cos\varphi.$$

Now apply the trick of the previous exercise, recognizing that the left-hand side is equal to $\frac{1}{2}\frac{d}{dt}(\dot{\varphi}^2)$ and the right-hand side equates to $3\omega^2\frac{d}{dt}(\frac{1}{2}\cos^2\varphi)$, so that we end up with

$$\frac{d}{dt}\left(\frac{1}{2}\dot{\varphi}^2 - \frac{3}{2}\omega^2\cos^2\varphi\right) = 0.$$

The constant of motion (in terms of φ) immediately follows from this,

$$\dot{\varphi}^2 - 3\omega^2\cos^2\varphi = \text{constant},$$

and substituting for φ and $\dot{\varphi}$ gives the required result.

Solution 1.8

Substituting $N_n = x_n/k$ into Equation (1.9) and multiplying through by k gives

$$x_{n+1} = ax_n - \frac{bx_n^2}{k} = ax_n \left(1 - \frac{bx_n}{ak}\right),$$

so setting $k = b/a$ leads to Equation (1.10).

Solution 1.9

The Newton–Raphson map, Equation (1.11), for $f(x) = x^2 - a$ (so that $f'(x) = 2x$) is $x_{n+1} = F(x_n)$ where

$$F(x) = x - \frac{x^2 - a}{2x}$$
$$= \frac{1}{2}\left(x + \frac{a}{x}\right).$$

This can be tested with Maple as follows:

```
>  restart:
>  a := 5:
>  x := 1:
>  for k from 1 to 8 do
>     x := evalf[20]((x+a/x)/2);
>     print(k,x);
>  end do:
```

            1, 3.
        2, 2.3333333333333333334
        3, 2.2380952380952380953
        4, 2.2360688956433637284
        5, 2.2360679774999781941
        6, 2.2360679774997896964
        7, 2.2360679774997896964
        8, 2.2360679774997896964

The results can be compared with direct evaluation through

```
>  evalf[20](sqrt(a));
```
            2.2360679774997896964

Note how very rapidly the iterates converge to the root.

Solution 1.10

With $f(x) = e^x - a$, the Newton–Raphson map function is now

$$F(x) = x - \frac{e^x - a}{e^x}$$
$$= x - 1 + ae^{-x},$$

which can be tested with Maple as follows:

```
>  restart:
>  a := 2:
>  x := 1:
>  for k from 1 to 6 do
>     x := evalf[20](x-1+a*exp(-x));
>     print(k,x);
>  end do:
```

        1, 0.73575888234288464320
        2, 0.69404229991891527920
        3, 0.69314758105977141504
        4, 0.69314718056002550946
        5, 0.69314718055994530942
        6, 0.69314718055994530942

Direct evaluation gives

```
>  evalf[20](ln(a));
```
            0.69314718055994530942

Again, note the rapid convergence of the iterates.

Solution 1.11

Here, we need to find the positive zero of $f(x) = x^p - a$, for which the Newton–Raphson map function is

$$F(x) = x - \frac{x^p - a}{px^{p-1}}$$
$$= \left(1 - \frac{1}{p}\right)x + \frac{a}{p}x^{1-p}.$$

Note that for $p = 2$ this coincides with the solution to Exercise 1.9. It is tested with Maple as follows:

```
>  restart:
>  p := 7:
>  a := 3:
>  x := 1:
>  for k from 1 to 8 do
>     x := evalf[20]((1-1/p)*x+a*x^(1-p)/p);
>     print(k,x);
>  end do:
```

        1, 1.2857142857142857143
        2, 1.1969168232586265552
        3, 1.1716890505387113380
        4, 1.1699387082325357493
        5, 1.1699308129185357889
        6, 1.1699308127586868865
        7, 1.1699308127586868864
        8, 1.1699308127586868864

and compared to direct evaluation by:

```
>  evalf[20](a^(1/p));
```
            1.1699308127586868865

The discrepancy in the last digit is due to rounding.

Solution 1.12

(a) With $B = 0$, the initial-value problem is

$$\dot{x} = Ax, \quad x(0) = x_0.$$

But this is just a linear equation with constant coefficient whose solution (satisfying the initial condition) is

$$x(t) = x_0 \exp(At),$$

which, as t increases, grows exponentially (with rate A) when $A > 0$ but decays exponentially when $A < 0$.

(b) Applying the Euler approximation, Equation (1.13), directly to the logistic differential equation (i.e. substituting $f(x) = Ax - Bx^2$ into the right-hand side of Equation (1.13)) gives a map of the form quoted in the question with $a = 1 + hA$ and $b = hB$. Note that the resulting map is the same as that given in Equation (1.9). That $A > 0$ implies initial growth (provided $B \geq 0$ and x_0 is not too large) is consistent with the condition that $a > 1$ for initial growth as stated in the discussion immediately preceding Equation (1.9).

Solution 1.13

Using the methods leading to Equations (1.3) on page 10 gives the two-dimensional system
$$\dot{x} = y,$$
$$\dot{y} = -g(x)y - f(x). \tag{1.48}$$
Approximating $\dot{x}(nh)$ and $\dot{y}(nh)$ by the Euler forward differences $(x_{n+1} - x_n)/h$ and $(y_{n+1} - y_n)/h$, respectively (with $y(nh) = y_n$), and substituting into Equations (1.48) gives the two-dimensional map given in the question.

Solution 1.14

Recognize that the differential equation is in the form $\dot{x} = g(t)x$ where
$$g(t) = 1 - \cos t,$$
which has period 2π, and that the discrete points are $x_n = x(2n\pi)$. This is a particular case of Equation (1.18), so we can apply the same methods as were used to treat that equation. We obtain, from Equation (1.19), $x_1 = F(x_0)$ with $F(x) = bx$, where
$$b = \exp\left(\int_0^{2\pi} (1 - \cos t)\, dt\right).$$
But
$$\int_0^{2\pi} (1 - \cos t)\, dt = 2\pi$$
(since $\int_0^{2\pi} \cos t\, dt = 0$), so the time-$2\pi$ map function is $F(x) = e^{2\pi}x$.

Solution 1.15

We need first to solve Equation (1.22), with initial conditions $x(0) = x_0$ and $\dot{x}(0) = y_0$, to determine $x(t)$ and $y(t) = \dot{x}(t)$, and then to compute $x_1 = x(T)$ and $y_1 = y(T)$. The solution of Equation (1.22) consists of the complementary function, a linear combination of $\cos(\omega t)$ and $\sin(\omega t)$, and the particular integral, which is $R\sin(\Omega t)$. Substituting this last expression into Equation (1.22) determines R, which is given by $(\omega^2 - \Omega^2)R = \Gamma$. So the general solution is
$$x(t) = A\cos(\omega t) + B\sin(\omega t) + R\sin(\Omega t), \tag{1.49}$$
and therefore
$$y(t) = -\omega A\sin(\omega t) + \omega B\cos(\omega t)$$
$$+ R\Omega\cos(\Omega t). \tag{1.50}$$

Applying the initial conditions gives
$$x(0) = A = x_0$$
and
$$y(0) = \omega B + R\Omega = y_0,$$
giving $B = (y_0 - R\Omega)/\omega$. Substituting A and B into Equations (1.49) and (1.50), and then putting $t = T$ into these equations, noting that $\sin(\Omega T) = 0$ and $\cos(\Omega T) = 1$, gives the equations
$$x_1 = x(T) = cx_0 + \frac{sy_0}{\omega} - \frac{R\Omega s}{\omega},$$
$$\frac{y_1}{\omega} = \frac{y(T)}{\omega} = -sx_0 + \frac{cy_0}{\omega} + \frac{R\Omega(1 - c)}{\omega},$$
where $s = \sin(\omega T)$ and $c = \cos(\omega T)$. This can be written in matrix form as
$$\begin{pmatrix} x_1 \\ y_1/\omega \end{pmatrix} = \begin{pmatrix} c & s \\ -s & c \end{pmatrix} \begin{pmatrix} x_0 \\ y_0/\omega \end{pmatrix} + \begin{pmatrix} -s \\ 1 - c \end{pmatrix} R\Omega/\omega,$$
giving the map taking $\mathbf{x}_0$ to $\mathbf{x}_1$ and therefore also that taking $\mathbf{x}_n$ to $\mathbf{x}_{n+1}$.

Solution 1.16

(a) The zeros of $f(x) = x(1 - x^2)$ occur at $x = 0$ and $x = \pm 1$, which are therefore the locations of the fixed points. Taking the derivative, $f'(x) = 1 - 3x^2$, we see that $f'(0) = 1 > 0$, implying that $x = 0$ is an *unstable* fixed point, whereas $f'(\pm 1) = -2 < 0$, implying that $x = \pm 1$ are *stable* fixed points. This can also be deduced from sketching the phase flow as shown in Figure 1.39.

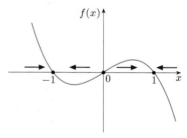

Figure 1.39 Sketch of $f(x) = x(1 - x^2)$ with the phase flow along the real line indicated by the bold arrows whose directions are given by the sign of $f(x)$

(b) There is only one zero of $f(x) = -x^3$, which is at $x = 0$, the location of the only fixed point. Note that in this case $f'(0) = 0$, so the stability of the fixed point cannot be determined by considering the sign of the derivative. Instead, the stability can be deduced from sketching the phase flow as in Figure 1.40, from which it can be seen that the fixed point is *stable*.

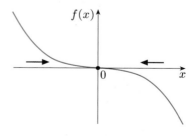

Figure 1.40 Sketch of $f(x) = -x^3$ and the phase flow

(c) The zeros of $f(x) = x^2(1-x)$ occur at $x = 0$ and $x = 1$, which are the locations of the fixed points. From $f'(x) = 2x - 3x^2$, we see that $f'(0) = 0$, so nothing can be deduced from the derivative about the stability of the fixed point at $x = 0$, but $f'(1) = -1 < 0$, implying that $x = 1$ is a *stable* fixed point. A sketch of the phase flow, Figure 1.41, shows that orbits flow into the fixed point at $x = 0$ from negative x, but flow away from this fixed point for $0 < x < 1$. Therefore the fixed point at $x = 0$ is neither stable nor unstable.

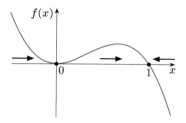

Figure 1.41 Sketch of $f(x) = x^2(1-x)$ and the phase flow

(d) The zeros of $f(x) = \sin x$ occur at $x = n\pi$ with $n = 0, \pm 1, \pm 2, \ldots$, which are the locations of the fixed points. From $f'(x) = \cos x$, we find that $f'(n\pi) = \cos(n\pi) = (-1)^n$, showing that the fixed point at $x = n\pi$ is *unstable* when n is *even* (including 0), and *stable* when n is *odd*. The phase flow is sketched in Figure 1.42.

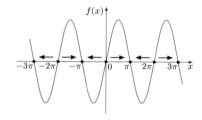

Figure 1.42 Sketch of $f(x) = \sin x$ and the phase flow

Solution 1.17

First consider the case when $A = 0$, so that $f(x) = -Bx^2$. In this case there is just one fixed point, at $x = 0$. But for $B > 0$, the orbits always flow in the negative x-direction except at $x = 0$ where the derivative is zero; so the orbit approaches the fixed point when positive but flows away when negative, and so the fixed point is neither stable nor unstable. A similar argument holds for $A = 0$ and $B < 0$, only this time the orbits always flow in the positive x-direction except at $x = 0$ where the derivative is zero; they flow away from the fixed point when x is positive and towards it when x is negative, and so, again, it is neither stable nor unstable.

Now consider $\dot{x} = f(x) = Ax - Bx^2$ for $A \neq 0$. The fixed points are given by $f(x) = x(A - Bx) = 0$, which occur at $x = 0$ and $x = A/B$. Since $f'(x) = A - 2Bx$,

we have $f'(0) = A$ and $f'(A/B) = -A$, showing that the stability of the fixed points is independent of B and depends only on the *sign* of A. Thus for $A > 0$ there is an *unstable* fixed point at $x = 0$ and a *stable* fixed point at $x = A/B$, whereas for $A < 0$ there is a *stable* fixed point at $x = 0$ and an *unstable* fixed point at $x = A/B$. The phase flows for the various signs of A and B are shown in Figures 1.43 to 1.46.

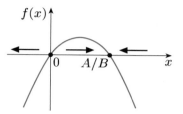

Figure 1.43 Logistic phase flow for $A > 0$ and $B > 0$

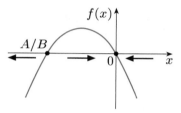

Figure 1.44 Logistic phase flow for $A < 0$ and $B > 0$

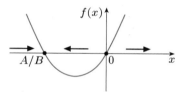

Figure 1.45 Logistic phase flow for $A > 0$ and $B < 0$

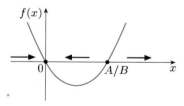

Figure 1.46 Logistic phase flow for $A < 0$ and $B < 0$

Solution 1.18

Since $\mathbf{A}$ and $\mathbf{h}$ are constants, we have $\dot{\mathbf{x}} = \dot{\mathbf{v}}$. Substituting Equation (1.28) into the right-hand side of Equation (1.27) gives

$$\mathbf{Ax} + \mathbf{h} = \mathbf{Av} - \mathbf{AA}^{-1}\mathbf{h} + \mathbf{h} = \mathbf{Av},$$

with the last equality following since $\mathbf{AA}^{-1} = \mathbf{I}$, the identity matrix. So $\dot{\mathbf{v}} = \mathbf{Av}$, as required.

Solution 1.19

Taking $\mathbf{A}$ to be the general matrix given by Equation (1.26), the equation for the characteristic polynomial, Equation (1.30), is equivalent to Equation (1.31). Expanding out the determinant in this equation gives

$$\begin{vmatrix} a - \lambda & b \\ c & d - \lambda \end{vmatrix} = (a - \lambda)(d - \lambda) - bc$$

$$= \lambda^2 - (a + d)\lambda + ad - bc.$$

But $\operatorname{tr} \mathbf{A} = a + d$ and $\det \mathbf{A} = ad - bc$, and substituting these into the above gives

$$\begin{vmatrix} a - \lambda & b \\ c & d - \lambda \end{vmatrix} = \lambda^2 - (\operatorname{tr} \mathbf{A})\lambda + \det \mathbf{A},$$

so Equations (1.31) and (1.32) are equivalent.

Solution 1.20

If λ_1 and λ_2 are eigenvalues of $\mathbf{A}$, then they are roots of the characteristic polynomial (a quadratic). Therefore the characteristic polynomial can be written as

$$(\lambda - \lambda_1)(\lambda - \lambda_2) = 0,$$

which can be expanded to give

$$\lambda^2 - (\lambda_1 + \lambda_2)\lambda + \lambda_1 \lambda_2 = 0.$$

Comparing this last equation with Equation (1.32) leads to the required relations.

Solution 1.21

It follows immediately from Equation (1.36) that $\mathbf{x}(0) = \mathbf{x}_0$, so $\mathbf{x}(t)$ satisfies the initial condition. Now, substituting $\mathbf{x}(t)$ into the left-hand side of Equation (1.25) gives

$$\dot{\mathbf{x}} = c_1 \frac{d}{dt}\left(e^{\lambda_1 t}\right)\mathbf{u}_1 + c_2 \frac{d}{dt}\left(e^{\lambda_2 t}\right)\mathbf{u}_2$$

$$= c_1 \lambda_1 e^{\lambda_1 t}\mathbf{u}_1 + c_2 \lambda_2 e^{\lambda_2 t}\mathbf{u}_2.$$

Substituting $\mathbf{x}(t)$ into the right-hand side of Equation (1.25) gives

$$\mathbf{A}\mathbf{x} = c_1 e^{\lambda_1 t}\mathbf{A}\mathbf{u}_1 + c_2 e^{\lambda_2 t}\mathbf{A}\mathbf{u}_2$$

$$= c_1 e^{\lambda_1 t}\lambda_1 \mathbf{u}_1 + c_2 e^{\lambda_2 t}\lambda_2 \mathbf{u}_2,$$

using the fact that $\mathbf{A}\mathbf{u}_j = \lambda_j \mathbf{u}_j$, $j = 1, 2$. Thus the left-hand and right-hand sides are equal, and hence $\mathbf{x}(t)$ given by Equation (1.36) is a solution to Equation (1.25).

Solution 1.22

(a) When the system is expressed in the form $\dot{\mathbf{x}} = \mathbf{A}\mathbf{x}$, the matrix $\mathbf{A}$ is given by

$$\mathbf{A} = \begin{pmatrix} 2 & 2 \\ -2 & -1 \end{pmatrix},$$

so $\operatorname{tr} \mathbf{A} = 1$ and $\det \mathbf{A} = 2$. Applying the formula in Equation (1.33), the eigenvalues of $\mathbf{A}$ are given by

$$2\lambda = 1 \pm \sqrt{1 - 8},$$

so they are the complex conjugate pair $\frac{1}{2}(1 \pm i\sqrt{7})$ and they have positive real parts. The fixed point is therefore an *unstable spiral*.

(b) The matrix $\mathbf{A}$ is given by

$$\mathbf{A} = \begin{pmatrix} -2 & 1 \\ 1 & -2 \end{pmatrix},$$

so $\operatorname{tr} \mathbf{A} = -4$ and $\det \mathbf{A} = 3$. Applying Equation (1.33), the eigenvalues are given by

$$2\lambda = -4 \pm \sqrt{16 - 12},$$

so $\lambda_1 = -3$ and $\lambda_2 = -1$, and therefore $\lambda_1 < \lambda_2 < 0$. Hence the fixed point is a *stable node*.

(c) The matrix $\mathbf{A}$ is given by

$$\mathbf{A} = \begin{pmatrix} 3 & -1 \\ 1 & 1 \end{pmatrix},$$

so $\operatorname{tr} \mathbf{A} = 4$ and $\det \mathbf{A} = 4$. Since $(\operatorname{tr} \mathbf{A})^2 = 4 \det \mathbf{A}$, the eigenvalues are repeated and, applying Equation (1.33), are given by $\lambda_1 = \lambda_2 = 2$. Hence, since $\mathbf{A}$ is non-diagonal, the fixed point is an *unstable improper node*.

(d) The matrix $\mathbf{A}$ is given by

$$\mathbf{A} = \begin{pmatrix} 2 & -3 \\ 2 & -2 \end{pmatrix},$$

so $\operatorname{tr} \mathbf{A} = 0$ and $\det \mathbf{A} = 2$. Applying Equation (1.33), the eigenvalues are given by

$$2\lambda = \sqrt{-8},$$

so the eigenvalues are the *purely imaginary* complex conjugate pair $\pm i\sqrt{2}$. Hence the fixed point is a *centre*.

Solution 1.23

From the solution to Exercise 1.2, the matrix $\mathbf{A}$ is given by

$$\mathbf{A} = \begin{pmatrix} 0 & 1 \\ -\omega^2 & -c \end{pmatrix},$$

so $\operatorname{tr} \mathbf{A} = -c$ and $\det \mathbf{A} = \omega^2$. Hence, using Equation (1.33), the eigenvalues of $\mathbf{A}$ are given by

$$2\lambda = -c \pm \sqrt{c^2 - 4\omega^2}.$$

Now we consider each case in turn.

For $c > 2\omega$ (strong damping), both eigenvalues are real and $\lambda_1 < \lambda_2 < 0$, so the origin is a *stable node*.

For $c = 2\omega$ (critical damping), $\lambda_1 = \lambda_2 = -c/2 < 0$ and $\mathbf{A}$ is non-diagonal, so the origin is a *stable improper node*.

For $0 < c < 2\omega$ (weak damping), the eigenvalues are complex with a negative real part, so the origin is a *stable spiral*.

For $c = 0$ (no damping), $\lambda_{1,2} = \pm i\omega$, i.e. the eigenvalues are purely imaginary, so the origin is a *centre*.

Solution 1.24

(a) Here, $f(x, y) = y$ and $g(x, y) = x^2 - 3x + y + 2$. The fixed points satisfy $f(x, y) = 0$, which implies $y = 0$, and $g(x, y) = 0$, implying that

$$x^2 - 3x + 2 = (x - 1)(x - 2) = 0,$$

with solutions $x = 1$ and $x = 2$. So the fixed points are at $(1, 0)$ and $(2, 0)$.

Now, $f_x = 0$, $f_y = 1$, $g_x = 2x - 3$ and $g_y = 1$, so the Jacobian is

$$\mathbf{J}(x,y) = \begin{pmatrix} 0 & 1 \\ 2x - 3 & 1 \end{pmatrix},$$

from which we have $\operatorname{tr} \mathbf{J}(x,y) = 1$ and $\det \mathbf{J}(x,y) = 3 - 2x$.

For the fixed point at $(1,0)$, $\operatorname{tr} \mathbf{J}(1,0) = 1$ and $\det \mathbf{J}(1,0) = 1$, and applying Equation (1.33) gives $2\lambda = 1 \pm i\sqrt{3}$, so the eigenvalues are a complex conjugate pair with positive real part. Therefore $(1,0)$ is an *unstable spiral*.

For the fixed point at $(2,0)$, $\operatorname{tr} \mathbf{J}(2,0) = 1$ and $\det \mathbf{J}(2,0) = -1$, and applying Equation (1.33) gives $2\lambda = 1 \pm \sqrt{5}$, so the eigenvalues satisfy $\lambda_1 > 0 > \lambda_2$. Therefore $(2,0)$ is a *saddle point*.

(b) Here, $f(x,y) = -2x + y$ and $g(x,y) = x^2 + y^2 - 5$. The fixed points satisfy $f(x,y) = 0$, which implies $y = 2x$, and $g(x,y) = 0$, implying that

$$x^2 + (2x)^2 - 5 = 5x^2 - 5 = 0,$$

with solutions $x = \pm 1$. So the fixed points are at $(1,2)$ and $(-1,-2)$. Now, $f_x = -2$, $f_y = 1$, $g_x = 2x$ and $g_y = 2y$, so the Jacobian is

$$\mathbf{J}(x,y) = \begin{pmatrix} -2 & 1 \\ 2x & 2y \end{pmatrix},$$

from which we have $\operatorname{tr} \mathbf{J}(x,y) = 2(y-1)$ and $\det \mathbf{J}(x,y) = -2(x+2y)$.

For the fixed point at $(1,2)$, $\operatorname{tr} \mathbf{J}(1,2) = 2$ and $\det \mathbf{J}(1,2) = -10$, and applying Equation (1.33) gives $2\lambda = 2 \pm 2\sqrt{11}$, so $\lambda_1 > 0 > \lambda_2$. Therefore $(1,2)$ is a *saddle point*.

For the fixed point at $(-1,-2)$, $\operatorname{tr} \mathbf{J}(-1,-2) = -6$ and $\det \mathbf{J}(-1,-2) = 10$, and applying Equation (1.33) gives $2\lambda = -6 \pm 2i$, so the eigenvalues are a complex conjugate pair with negative real part. Therefore $(-1,-2)$ is a *stable spiral*.

Solution 1.25

By taking time derivatives of $x = r\cos\theta$ and $y = r\sin\theta$ we obtain

$$\dot{x} = \dot{r}\cos\theta - r\dot{\theta}\sin\theta,$$
$$\dot{y} = \dot{r}\sin\theta + r\dot{\theta}\cos\theta, \tag{1.51}$$

from which it follows that

$$\dot{x}\cos\theta + \dot{y}\sin\theta = \dot{r},$$
$$\dot{y}\cos\theta - \dot{x}\sin\theta = r\dot{\theta}.$$

Now it is possible to express $\dot{r}$ and $\dot{\theta}$ in terms of $\dot{x} = f(x,y)$ and $\dot{y} = g(x,y)$. Hence

$$\dot{r} = f(x,y)\cos\theta + g(x,y)\sin\theta,$$
$$r\dot{\theta} = g(x,y)\cos\theta - f(x,y)\sin\theta, \tag{1.52}$$

and substituting $x = r\cos\theta$ and $y = r\sin\theta$ into the right-hand sides of Equations (1.52) gives the required result.

Solution 1.26

From Equations (1.51), in the solution to the previous exercise, we can write

$$\dot{x} = \frac{\dot{r}x}{r} - y\dot{\theta},$$
$$\dot{y} = \frac{\dot{r}y}{r} + x\dot{\theta},$$

and substituting $\dot{r} = r(1 - r^2)$ and $\dot{\theta} = 1$ into the above gives

$$\dot{x} = x(1 - r^2) - y,$$
$$\dot{y} = y(1 - r^2) + x.$$

Substituting $r^2 = x^2 + y^2$ into this final expression gives the required result.

For the second part, note that the system linearized at the fixed point at the origin is

$$\dot{x} = x - y,$$
$$\dot{y} = x + y,$$

for which the $\mathbf{A}$ matrix is

$$\mathbf{A} = \begin{pmatrix} 1 & -1 \\ 1 & 1 \end{pmatrix},$$

so $\operatorname{tr} \mathbf{A} = 2$ and $\det \mathbf{A} = 2$. Using Equation (1.33), its eigenvalues are given by $2\lambda = 2 \pm \sqrt{4 - 8}$ or, more simply, $\lambda = 1 \pm i$, which are the eigenvalues of an unstable spiral, since they are complex with positive real part.

Solution 1.27

Use the results of Exercise 1.25 to express the system in polar form. Thus

$$\dot{r} = \big((1 - r^2)(r^2 - 4)r\cos\theta - r\sin\theta\big)\cos\theta + \big((1 - r^2)(r^2 - 4)r\sin\theta + r\cos\theta\big)\sin\theta$$
$$= r(1 - r^2)(r^2 - 4)$$

and

$$r\dot{\theta} = \big((1 - r^2)(r^2 - 4)r\sin\theta + r\cos\theta\big)\cos\theta - \big((1 - r^2)(r^2 - 4)r\cos\theta - r\sin\theta\big)\sin\theta$$
$$= r,$$

so the polar coordinates decouple into the pair

$$\dot{r} = r(1 - r^2)(r^2 - 4), \quad \dot{\theta} = 1.$$

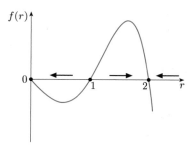

Figure 1.47 Flow of the radial coordinate with $\dot{r} = f(r) = r(1 - r^2)(r^2 - 4)$

To deduce the phase portrait, apply the methods of Subsection 1.4.1 to the radial coordinate r. So, plotting $\dot{r} = f(r) = r(1 - r^2)(r^2 - 4)$ against r in

Figure 1.47, we see that the r-coordinate of the orbits flows in the negative r-direction for $0 < r < 1$ and $r > 2$, but in the positive r-direction for $1 < r < 2$, with fixed points in r at $r = 0$ (stable), $r = 1$ (unstable), and $r = 2$ (stable). This implies that in the xy-plane there is a *stable* spiral at the origin, an *unstable* limit cycle at $r = 1$ (i.e. at $x^2 + y^2 = 1$), and a *stable* limit cycle at $r = 2$ (i.e. at $x^2 + y^2 = 4$).

Solution 1.28

Use the methods of Subsection 1.4.1 to examine the flow of the r-coordinate of the orbits. Proceed by plotting $\dot{r} = f(r) = -r(1 - r^2)^2$ against r as in Figure 1.48. There are fixed points in r at $r = 0$ and $r = 1$. But away from these fixed points the r-coordinate of the orbits is always flowing in the negative r-direction. Therefore the fixed point in r at $r = 0$ is stable, but at $r = 1$ it is neither stable nor unstable, since for $r > 1$ orbits flow into it but for $r < 1$ orbits flow out of it. This means that in the xy-plane there is a *stable* spiral at the origin but a *half-stable* limit cycle at $r = 1$ (i.e. at $x^2 + y^2 = 1$), with orbits spiralling into it for $r > 1$ but spiralling away from it towards the origin for $0 < r < 1$.

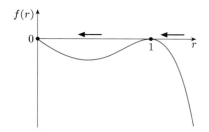

Figure 1.48   Flow of the radial coordinate with $\dot{r} = f(r) = -r(1 - r^2)^2$

Solution 1.29

The steady-state solution $x_{\mathrm{ss}}(t)$ is the particular integral for Equation (1.43). So choose
$$x_{\mathrm{ss}}(t) = A\cos(\Omega t) + B\sin(\Omega t) = R\cos(\Omega t + \phi),$$
so that $A = R\cos\phi$ and $B = -R\sin\phi$ and therefore
$$R^2 = A^2 + B^2. \tag{1.53}$$
Now, substituting this form of $x_{\mathrm{ss}}(t)$ into Equation (1.43) and equating terms in $\sin(\Omega t)$ leads to
$$\left(\omega^2 - \Omega^2\right)B - cA\Omega = \Gamma, \tag{1.54}$$
while equating terms in $\cos(\Omega t)$ gives
$$\left(\omega^2 - \Omega^2\right)A + cB\Omega = 0. \tag{1.55}$$
Equation (1.55) gives
$$B = \left(\Omega^2 - \omega^2\right)A/(c\Omega), \tag{1.56}$$
which, when substituted into (1.54), leads to
$$-\left(\Omega^2 - \omega^2\right)^2\frac{A}{c\Omega} - cA\Omega = \Gamma.$$
Rearranging gives
$$A = \frac{-c\Omega\Gamma}{\left(\Omega^2 - \omega^2\right)^2 + c^2\Omega^2},$$

and substituting this back into (1.56) gives
$$B = \frac{\left(\omega^2 - \Omega^2\right)\Gamma}{\left(\Omega^2 - \omega^2\right)^2 + c^2\Omega^2}.$$
These values of A and B are then substituted into Equation (1.53), giving the final expression for R.

Solution 1.30

The system of first-order differential equations is
$$\dot{x} = y,$$
$$\dot{y} = x - x^3 - cy + \Gamma\sin(\Omega t).$$
With $\Gamma = 0$, all the fixed points have $y = 0$ as required, from $\dot{x} = 0$. From $\dot{y} = 0$, the x-coordinate of the fixed points must satisfy $x(1 - x^2) = 0$, which has the three solutions $x = 0, \pm 1$, and therefore the three fixed points are at $(0,0)$, $(1,0)$ and $(-1,0)$. The Jacobian matrix is
$$\mathbf{J}(\mathbf{x}) = \begin{pmatrix} 0 & 1 \\ 1 - 3x^2 & -c \end{pmatrix},$$
and therefore $\operatorname{tr}\mathbf{J}(\mathbf{x}) = -c$ and $\det\mathbf{J}(\mathbf{x}) = 3x^2 - 1$. So, using Equation (1.33) on page 36, the eigenvalues of $\mathbf{J}(\mathbf{x})$ are given by
$$2\lambda = -c \pm \sqrt{c^2 - 4(3x^2 - 1)}.$$
For $x = 0$, $2\lambda = -c \pm \sqrt{c^2 + 4}$, so $\lambda_1 > 0 > \lambda_2$ and therefore $(0,0)$ is a saddle point for all c.

For $x = \pm 1$, $2\lambda = -c \pm \sqrt{c^2 - 8}$, and we now consider how this depends on c. For $c > 2\sqrt{2}$, the eigenvalues are real with $\lambda_1 < \lambda_2 < 0$ and so $(\pm 1, 0)$ are stable nodes. For $c = 2\sqrt{2}$, the eigenvalues are real but repeated with $\lambda_1 = \lambda_2 < 0$, and since $\mathbf{J}(\mathbf{x})$ is non-diagonal, $(\pm 1, 0)$ are stable improper nodes. For $0 < c < 2\sqrt{2}$, the eigenvalues are complex with negative real parts and therefore $(\pm 1, 0)$ are stable spirals. Finally, for $c = 0$, the eigenvalues are purely imaginary, implying that $(\pm 1, 0)$ are centres.

Solution 1.31

Since $x(t)$ is always close to 1, write $x = 1 + u$ (so that $y = \dot{x} = \dot{u}$ and $\ddot{x} = \ddot{u}$) and linearize Equation (1.45) by treating u as small. Since
$$-x + x^3 = -x(1 - x^2)$$
$$= -x(1 - x)(1 + x)$$
$$= -(1 + u)(-u)(2 + u)$$
$$= 2u + O(u^2),$$
Equation (1.45) becomes
$$\ddot{u} + c\dot{u} + 2u = \Gamma\sin(\Omega t)$$
to linear order in u. But this is identical to Equation (1.43) with u substituted for x and $\omega^2 = 2$. Therefore its steady-state phase curve is given by $u^2 + (y^2/\Omega^2) = R^2$, where R is as given in Exercise 1.29 but with $\omega^2 = 2$. Given that $u = x - 1$, this completes the solution.

Solution 1.32

To identify the mapping function $F(x)$ we need to solve the equation with initial value $x(0) = x_0$, and where $x_1 = x(T) = F(x_0)$. Express the differential equation as

$$\dot{x} + cx = A\cos(\Omega t),$$

and note that this can be solved with an integrating factor e^{ct}. Hence the equation becomes

$$\frac{d}{dt}\left(e^{ct}x\right) = Ae^{ct}\cos(\Omega t),$$

which, when integrated such that $x(0) = x_0$, gives

$$e^{ct}x(t) = A\int_0^t ds\, e^{cs}\cos(\Omega s) + x_0.$$

The integral on the right-hand side can be evaluated using the hint to give

$$x(t) = \frac{A}{c^2 + \Omega^2}\left(c\cos(\Omega t) + \Omega\sin(\Omega t) - ce^{-ct}\right) + e^{-ct}x_0.$$

Now, putting $t = T = 2\pi/\Omega$ into the above expression, noting that $\cos(2\pi) = 1$ and $\sin(2\pi) = 0$, gives

$$x(T) = x_1 = \frac{Ac\left(1 - e^{-cT}\right)}{c^2 + \Omega^2} + e^{-cT}x_0,$$

and hence the mapping function is

$$F(x) = \frac{Ac\left(1 - e^{-cT}\right)}{c^2 + \Omega^2} + e^{-cT}x.$$

Solution 1.33

Since $\dot{\theta} = 1$, $\theta(t) = t + \theta_0$, which implies that if the orbit starts on Σ it will take time 2π to return to Σ. So if r_0 is the value of $r(t)$ at $t = 0$, say, and r_1 is its value at $t = 2\pi$, then r_0 and r_1 are related via the Poincaré return map $r_1 = P(r_0)$. So we need to solve $\dot{r} = r(1 - r^2)$ with initial condition $r(0) = r_0$, and obtain $r(2\pi) = r_1$. The differential equation for r can be rearranged to give

$$\int \frac{dr}{r(1 - r^2)} = \int dt,$$

and integrating with the required initial value gives

$$\int_{r_0}^{r_1} \frac{dr}{r(1 - r^2)} = \int_0^{2\pi} dt = 2\pi.$$

Using the hint to integrate the left-hand side gives

$$\tfrac{1}{2}\ln\left|\frac{1 - r_0^{-2}}{1 - r_1^{-2}}\right| = 2\pi,$$

and rearranging further gives

$$1 - r_1^{-2} = e^{-4\pi}\left(1 - r_0^{-2}\right).$$

Final rearrangement gives

$$r_1 = P(r_0) = \left(1 + e^{-4\pi}\left(r_0^{-2} - 1\right)\right)^{-1/2},$$

leading to the required result.

Solution 1.34

(a) Defining the functions

$$f(x, y, z) = \sigma(y - x),$$
$$g(x, y, z) = rx - y - xz,$$
$$h(x, y, z) = xy - bz,$$

the fixed points are the solutions of $f = g = h = 0$.

Now, $f = 0$ implies that $y = x$ at the fixed points, and substituting this into the remaining equations, $g = h = 0$, gives

$$(r - 1)x = xz \tag{1.57}$$

from $g = 0$ and

$$x^2 = bz \tag{1.58}$$

from $h = 0$. Now, $x = 0$ is a solution of Equation (1.57) for *all* r, in which case $y = x = 0$ and, from Equation (1.58), $z = 0$. Therefore the origin $(0, 0, 0)$ is a fixed point for all $r > 0$. In addition, if $x = y \neq 0$ then a solution of (1.57) is $z = r - 1$, and substituting this into Equation (1.58) gives $x^2 = b(r - 1)$. Provided that $r > 1$ (since $b > 0$ and x must be real), this last equation has the solutions $x = \pm\sqrt{b(r - 1)}$. So for $r > 1$ only, in addition to the fixed point at the origin, there are two more fixed points, at

$$\left(\sqrt{b(r - 1)}, \sqrt{b(r - 1)}, r - 1\right)$$

and

$$\left(-\sqrt{b(r - 1)}, -\sqrt{b(r - 1)}, r - 1\right).$$

Note that these coincide with $(0, 0, 0)$ at $r = 1$. For $0 < r < 1$, the origin is the only fixed point.

(b) Many of the arguments in Subsection 1.4.2 extend to three dimensions. To determine the stability of the fixed point at $(0, 0, 0)$, we need to linearize about this point, which gives a 3×3 Jacobian matrix

$$\mathbf{J} = \begin{pmatrix} f_x & f_y & f_z \\ g_x & g_y & g_z \\ h_x & h_y & h_z \end{pmatrix}.$$

This leads to the linear system $\dot{\mathbf{x}} = \mathbf{J}(0)\mathbf{x}$, which can be analysed in terms of the eigenvalues of $\mathbf{J}$, as before, only now there are three eigenvalues since $\mathbf{J}$ is a 3×3 matrix. Thus Equation (1.36), on page 36, becomes

$$\mathbf{x}(t) = c_1 e^{\lambda_1 t}\mathbf{u}_1 + c_2 e^{\lambda_2 t}\mathbf{u}_2 + c_3 e^{\lambda_3 t}\mathbf{u}_3, \tag{1.59}$$

and the task is to find the three eigenvalues, λ_1, λ_2 and λ_3, of the Jacobian. Note that $f_x = -\sigma$, $f_y = \sigma$, $f_z = 0$, $g_x = r - z$, $g_y = -1$, $g_z = -x$, $h_x = y$, $h_y = x$ and $h_z = -b$, so the Jacobian matrix at $(0, 0, 0)$ is

$$\mathbf{J}(0) = \begin{pmatrix} -\sigma & \sigma & 0 \\ r & -1 & 0 \\ 0 & 0 & -b \end{pmatrix}.$$

The eigenvalues are determined by $\det(\mathbf{J}(0) - \lambda\mathbf{I}) = 0$, which can be expressed as

$$(\lambda + b)\left((\lambda + \sigma)(\lambda + 1) - r\sigma\right) = 0.$$

So one of the eigenvalues is $\lambda_3 = -b$, and since $b > 0$, $\lambda_3 < 0$. The other two are solutions of the quadratic

$$\lambda^2 + (1 + \sigma)\lambda - \sigma(r - 1) = 0.$$

These solutions are given by

$$2\lambda = -(1 + \sigma) \pm \sqrt{\Delta},$$

where

$$\Delta = (1 + \sigma)^2 + 4\sigma(r - 1) \tag{1.60}$$
$$= (1 - \sigma)^2 + 4\sigma r, \tag{1.61}$$

with (1.61) implying that $\Delta > 0$ (since all terms on the right-hand side are positive) and therefore all the eigenvalues are real.

Now, when $0 < r < 1$, Equation (1.60) implies that $\Delta < (1 + \sigma)^2$ (recall that $\sigma > 0$, so $\sigma(r - 1) < 0$), so the remaining eigenvalues, λ_1 and λ_2, are both negative. Thus, since all three eigenvalues are negative, Equation (1.59) shows that the origin is a three-dimensional version of a *stable node* when $0 < r < 1$.

Turning now to $r > 1$, for this case Equation (1.60) implies that $\Delta > (1 + \sigma)^2$, so that one of the remaining eigenvalues is positive but the other is negative, $\lambda_1 > 0 > \lambda_2$. Thus for $r > 1$, one eigenvalue, λ_1, is positive and the other two, λ_2 and λ_3, are both negative and so, by referring to Equation (1.59), the fixed point at the origin is a three-dimensional version of a *saddle point*.

UNIT 2 One-dimensional maps

Study guide

There are five sections in this unit. You will probably find Sections 2.1, 2.2 and 2.3 heaviest in terms of workload. Section 2.4 is relatively short (although mathematically subtle in places), and Section 2.5 is shorter still and mainly descriptive with little mathematics.

Section 2.1 does not use Maple at all and can therefore be worked through without a computer. Maple is used quite extensively in Sections 2.2 and 2.3, and to a much lesser extent in Sections 2.4 and 2.5.

Introduction

The purpose of this unit is to study some properties of autonomous one-dimensional maps, paying particular attention to periodic orbits and chaotic orbits. In many ways, one-dimensional maps are the simplest dynamical systems in which to study chaotic phenomena, and they enable us to arrive at a mathematically precise definition of a chaotic orbit.

The unit starts by introducing some basic definitions and notations for maps, which are then illustrated with *linear maps* in Subsection 2.1.1. In Subsection 2.1.2, *fixed points* are defined and discussed. Also in this subsection, *cobweb plots* are introduced. These are graphical representations of orbits and are useful in visualizing their properties, particularly near fixed points. In Subsection 2.1.3, the concept of *invariant sets* is introduced. As with differential equations, fixed points of maps can be either *stable* (the fixed point is then called a *sink*) or *unstable* (where the fixed point is called a *source*). The condition which determines the *stability* of a fixed point is given in an important theorem in Subsection 2.1.4.

Sections 2.2 and 2.3 are concerned mainly with the *logistic map* in order to illustrate ideas leading to *period doubling* and *chaos*. In Subsection 2.2.1, it will be shown how orbits for the logistic map are evaluated numerically and plotted using Maple. In Subsection 2.2.2, these methods are used to find periodic orbits and, in particular *bifurcations* to *period-2 orbits*, *period-4 orbits*, etc. In general, one may find *period-k orbits*. Like fixed points, period-k orbits can be either stable, called *period-k sinks*, or unstable, called *period-k sources*. The stability condition for period-k orbits is given in Subsection 2.2.3. It is possible to construct a diagram which plots the set of points to which orbits are attracted as a parameter is varied. Such a diagram is called a *bifurcation diagram* and, in Subsection 2.2.4, Maple is used to plot this for the logistic map.

Notions of chaos characterized by an extreme sensitivity to initial conditions are discussed in Subsection 2.3.1. This leads naturally to defining the *Lyapunov number* and *Lyapunov exponent* for an orbit, which is done in Subsection 2.3.2. Orbits which eventually become periodic are called *asymptotically periodic*, and these are also defined in this subsection. The Lyapunov exponent, which in Subsection 2.3.3 is calculated numerically using Maple for orbits of the logistic map, is particularly useful in that a bounded orbit, which is *not* asymptotically periodic, is defined as chaotic when its Lyapunov exponent is positive. This definition is expanded upon at the end of Section 2.3.

Another map, the *tent map*, is explored in Section 2.4. This map, introduced in Subsection 2.4.1, is similar to the logistic map in that it has chaotic orbits, but it is simpler to analyse and much can be inferred without numerical computation. In particular, it is explicitly shown (without numerics) in Subsection 2.4.2 that, for a particular parameter value of the tent map, orbits can be chaotic. The arguments make use of *binary* fractions, and, moreover, the tent map at that parameter value is equivalent to the logistic map at a particular value of its parameter. This then substantiates the numerical evidence for chaos in the logistic map.

The unit ends in Section 2.5 with a brief discussion of some universal aspects generic to a wide class of one-dimensional maps where chaos occurs. In particular, *Feigenbaum's universal constant*, emerging from the period-doubling route to chaos, is defined. This section is mainly descriptive with few mathematical details or exercises.

2.1   Maps and orbits

In this unit we shall confine ourselves to the study of one-dimensional maps of the type

$$x_{n+1} = f(x_n) \tag{2.1}$$

where $f : \mathbb{R} \longrightarrow \mathbb{R}$. This defines the 'discrete-time' development of some variable x_n on $\mathbb{R}$, with n being the discrete time. The variable x_n takes the value x_0 at the initial time $n = 0$; this is the **initial value**. Equation (2.1) then determines x_n for all subsequent $n \geq 1$, so that $x_1 = f(x_0)$, $x_2 = f(x_1) = f(f(x_0))$, etc.

We now define some useful notation. The symbol '∘' is used to denote the **composition** of two functions, $f(x)$ and $g(x)$, say, as follows:

$$(f \circ g)(x) = f(g(x)),$$

i.e. the function, f, of another function, g. In addition, another notation is often used to denote the composition of a function with itself, as in

$$f^2(x) = (f \circ f)(x) = f(f(x))$$

or, more generally for $k \geq 1$,

$$f^k(x) = (\underbrace{f \circ f \circ \cdots \circ f}_{k \text{ times}})(x) = f\left(f\left(\ldots f\left(f(x)\right)\ldots\right)\right),$$

and we use the convention that $f^0(x) = x$. It might be helpful to note that $f^k(x) = f(f^{k-1}(x))$ (you will observe that this holds for the case $k = 1$), and it is *very* important not to confuse $f^k(x)$ with $f^{(k)}(x)$, the latter denoting the kth derivative of $f(x)$ with respect to x (the parentheses in the superscript play a crucial role here). Moreover, one must *not* confuse $f^k(x)$ with $(f(x))^k$; the latter means, of course, that $f(x)$ has been raised to the kth power.

Let us look at an example.

> Note that for some named functions (e.g. sin, cos, etc.), the superscript convention does refer to raising the result of the function application to a power, e.g. $\sin^3 x = (\sin x)^3$.

Example 2.1

Consider the map $f(x) = 1 + x^2$. Evaluate $f^2(x)$ and $f^3(x)$.

Solution

$$f^2(x) = f(f(x)) = f(1 + x^2) = 1 + (1 + x^2)^2 = 2 + 2x^2 + x^4$$

and

$$f^3(x) = f(f^2(x)) = 1 + (2 + 2x^2 + x^4)^2 = 5 + 8x^2 + 8x^4 + 4x^6 + x^8.$$

Note that $f^3(x)$ is a polynomial of degree 8, whereas $f(x)^3 = (f(x))^3$ would be a polynomial of degree 6. ◆

Returning now to the map (2.1), given the initial value x_0, the map generates the sequence of points

$$\{x_0, x_1, x_2, \ldots\} = \{x_0, f(x_0), f^2(x_0), \ldots\}.$$

This sequence, also denoted $\{x_n\}_{n \geq 0} = \{f^n(x_0)\}_{n \geq 0}$, is referred to as the **orbit** of x_0 under f.

> Note that the curly-bracket set notation, { }, is used for orbits, but in *this* case the elements of the set are *ordered* and can take repeating values.

2.1.1 Linear maps

In order to illustrate the above ideas, we consider linear maps. These are relatively simple, and understanding them will prove useful later in the analysis of more complicated maps where much can be understood from linearizations about certain points.

Consider the following **linear map**:

$$f(x) = bx, \tag{2.2}$$

with initial value x_0, and b some real constant. Clearly,

$$x_1 = bx_0,$$
$$x_2 = bx_1 = b^2 x_0,$$

etc., or, more generally,

$$x_n = b^n x_0. \tag{2.3}$$

> A linear map is any map whose mapping function $f(x)$ has the form $f(x) = a + bx$, where a and b are constants.

Thus x_n changes *exponentially* with n. So the orbit of x_0 under f given by (2.2) is

$$\{x_0, bx_0, b^2 x_0, \ldots, b^n x_0, \ldots\}.$$

We now examine the behaviour of this orbit as b is varied. For the time being, it is assumed that $x_0 \neq 0$. First, it is trivial to see that if $b = 0$, then $x_n = 0$ for all $n \geq 1$. For other values of b, we consider positive and negative values separately. For $0 < b < 1$, $x_n \to 0$ *monotonically* as $n \to \infty$, or in other words, the orbit converges monotonically to the point $x = 0$ as n becomes large. On the other hand, for $b > 1$, $x_n \to \pm\infty$ ($+\infty$ for $x_0 > 0$ and $-\infty$ for $x_0 < 0$) as $n \to \infty$, so the orbit monotonically diverges as n becomes large. The special case of $b = 1$ gives $x_n = x_0$ for all n. For

> Recall the definition of the term *monotonic*: if a variable is varying monotonically, then it is changing in one direction only, either always increasing or always decreasing.

negative b, let us set $b = -|b|$ in Equation (2.3) so that it becomes

$$x_n = (-1)^n |b|^n x_0. \tag{2.4}$$

Hence we see that for $-1 < b < 0$, x_n converges to 0 as $n \to \infty$ (converges since $0 < |b| < 1$), although *not* monotonically but with a sign which alternates between successive terms. For $b < -1$, the orbit diverges with alternating sign as $n \to \infty$. Finally, for $b = -1$, $x_n = (-1)^n x_0$, so x_n simply alternates between the two values $\pm x_0$ for all n.

Exercise 2.1

Show that the orbit of x_0 under the linear map

$$f(x) = a + bx$$

is $\{x_n\}_{n \geq 0}$ where

$$x_n = \begin{cases} b^n x_0 + \dfrac{(1 - b^n)a}{1 - b} & \text{if } b \neq 1, \\ x_0 + na & \text{if } b = 1. \end{cases}$$

[*Hint*: Write $x_n = u_n + \alpha$, and find α such that the map for u_n reduces to that for x_n in Equation (2.2).]

2.1.2 Fixed points and cobweb plots

The point $x = 0$ played a special role in the orbit under the linear map (2.2) in the preceding subsection. The orbit could be described in terms of its behaviour in relation to this point: for $|b| < 1$, the orbit of x_0 converges to this point, whereas for $|b| > 1$, it diverges away from it. If we set $x_0 = 0$, then $x_n = 0$ for *all* $n \geq 0$ *regardless* of the value of b, i.e. the orbit never leaves this point. The point $x = 0$ stays fixed under the map f in (2.2) and is therefore referred to as a fixed point.

For a general map $f(x)$, the **fixed point** x^* solves the equation

$$f(x^*) = x^*. \tag{2.5}$$

Thus if $x_n = x^*$, then $x_m = x^*$ for all $m \geq n$; the orbit of x_n stays at x^*. For the linear map (2.2) with $b \neq 1$, the *only* solution of Equation (2.5) is $x^* = 0$.

We can visualize orbits through the following graphical representation of the map

$$x_{n+1} = f(x_n). \tag{2.6}$$

Consider Figure 2.1, which shows a plot of $y = f(x)$ with the restriction that $f'(x) > 0$. This restriction is chosen for convenience of presentation – other cases will be considered later. In this example it turns out that $0 < f'(x^*) < 1$, but other cases will be considered below. Also shown is the line $y = x$, which crosses $y = f(x)$ at the fixed point x^*, since this is where $x = f(x)$.

On a point of notation, the asterisk in x^* has, of course, nothing to do with the complex conjugate. (Throughout, we shall consider only real-valued variables.) Note also that for the differential equations in *Unit 1*, x_f was used to denote a fixed point of a flow.

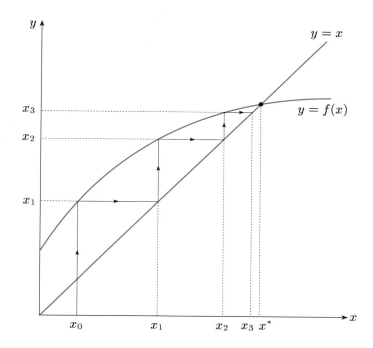

Figure 2.1   Cobweb plot (shown in red) for the orbit of x_0 under f with $0 < f'(x^*) < 1$

We now describe how to construct a graphical representation of the orbit of x_0 under f. Let x_0 be some point on the x-axis, and proceed with the following two steps.

Step (i)   Draw the vertical line from $(x_0, 0)$ until it meets the curve $y = f(x)$. The y-coordinate of this point of intersection is x_1 since $y = f(x_0) = x_1$ using Equation (2.6).

Step (ii)   Now draw the horizontal line $y = x_1$ until it intersects the line $y = x$. The x-coordinate of this point of intersection is clearly x_1, as can be seen in Figure 2.1 by tracing along the vertical broken line between the point and the x-axis.

Thus we have been able to give graphical expression to the map $x_0 \longmapsto x_1 = f(x_0)$, by drawing the line joining the points $(x_0, 0)$ and (x_0, x_1) together with the line joining (x_0, x_1) and (x_1, x_1). These two steps can be repeated on the point (x_1, x_1) so that a vertical line is drawn to the point $(x_1, f(x_1)) = (x_1, x_2)$ (Step (i)), followed by a horizontal line to the point (x_2, x_2) (Step (ii)). These latter two lines represent the map $x_1 \longmapsto x_2 = f(x_1)$. Steps (i) and (ii) can be continued repeatedly so that a picture of the orbit is built up as shown by the 'staircase' of arrowed lines in Figure 2.1. This way of visualizing the orbit is called the **cobweb plot** for the orbit of the map f. Notice that the staircase converges to the fixed point x^*; this is an example of an attracting fixed point.

Attracting (and repelling) fixed points will be discussed more fully in Subsection 2.1.4.

Exercise 2.2

The cobweb plot in Figure 2.1 was constructed for the case when $x_0 < x^*$. Construct a cobweb plot for the same map but with $x_0 > x^*$.

So far we have described the construction of a cobweb plot for the case where $f'(x) > 0$. Figure 2.2 shows a cobweb for the case where $f'(x) < 0$.

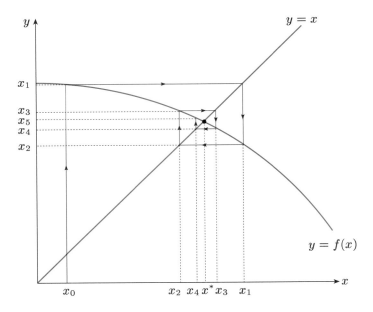

Figure 2.2   Cobweb plot (shown in red) for the orbit of x_0 under f with $-1 < f'(x^*) < 0$

The cobweb was constructed by following the same Steps (i) and (ii) above, except that now we find that the direction of the horizontal line in Step (ii) alternates at each iteration of the map, first rightwards then leftwards then rightwards, etc. This builds up a graphical representation of the orbit which consists of the 'spiral' of arrowed lines winding round the fixed point. You can now begin to see why these are called cobweb plots. Notice that in this case the spiral converges to the fixed point x^*, in ever-decreasing 'circles'. This is another example of an attracting fixed point.

As a simple illustration of these ideas, consider the linear map $f(x) = bx$. It has already been mentioned that $x = 0$ is the fixed point for this map. We now present cobweb plots for this map for various values of b. First, we plot cobwebs for the orbits for positive values of b (with $b \neq 1$), shown in Figure 2.3.

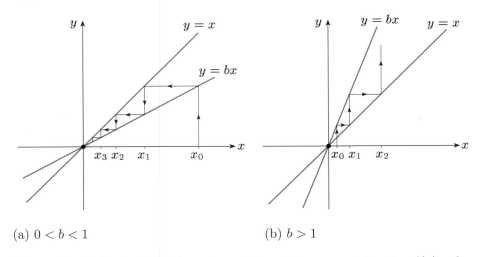

(a) $0 < b < 1$ (b) $b > 1$

Figure 2.3   Cobweb plots (shown in red) for orbits generated under $f(x) = bx$ with positive b $(b \neq 1)$

Recall that for $0 < b < 1$ the orbit converges to the fixed point no matter where x_0 is. This can be seen graphically from the cobweb in Figure 2.3(a), where the origin is an **attracting** fixed point. On the other hand, for $b > 1$, the orbit diverges to infinity for all $x_0 \neq 0$, as illustrated by the cobweb plot in Figure 2.3(b); in this case we call the origin a **repelling** fixed point.

We also consider orbits for negative values of b. The cobweb plots for these are shown in Figure 2.4.

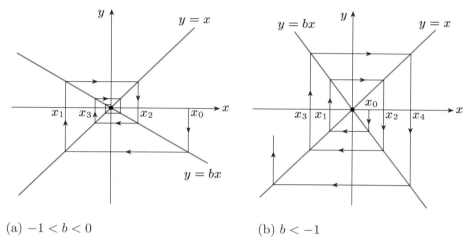

(a) $-1 < b < 0$ (b) $b < -1$

Figure 2.4 Cobweb plots (shown in red) for orbits generated under $f(x) = bx$ with negative b ($b \neq -1$)

Note that Figure 2.4(a) (where $-1 < b < 0$) represents graphically the orbit of a point near an attracting fixed point, whereas Figure 2.4(b) (where $b < -1$) shows the orbit of a point near a repelling fixed point. You should compare the cobweb plots of the orbits shown in Figures 2.3 and 2.4 with the analytical results derived in Subsection 2.1.1. Note that the alternating sign in Equation (2.4) is consistent with the spiralling cobwebs in Figure 2.4.

Exercise 2.3

Consider the map $f(x) = a + bx$ in Exercise 2.1, keeping $a > 0$ and $b \neq 1$.

(a) Determine the fixed point of the map.

(b) Draw cobweb plots of its orbits for $0 < b < 1$ and $b > 1$.

Comment on the case $b = 1$ and the limits $b \uparrow 1$ and $b \downarrow 1$.

Notation: the expression $x \uparrow a$ denotes taking the limit $x \to a$ from below (i.e. whilst keeping $x < a$), and $x \downarrow a$ denotes taking the limit $x \to a$ from above (i.e. whilst keeping $x > a$).

By now, you may have noticed a useful rule of thumb for constructing the graphical representation of the orbit: if the graph $y = f(x)$ is *above* the line $y = x$, the orbit moves to the *right*, whereas if the graph is *below* the line $y = x$, the orbit moves to the *left*.

Hence, by applying this rule, you can readily see that if $y = f(x)$ crosses the line $y = x$ in the manner shown in Figure 2.5(a), then the point of intersection is an *attracting* fixed point, whereas if it crosses as in Figure 2.5(b), then it gives rise to a *repelling* fixed point.

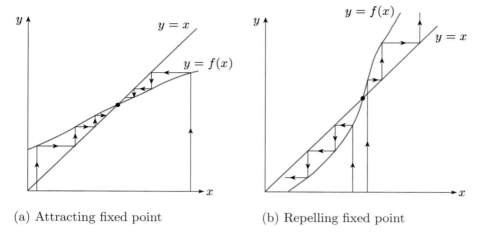

(a) Attracting fixed point   (b) Repelling fixed point

Figure 2.5   Cobweb plots (shown in red) for orbits generated under $f(x)$ near fixed points

2.1.3 Invariant sets

Here we shall introduce the concept of an **invariant set** for a one-dimensional map f. The set $S \subset \mathbb{R}$ is **invariant** under the map f if $x \in S \Rightarrow f(x) \in S$. In other words, an invariant set is mapped into itself under the map. However, when developing an overall picture of the dynamics of a map, one usually considers the **elementary invariant sets** under the map. The elementary invariant sets of a map are the largest invariant sets that *cannot* be decomposed into smaller invariant sets. Note that if x^* is a fixed point of the map f, then the one-element set $\{x^*\}$ is an invariant set under f and is clearly an elementary invariant set. Let us look at an example.

Example 2.2

Consider the linear map $f(x) = bx$, whose cobweb plots were constructed in Subsection 2.1.2. Find all the *elementary* invariant sets of this map when

(a) $b > 0$ $(b \neq 1)$,   (b) $b < 0$ $(b \neq -1)$.

Solution

(a) By examining Figure 2.3, we see that for $b > 0$ there are *three* elementary invariant sets under f, namely $(-\infty, 0)$, $\{0\}$ and $(0, \infty)$. Note that a set such as $[0, \infty)$ is an invariant set but *not* an elementary invariant set because $[0, \infty)$ can be decomposed into smaller invariant sets: $[0, \infty) = \{0\} \cup (0, \infty)$.

(b) By looking at Figure 2.4, and noting the alternating character of the orbit, we find just *two* elementary invariant sets for $b < 0$, namely $\{0\}$ and $\mathbb{R} \setminus \{0\} = (-\infty, 0) \cup (0, \infty)$. Note that $\mathbb{R}$ is an invariant set but not an elementary one since it can be decomposed into smaller invariant sets via $\mathbb{R} = \{(-\infty, 0) \cup (0, \infty)\} \cup \{0\}$. ◆

Exercise 2.4

Find all the elementary invariant sets for the map in Exercise 2.1 for both $b > 0$ and $b < 0$.

2.1.4 Stability of fixed points

The previous discussions regarding cobweb plots help us develop an intuitive feel for the behaviour of orbits near fixed points. A question that needs to be asked is what determines whether a fixed point of a map $f(x)$ is attracting or repelling. The cobweb plots in Figure 2.5, together with considerations based on those for the linear map shown in Figures 2.3 and 2.4, seem to indicate that it is the *slope* of $f(x)$ at x^* that determines the **stability** of x^*, that is, whether the fixed point is attracting, and therefore **stable**, or repelling, and therefore **unstable**. One could go further and guess that x^* is attracting if $|f'(x^*)| < 1$ and repelling if $|f'(x^*)| > 1$. This is certainly confirmed by the linear map $f(x) = bx$ in the examples considered above, and also for the more general picture in Figure 2.5. In fact, we shall *prove* that this is indeed the case. But first we need to give more precise definitions of attracting and repelling fixed points, and introduce the notion of the neighbourhood of a fixed point.

So far, we have rather loosely used phrases like 'behaviour of orbits near a fixed point' but, in order to progress further, we now need to quantify more precisely what we mean by the word 'near'. We do this by introducing the **epsilon neighbourhood**, $N_\varepsilon(x^*)$, of the fixed point x^*. This is just an interval in $\mathbb{R}$ of all points within a distance ε of x^*, and it can be expressed as

$$N_\varepsilon(x^*) = \{x \in \mathbb{R} : |x - x^*| < \varepsilon\} = (x^* - \varepsilon, x^* + \varepsilon). \tag{2.7}$$

Now, consider the map $f(x)$ on $\mathbb{R}$ with a fixed point x^* such that $f(x^*) = x^*$. We say that x^* is an **attracting fixed point**, also called a **sink**, if points sufficiently close to x^* converge to x^* under f. More precisely, given some $\varepsilon > 0$ (which may be small), x^* is a sink if $\lim_{k \to \infty} f^k(x) = x^*$ for all $x \in N_\varepsilon(x^*)$. Conversely, we say that x^* is a **repelling fixed point**, also called a **source**, if points sufficiently close to x^* move increasingly away from x^* under f. Again, more precisely, x^* is a source if there exists some $\varepsilon > 0$ such that for all $x \in N_\varepsilon(x^*)$ except x^* itself, x eventually maps outside $N_\varepsilon(x^*)$ under repeated application of f.

The stability of x^* is now given by the following theorem, which applies to all **smooth** functions f. A smooth function is a function with a continuous first derivative (that is, it is continuously differentiable).

Smooth functions are sometimes called functions of class C^1.

Theorem 2.1

Let f be a smooth map on $\mathbb{R}$ with fixed point x^*.

(a) If $|f'(x^*)| < 1$, then x^* is a stable fixed point, i.e. a sink.

(b) If $|f'(x^*)| > 1$, then x^* is an unstable fixed point, i.e. a source.

A smooth map is a map whose mapping function, $f(x)$, is smooth.

Note that Theorem 2.1 does not specify the stability of the fixed point when $|f'(x^*)| = 1$.

Proof We start by noting that $|f'(x^*)|$ is given by the limit

$$\lim_{x \to x^*} \frac{|f(x) - f(x^*)|}{|x - x^*|} = |f'(x^*)|. \tag{2.8}$$

We now prove the parts of the theorem in turn.

(a) Let c be *any* number such that $|f'(x^*)| < c < 1$. Then the limit (2.8) and the smoothness of $f(x)$ guarantee that there exists an epsilon neighbourhood $N_\varepsilon(x^*)$ such that

$$\frac{|f(x) - f(x^*)|}{|x - x^*|} \le c \quad \text{for all } x \in N_\varepsilon(x^*).$$

Since $f(x^*) = x^*$, this last expression can be rewritten as

$$|f(x) - x^*| \le c|x - x^*| \quad \text{for all } x \in N_\varepsilon(x^*). \tag{2.9}$$

Since $|f'(x^*)| < c < 1$, (2.9) implies that when x is in $N_\varepsilon(x^*)$, $f(x)$ is closer than x to x^*. We can then have the map act on $f(x)$ to show that $f^2(x)$ is closer than $f(x)$ to x^*. Continuing in this way shows that $f^3(x)$ is closer still, etc. Thus $f^k(x)$ gets progressively closer to x^* as k increases, provided that $x \in N_\varepsilon(x^*)$. Furthermore, substituting $f(x)$ for x in (2.9) shows that

$$|f^2(x) - x^*| \le c|f(x) - x^*| \le c^2|x - x^*|$$

for all $x \in N_\varepsilon(x^*)$, where the second inequality follows directly from (2.9). Hence, by induction, it follows that

$$|f^k(x) - x^*| \le c^k|x - x^*|, \tag{2.10}$$

and therefore, since $|f'(x^*)| < c < 1$,

$$\lim_{k \to \infty} |f^k(x) - x^*| = 0 \quad \text{for all } x \in N_\varepsilon(x^*),$$

thus proving the first part of the theorem.

(b) The proof for this part follows along similar lines to that for part (a). Now let c be *any* number satisfying $1 < c < |f'(x^*)|$. Then the limit (2.8) implies that there exists an epsilon neighbourhood $N_\varepsilon(x^*)$ such that

$$\frac{|f(x) - f(x^*)|}{|x - x^*|} \ge c \quad \text{for all } x \in N_\varepsilon(x^*)$$

or, in other words,

$$|f(x) - x^*| \ge c|x - x^*| \quad \text{for all } x \in N_\varepsilon(x^*). \tag{2.11}$$

Thus, since $c > 1$, $f(x)$ will be further away than x from x^* for all $x \in N_\varepsilon(x^*)$. If $f(x)$ lies within $N_\varepsilon(x^*)$, we can apply inequality (2.11) with $f(x)$ instead of x, showing that $f^2(x)$ is even further than $f(x)$ from x^*. We continue this process recursively, and an inductive argument similar to that in part (a) shows that

$$|f^k(x) - x^*| \ge c^k|x - x^*|$$

provided that $f^0(x), f^1(x), f^2(x), \ldots, f^{k-1}(x)$ continue to lie within $N_\varepsilon(x^*)$. However, since $1 < c < |f'(x^*)|$, we will be able to find a k big enough such that $f^k(x)$ eventually lies outside $N_\varepsilon(x^*)$ for any $x \in N_\varepsilon(x^*)$. This completes the proof of the second part of the theorem. $\square$

This proof gives us some important insights. In particular, in the case of sinks, (2.10) shows that the orbit approaches the sink *exponentially* fast with k. Moreover, c can be chosen to be arbitrarily close to $|f'(x^*)|$. In particular, for a sink where $f'(x^*) = 0$, the orbit must converge to x^* *faster* than any exponential. This can be seen from (2.10) where, since c can be chosen to be arbitrarily close to 0, an orbit converging exponentially to x^* would eventually violate this inequality. Such a sink is called **superstable** and is determined by the condition $f'(x^*) = 0$.

An exponential convergence to x^* is where $|f^k(x) - x^*| \simeq b^k|x - x^*|$ as $k \to \infty$ and $0 < b < 1$.

Example 2.3

Find and classify the fixed points of the map $f(x) = x^2$.

Solution

The fixed points x^* satisfy $f(x^*) = x^*$, so x^* solves $(x^*)^2 = x^*$. This has two solutions, one at $x = 0$ and the other at $x = 1$. Now, $f'(x) = 2x$, so for the fixed point at $x = 0$, $f'(0) = 0$, and for that at $x = 1$, $f'(1) = 2$. Hence the fixed point at $x = 0$ is a *sink* (in fact, a superstable sink), and the fixed point at $x = 1$ is a *source*. ◆

For the superstable sink found in Example 2.3, one can show explicitly that orbits converge to this fixed point faster than any exponential since the orbits themselves can be written down explicitly. This is done as follows. Since $x_{n+1} = x_n^2$, we have

$$x_1 = x_0^2, \quad x_2 = x_1^2 = x_0^4, \quad x_3 = x_2^2 = x_0^8, \quad \text{etc.,}$$

and in general we can see that

$$x_n = x_0^{2^n}.$$

Thus, for $|x_0| < 1$, x_n converges to 0 as $n \to \infty$ faster than any exponential (compare with b^n for any $0 < b < 1$).

That $x_n = x_0^{2^n}$ can be seen inductively. It is clearly true for $n = 1$, and if true for n then true for $n + 1$ since $x_{n+1} = x_n^2 = (x_0^{2^n})^2 = x_0^{2^{n+1}}$.

Exercise 2.5

Recall that the Newton–Raphson method for finding the solution of the equation $f(x) = 0$ at $x = x_s$ is based on the iterative map

$$x_{n+1} = F(x_n), \quad F(x) = x - \frac{f(x)}{f'(x)},$$

with the fixed point at $x^* = x_s$. It was noted in the exercises in *Unit 1* that the iterates of the Newton–Raphson maps considered there converge very rapidly to the solution $x = x_s$. Show that the fixed point of the general Newton–Raphson map $F(x)$ is *superstable* provided that $f'(x_s) \neq 0$ (hence the reason for the rapid convergences observed in the *Unit 1* exercises).

The definition of a sink requires that there exists an epsilon neighbourhood $N_\varepsilon(x^*)$ such that *all* orbits starting in $N_\varepsilon(x^*)$ eventually converge to x^*. For this to happen, ε may need to be very small. However, this is often not the case, and one can find sinks which attract orbits starting at points some distance away. Indeed, we define the set of *all* initial values whose orbits converge to the sink x^* as the **basin of attraction** of x^*. For an example of this, consider the map

$$f(x) = 2x(1 - x).$$

The fixed points are solutions of the equation

$$2x^*(1 - x^*) = x^*,$$

and hence there are two fixed points: $x^* = 0$ and $x^* = \frac{1}{2}$. Now, $f'(x) = 2 - 4x$, so $f'(0) = 2 > 1$ and $f'(\frac{1}{2}) = 0 < 1$. Thus, using Theorem 2.1, the fixed point at $x = 0$ is a *source* (because $|f'(0)| > 1$), whereas that at $x = \frac{1}{2}$ is a *sink* (because $|f'(\frac{1}{2})| < 1$). In fact, since $f'(\frac{1}{2}) = 0$, it is a *superstable* sink. The nature of these fixed points is also evident graphically by examining the cobweb plots shown in Figure 2.6.

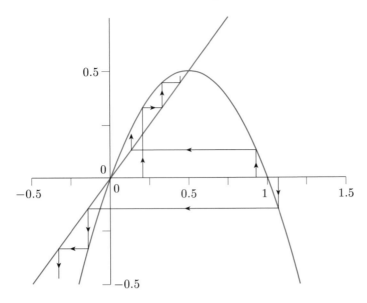

Figure 2.6   Cobweb plots (shown in red) for orbits under $f(x) = 2x(1 - x)$ with various initial values

These cobweb plots are particularly useful for determining the basin of attraction of the sink at $x = \frac{1}{2}$. The graphical construction shows that all orbits starting in the region $x < 0$ are repelled by the source at $x = 0$ and diverge to $x = -\infty$. Also, all orbits starting in the region $x > 1$ immediately jump to the region $x < 0$ at the first iteration and thus diverge to $x = -\infty$ as before. However, one can see that all orbits starting in the region $0 < x < 1$ will converge to the sink at $x = \frac{1}{2}$. Note that the orbit of the point $x = 1$ will go straight to the fixed point at $x = 0$ at the first iteration. (However, this does not stop $x = 0$ being a source because there still exists a neighbourhood of $x = 0$ which satisfies the definition of a source.) Thus the basin of attraction of the superstable sink at $x = \frac{1}{2}$ is the open interval $(0, 1)$.

Exercise 2.6

Show, graphically, that for the map $f(x) = x^2$ considered in Example 2.3, the basin of attraction of the superstable sink at $x = 0$ is the open interval $(-1, 1)$.

Exercise 2.7

Consider the map

$$f(x) = x(3 - x^2)/2.$$

(a) Locate its fixed points, and determine whether they are sources, sinks or otherwise.

(b) Show, graphically, that the open interval $(0, \sqrt{3})$ belongs to the basin of attraction of a sink of this map. Is this the *complete* basin of attraction?

[*Hint*: Consider orbits starting in the region $-2 \leq x < -\sqrt{3}$.]

Recall that Theorem 2.1 does not specify the nature of a fixed point in the case where $|f'(x^*)| = 1$. Bearing this in mind, attempt the following instructive exercise.

Exercise 2.8

Each of the following maps has a fixed point at the origin. Sketch cobweb plots to determine the nature of these fixed points, specifying whether they are sinks, sources or neither.

(a) $f(x) = x + x^2$ (b) $f(x) = x - x^2$

(c) $f(x) = x + x^3$ (d) $f(x) = x - x^3$

2.2   The period-doubling route to chaos

In the previous unit you were introduced to a quadratic map called the *logistic map*, which was used as a model for population dynamics in biological systems. This map will feature frequently in this unit and will be studied in considerable detail, particularly in this section and the next. Although the map is relatively simple, just a quadratic function, it nevertheless gives rise to some very complicated dynamics, including chaos. Indeed, that one can find such rich and complicated behaviour from such simple maps is one of the most fascinating aspects of this subject. However, as you work through this section, you may begin to wonder why so much effort is being spent on just this one map, albeit one with such interesting properties. Part of the reason for this is that many of the properties of the logistic map, such as the type of orbits found and the nature of the transition to chaos through a period-doubling process, are generic to a wide class of maps of the type shaped as in Figure 2.7, i.e. maps under a smooth function $f(x)$ which has a single maximum and is downward concave. Such maps are called **unimodal**. Clearly, they must be *nonlinear*.

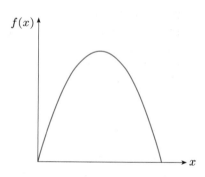

Figure 2.7   Unimodal map $f(x)$

2.2.1   Introduction to the logistic map

Recall that the **logistic map** is the simple nonlinear map given by the equation

$$f_a(x) = ax(1 - x). \tag{2.12}$$

The behaviour of its orbits as the parameter a is varied will be investigated. In particular, it will be shown that for certain values of a, the orbits are *chaotic*, being highly sensitive to their initial values x_0. Note that $f_a(x)$ has a form similar to that illustrated in Figure 2.7, i.e. it is unimodal.

Exercise 2.9

Show that for $0 < a \le 4$, the closed interval $[0, 1]$ is an *invariant set* under the logistic map $f_a(x)$.

Exercise 2.10

The logistic map $f_a(x)$ has a fixed point at the origin since $f_a(0) = 0$.
Show that this fixed point is a sink for $|a| < 1$ and a source for $|a| > 1$.
Show that the map has another fixed point, given by

$$x^* = 1 - \frac{1}{a}, \tag{2.13}$$

which is a *sink* when $1 < a < 3$ and a *source* when $a > 3$ or $a < 1$.

Now, let us *numerically* generate some orbits of f_a using Maple. Start up
Maple and type in the following procedure.

```
>   # Procedure to generate an orbit under the Logistic Map
>   orbit := proc(x0,a,N::posint)  local k,x,xorbit,orb;
>     x := x0:
>     xorbit := [0,x]:
>     for k from 1 to N do
>       x := evalf(a*x*(1-x));
>       xorbit := xorbit,[k,x];
>     end do:
>     [xorbit];
>   end proc:
```

The procedure `orbit` will generate the orbit with initial value `x0` under the
logistic map f_a (with the a specified by the second argument, `a`, of `orbit`),
and `N` is the number of iterates of the orbit. Maple outputs the orbit
$\{x_n\}_{n=0}^N$ as the list

$$[[0, x_0], [1, x_1], \ldots, [n, x_n], \ldots, [N, x_N]],$$

in `[xorbit]`. So, for example, after typing

```
>   orbit(0.2,2.4,20);
```

Maple will determine the orbit of 0.2 under the logistic map with $a = 2.4$
up to $n = 20$, and display the result in the following form:

$$[[0, .2], [1, .384], [2, .5677056], [3, .5889982841], [4, .5809903331],$$
$$[5, .5842573581], [6, .5829616741], [7, .5834816656], [8, .5832739474],$$
$$[9, .5833570793], [10, .5833238335], [11, .5833371329], [12, .5833318135],$$
$$[13, .5833339411], [14, .5833330904], [15, .5833334305], [16, .5833332944]$$
$$[17, .5833333491], [18, .5833333271], [19, .5833333358], [20, .5833333324]]$$

Note that the orbit converges to the fixed-point value given by
Equation (2.13) since $x^* = 1 - \frac{1}{a} = 1 - \frac{1}{2.4} = 0.583\,33\ldots$. In what follows,
it will often be more illuminating to plot the orbit (as x_n against n). In
order to do this, it is convenient to introduce a second procedure, called
`plotorbit`, as follows:

```
>   # Procedure to generate and plot an orbit under the
    # Logistic Map
>   plotorbit := proc(xint,a,N::posint)  local orb;
>     orb := orbit(xint,a,N);
>     plot(orb,style=point,symbol=circle,color=black,
         title=cat("a=",convert(a,string)));
>   end proc:
```

So, to plot the orbit of 0.2 under the logistic map for $a = 2.4$ (up to $n = 20$) one enters

```
>  plotorbit(0.2,2.4,20);
```

Remember that you must keep the procedures orbit and plotorbit in the same worksheet.

with the resulting plot shown in the left panel of Figure 2.8. The other panel shows a plot of the orbit of 0.2 for a different value of a ($a = 2.8$, $N = 30$) as generated by plotorbit.

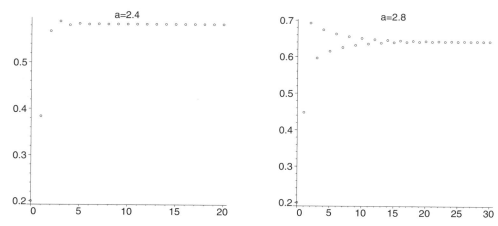

Figure 2.8   Maple plots of orbits generated under the logistic map $f_a(x)$, for $a = 2.4$ and 2.8. The abscissa is n.

Experiment with different values of a, keeping $1 < a < 3$ for the time being, and different initial values, and check that the numerically reached value of x^* agrees with Equation (2.13).

Exercise 2.11

Observe from Figure 2.8 that the orbit for $a = 2.8$ converges more slowly to x^* than that for $a = 2.4$. Why is this so? [*Hint*: Consider the linear approximation of the logistic map about its sink.]

2.2.2   Periodic orbits

In the previous subsection, you found that, for $1 < a < 3$, running the procedure plotorbit confirms that orbits under the logistic map converge to a single point, namely the sink at $x^* = 1 - \frac{1}{a}$. This is consistent with Exercise 2.10 where you showed that the fixed point is stable for $1 < a < 3$. You would also have observed that convergence gets slow as a approaches 3 from below (explanation given in Exercise 2.11), so that you need to increase the N argument in plotorbit somewhat to convince yourself that convergence is occurring. For example, with $a = 2.90$ you should execute plotorbit with $N = 40$ to get a convincing convergence.

We now investigate what happens for $a > 3$, where we know from Exercise 2.10 that the fixed point x^* is *unstable*. Start by running plotorbit for a just above 3, say $a = 3.10$. The plot for this value of a is shown in the left panel of Figure 2.9.

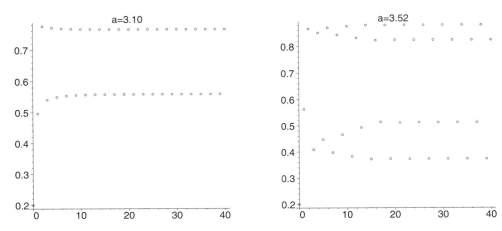

Figure 2.9   Maple plots of orbits generated under the logistic map $f_a(x)$ for $a = 3.10$ (period 2) and 3.52 (period 4). The abscissa is n.

Notice that for $a = 3.10$ the orbit, after a few iterations, approaches an orbit of alternating values, $x \simeq 0.56$ and $x \simeq 0.76$, instead of a single point. We say that the *limiting* orbit is periodic with period 2, i.e. the pattern repeats after 2 iterations, and it is therefore referred to as a **period-2 orbit**. Since the orbit converges to these alternating values, we say that the orbit under f_a at $a = 3.1$ approaches a **period-2 sink** denoted by $\{0.56, 0.76\}$. You have already met some simple examples of period-2 orbits: for the linear map $f(x) = bx$ in the example in Subsection 2.1.1, the orbit of x_0 for $b = -1$ is period-2, being just $\{(-1)^n x_0\}_{n \geq 0}$ (see the discussion after Equation (2.4)).

So, by playing with `plotorbit` with values of a below 3 and just above 3, we see that the fixed point at x^*, which is stable for $a < 3$, is replaced by a period-2 sink for a just above 3. This transition, which appears to occur at $a = 3$, is called a **bifurcation** since the single fixed point x^*, which can be regarded as a **period-1 sink**, has **bifurcated** into an orbit of two alternating values, i.e. the period-2 sink, and the periodicity of the orbit has doubled. Again, from Exercise 2.10, the fixed point x^* is known to be *unstable* for $a > 3$; this *repelling* fixed point is a **period-1 source**.

These numerically drawn conclusions will be mathematically substantiated in the following subsection, but what we have seen is that for a taking values just above 3 (but not too far above), the orbit is attracted to a *period-2 sink* and repelled by a *period-1 source*. You should re-run procedure `plotorbit` with $a = 3.10$ for different initial values to convince yourself that the *same* period-2 sink is reached, i.e. the period-2 sink is not dependent on the initial value. You should regard this as an important check on the stability of the period-2 sink. A graphical explanation for the appearance of the period-2 sink for $a = 3.10$ is shown by the cobweb plot in Figure 2.10. Note how the orbit converges to the period-2 sink, whose values are given by the points of intersection of the dotted lines with the horizontal axis.

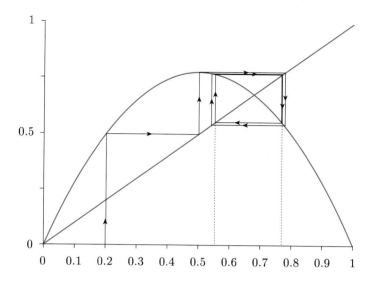

Figure 2.10   Cobweb plot (shown in red) for the orbit of 0.2 under $f_a(x) = 3.1x(1-x)$ showing convergence to the period-2 sink indicated by the intersection of the dotted lines with the x-axis

You should experiment with higher values of a using `plotorbit`. For instance, with $a = 3.20$, one finds very rapid convergence (within a few iterations) to the period-2 sink $\{0.5130, 0.7995\}$, to 4 significant figures. As a increases one finds that the period-2 sink bifurcates into a **period-4 sink**. For example, as indicated in Figure 2.9 (second panel), when $a = 3.52$ the orbit eventually settles into a pattern which repeats after every four iterates; this is a period-4 sink. In this case the period-4 sink has values given approximately by $\{0.879, 0.373, 0.823, 0.512\}$. So the period-2 sink is no longer stable at 3.52 and, instead, one finds a *stable* period-4 (attracting) orbit or sink. If you experiment by continuing to increase a, you will find further bifurcations leading to period-8 and higher period sinks, and eventually the orbit seems to degenerate into an indiscernible mess, without any apparent periodicity. This is the period-doubling route to chaos, and more will be said about this later. However, important questions to ask now are: what determines the stability of periodic points and why do they appear when they do? We shall endeavour to answer these questions, but first we need to define more carefully the meaning of periodic points and periodic orbits.

You will find a period-8 sink at $a = 3.55$.

Consider again period-2 orbits. Let $\{x_1^*, x_2^*\}$ denote a period-2 orbit under a map $f(x)$ on $\mathbb{R}$, which requires that $x_1^* \neq x_2^*$. Then

$$f(x_1^*) = x_2^*, \quad f(x_2^*) = x_1^*, \tag{2.14}$$

from which it immediately follows that

$$f^2(x_j^*) = x_j^* \quad \text{for } j = 1, 2. \tag{2.15}$$

Hence both iterates of the period-2 orbit, x_1^* and x_2^*, are *fixed points* of the map $f^2(x)$.

As an example, consider the limiting period-2 orbit of the logistic map $f_a(x)$ with $a = 3.20$, which is given to 4 significant figures by $\{0.5130, 0.7995\}$. One can easily check (simply with a pocket calculator) that, to 4 significant figures, $f_a(0.5130) \simeq 0.7995$, $f_a(0.7995) \simeq 0.5130$ and, therefore, $f_a^2(0.5130) \simeq 0.5130$ and $f_a^2(0.7995) \simeq 0.7995$.

These ideas can be generalized to **period-k orbits**. The orbit of x_j^*, $j = 1, \ldots, k$, under the map $f(x)$ on $\mathbb{R}$ is a period-k orbit of f, denoted $\{x_1^*, \ldots, x_k^*\}$, if it has the property

$$f(x_j^*) = \begin{cases} x_{j+1}^* & \text{if } 1 \leq j \leq k-1, \\ x_1^* & \text{if } j = k, \end{cases} \tag{2.16}$$

and all the x_j^* $(j = 1, \ldots, k)$ must be *distinct* in order for the orbit to be defined as period-k. This also means that

$$f^k(x_j^*) = x_j^* \quad \text{for } 1 \leq j \leq k, \tag{2.17}$$

and that k is the *smallest* positive integer for which this is true, so that points of a period-k orbit are *fixed points* of $f^k(x)$. This can be regarded as a *defining property* of a period-k orbit. Note that, with this in mind, a fixed point x^* of the map $f(x)$, as defined by Equation (2.5), can be alternatively regarded as a *period-1 orbit*. Note also that, after putting $k = 2$, Equations (2.16) and (2.17) reduce to Equations (2.14) and (2.15), respectively.

Exercise 2.12

Show that the property of period-k orbits expressed by Equation (2.16) implies the following.

(a) $x_j^* = f^{j-1}(x_1^*)$ for $2 \leq j \leq k$

(b) $x_j^* = \begin{cases} f^{j-2}(x_2^*) & \text{if } 3 \leq j \leq k \\ f^{k-1}(x_2^*) & \text{if } j = 1 \end{cases}$

2.2.3 Stability of periodic orbits

Recall that we have established a test for the stability of a fixed point (period-1 orbit): this is given by Theorem 2.1. Since a period-k orbit $\{x_1^*, \ldots, x_k^*\}$ of $f(x)$ is necessarily a fixed point of $f^k(x)$, the *same* stability test can be applied to f^k. Hence the period-k orbit is a **period-k sink** (i.e. an attracting period-k orbit) if $|(f^k)'(x_j^*)| < 1$ for all $j = 1, \ldots, k$, whereas it is a **period-k source** (i.e. a repelling period-k orbit) if $|(f^k)'(x_j^*)| > 1$ for all $j = 1, \ldots, k$. Before rephrasing this test in a more useful form, let us first consider period-2 orbits.

Recall the chain rule applied to the composition of two functions, $f(x)$ and $g(x)$:

$$(f \circ g)'(x) = g'(x) \, f'(g(x)). \tag{2.18}$$

Exercise 2.13

Suppose that $\{x_1^*, x_2^*\}$ is a period-2 orbit under a map $f(x)$. Show, using the chain rule (2.18), that

$$(f^2)'(x_1^*) = (f^2)'(x_2^*) = f'(x_1^*)f'(x_2^*). \tag{2.19}$$

The results of Exercise 2.13 lead to the following stability test for a period-2 orbit. The orbit is a period-2 sink if $|f'(x_1^*)f'(x_2^*)| < 1$, and a period-2 source if $|f'(x_1^*)f'(x_2^*)| > 1$. Moreover, note the importance of the identity $(f^2)'(x_1^*) = (f^2)'(x_2^*)$ in Equation (2.19). It shows consistency in that, for a period-2 orbit, x_1^* is an attracting (respectively repelling) fixed point of $f^2(x)$ if and only if x_2^* is an attracting (respectively repelling) fixed point of $f^2(x)$, as would be expected.

Now consider the period-k orbit $\{x_1^*, \ldots, x_k^*\}$ of $f(x)$, and do the following exercise.

Exercise 2.14

Show that

$$(f^k)'(x_1^*) = (f^k)'(x_2^*) = \cdots = (f^k)'(x_k^*) = \prod_{j=1}^{k} f'(x_j^*). \qquad (2.20)$$

[*Hint*: Write $f^k = f \circ f^{k-1}$ and apply the chain rule.]

Hence, with the help of Theorem 2.1 and the results of Exercise 2.14, we have arrived at the following **stability test for the period-k orbit**. This says that the periodic orbit is

$$\text{a period-}k \text{ sink if } \quad \left| \prod_{j=1}^{k} f'(x_j^*) \right| < 1 \qquad (2.21)$$

and

$$\text{a period-}k \text{ source if } \quad \left| \prod_{j=1}^{k} f'(x_j^*) \right| > 1. \qquad (2.22)$$

Note again the importance of the identity of $(f^k)'(x_j^*)$ for all $1 \leq j \leq k$ in ensuring consistency, similar to the case $k = 2$ in Exercise 2.13.

Exercise 2.15

Let x^* be a fixed point of the map $f(x)$.

(a) Show that $(f^2)'(x^*) \geq 0$.

(b) Show that x^* is a sink (respectively source) of $f(x)$ *if and only if* it is a sink (respectively source) of $f^k(x)$ for all $k \geq 1$.

Exercise 2.16

Let $\{x_1^*, x_2^*\}$ be a period-2 orbit of the map $f(x)$.

(a) Show that $(f^4)'(x_1^*) = (f^4)'(x_2^*) \geq 0$.

(b) Show that $\{x_1^*, x_2^*\}$ is a period-2 sink (respectively period-2 source) of $f(x)$ *if and only if* x_1^* and x_2^* are sinks (respectively sources) of $f^4(x)$.

Let us now return to the logistic map, $f_a(x)$. We found in the previous subsection that when $a = 3.10$, the map $f_a(x)$ has a period-2 sink which, for this value of a, is located at $\{0.5580, 0.7646\}$, to 4 significant figures. As a is increased, the period-2 orbit eventually becomes unstable so that we find instead a period-4 sink. For example, when $a = 3.52$, a period-4 sink was found at $\{0.8795, 0.3731, 0.8233, 0.5121\}$ to 4 significant figures. We have already established the condition for which a fixed point (period-1 orbit) of $f_a(x)$ is stable (see Exercise 2.10). The stability test for period-k orbits given by (2.21) and (2.22) allows us now to determine when a period-2 orbit is stable and the threshold above which it becomes unstable in favour of a period-4 sink.

Some insight is gained by examining plots of $y = f_a^k(x)$ for $k = 1, 2, 4$. Such plots, generated using Maple with $a = 3.52$, are shown in Figures 2.11 and 2.12 with $y = x$ plotted on the same axes to locate the fixed points.

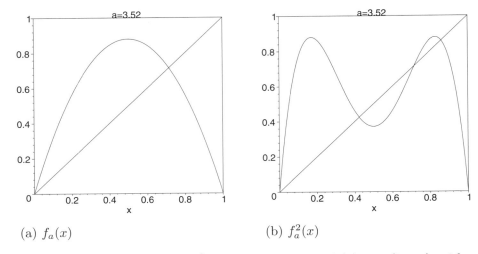

(a) $f_a(x)$ (b) $f_a^2(x)$

Figure 2.11   Plots of f_a and f_a^2 for the logistic map $f_a(x) = ax(1-x)$, with $a = 3.52$ in both cases. For both, the line $y = x$ is also plotted, intersections with which locate the fixed points.

First, look at Figure 2.11(a). There you will see 2 fixed points, one at $x = 0$, which is clearly a source, and the other at $x \simeq 0.716$, which we also know to be a source (because $a > 3$; see Exercise 2.10). Now turn to Figure 2.11(b). Here, you can see that $f_a^2(x)$ has 4 fixed points: one is the ubiquitous fixed point at $x = 0$, which is also obviously unstable; another is the fixed point of $f_a(x)$ at $x \simeq 0.716$ (which must be a fixed point of $f_a^2(x)$); the two other fixed points are at $x \simeq 0.424$ and $x \simeq 0.860$, points where $y = f_a^2(x)$ crosses $y = x$ with negative slope. These last two are the points of the *period-2 source*, period-2 orbits being fixed points of $f_a^2(x)$. Note that the fact that the fixed point of $f_a(x)$ at $x \simeq 0.716$ is a source is now *graphically explicit* from Figure 2.11, since it shows clearly that $(f_a^2)'(0.716) > 1$, implying that 0.716 is a source of $f_a^2(x)$ and hence, from Exercise 2.15, a source of $f_a(x)$.

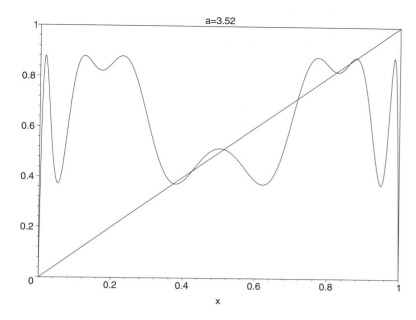

Figure 2.12   Plot of $f_a^4(x)$ with $a = 3.52$. The line $y = x$ is also plotted, intersections with which locate the fixed points.

Moving on to Figure 2.12, we see that $f_a^4(x)$ has 8 fixed points; 4 of these are where $y = f_a^4(x)$ crosses $y = x$ with *positive* slope, being the sources of $f_a(x)$ at $x = 0$ and $x \simeq 0.716$ and the period-2 source of $f_a(x)$ at $x \simeq 0.424$ and $x \simeq 0.860$. The other 4 fixed points are points of the *period-4 sink*, $x \simeq 0.3731, 0.5121, 0.8233, 0.8795$, and happen to be points where $y = f_a^4(x)$ meets $y = x$ with negative slope. Finally, we can see that the period-2 orbit at $\{0.424, 0.860\}$ is *manifestly* a period-2 *source*, since, clearly from Figure 2.12, $(f_a^4)'(0.424) = (f_a^4)'(0.860) > 1$, implying that both points are sources of $f_a^4(x)$ and therefore, from Exercise 2.16, sources of $f_a^2(x)$.

We are now in a position to determine, precisely, the values of a for which the period-2 orbit is stable. First we need to locate the period-2 points, $\{x_1^*, x_2^*\}$, of $f_a(x)$. Attempt the following exercise.

Exercise 2.17

The points x_1^*, x_2^* of the period-2 orbit for the logistic map $f_a(x)$ are solutions of the equation

$$f_a^2(x) = x. \qquad (2.23)$$

(a) Evaluate $f_a^2(x)$.

(b) Derive the cubic equation satisfied by the non-zero solutions of Equation (2.23).

(c) Recall that the fixed point x^* of $f_a(x)$, found in Exercise 2.10, is also a solution of Equation (2.23). Use this fact to factorize the cubic, and hence show that the period-2 points x_1^* and x_2^* are roots of the quadratic

$$a^2 x^2 - a(1 + a)x + 1 + a = 0. \qquad (2.24)$$

Thus, after solving the quadratic in Equation (2.24), we find that the points in the period-2 orbit $\{x_1^*, x_2^*\}$ are given by

$$x_1^* = \frac{1}{2a}\left(a + 1 - \sqrt{(a+1)(a-3)}\right), \tag{2.25}$$

$$x_2^* = \frac{1}{2a}\left(a + 1 + \sqrt{(a+1)(a-3)}\right). \tag{2.26}$$

Our interest in the logistic map is confined to the interval $0 < a \le 4$ (where the interval $[0,1]$ is an invariant set; see Exercise 2.9). In this interval, Equations (2.25) and (2.26) imply that *only* when $a > 3$ does a period-2 orbit exist. But, what of the *stability* of this period-2 orbit? We now apply the stability test for period-2 orbits. This tells us that the orbit $\{x_1^*, x_2^*\}$ is stable, i.e. a period-2 sink, when

$$-1 < f_a'(x_1^*)\, f_a'(x_2^*) < 1. \tag{2.27}$$

Since $f_a'(x) = a(1 - 2x)$, and using Equations (2.25) and (2.26), we have

$$f_a'(x_1^*) = -1 + \sqrt{(a+1)(a-3)},$$
$$f_a'(x_2^*) = -1 - \sqrt{(a+1)(a-3)},$$

which leads to

$$(f_a^2)'(x_1^*) = (f_a^2)'(x_2^*) = f_a'(x_1^*)f_a'(x_2^*) = 4 + 2a - a^2, \tag{2.28}$$

so the condition given in (2.27) implies that, for stability, a must satisfy

$$-1 < 4 + 2a - a^2 < 1. \tag{2.29}$$

Exercise 2.18

Show that the condition in (2.29) implies that, for positive a, the period-2 orbit is stable when $3 < a < 1 + \sqrt{6} \simeq 3.449\,49$.

We are now beginning to develop an understanding of the behaviour of the logistic map for orbits starting within the invariant set $[0,1]$ as a is varied for positive values. For $0 < a \le 1$, all orbits are attracted to the sink at $x = 0$. As a passes through 1, the sink at $x = 0$ becomes a source, but another fixed point occurs at $x^* = 1 - \frac{1}{a}$, which is a sink (period-1 orbit) for $1 < a < 3$. For $a > 3$ the fixed point x^* becomes a source, but a period-2 sink appears at $a = 3$, or, in other words, the period-1 sink at x^* *bifurcates* into a period-2 sink. As a is varied from 3 to $1 + \sqrt{6}$, Equation (2.28) shows that $(f_a^2)'(x_1^*)\ [= (f_a^2)'(x_2^*)]$ monotonically decreases from $+1$ (at $a = 3$) to -1 (at $a = 1 + \sqrt{6}$), implying that the period-2 orbit stays a period-2 sink throughout the interval $3 < a < 1 + \sqrt{6}$. For $a > 1 + \sqrt{6} \simeq 3.449\,49$, the period-2 orbit is a period-2 source.

2.2.4   Bifurcation diagrams

One can use the explicit expressions for x^*, x_1^* and x_2^* as functions of a (i.e. Equations (2.13), (2.25) and (2.26)) to plot a **bifurcation diagram** for the logistic map. This is shown in Figure 2.13, which illustrates the bifurcation of the period-1 sink to the period-2 sink at $a = 3$. We suspect, from the previous numerical investigations, that a further period-doubling bifurcation occurs at $a = 1 + \sqrt{6}$ giving rise to a period-4 sink (such as that shown in Figure 2.9 for $a = 3.52$), but, in any case, we have shown that beyond this point the period-2 orbit becomes unstable. Unfortunately, we cannot proceed much further with exact analytical expressions. We will need to use numerical methods in order to construct a more complete bifurcation diagram which will give a more comprehensive overview of the type of attracting orbits present in the logistic map.

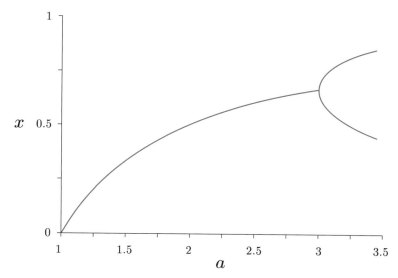

Figure 2.13   Plot of the attracting points of the logistic map $f_a(x) = ax(1 - x)$ against a for $1 \leq a \leq 1 + \sqrt{6} \simeq 3.449\,49$. The sink of $f_a(x)$, x^*, is depicted for $1 \leq a \leq 3$, which bifurcates at $a = 3$ to the period-2 sink $\{x_1^*, x_2^*\}$, with x_1^* (respectively x_2^*) plotted as the lower (respectively upper) branch. The period-2 orbit becomes unstable at $a = 1 + \sqrt{6}$, bifurcating into a period-4 sink (not shown here).

By experimenting with the Maple procedure `plotorbit` in the earlier subsections, for various a between 3.5 and 4, you should have found, in addition to the orbits displayed in Figure 2.9, evidence of further period-doubling bifurcations with orbits attracted to period-8 sinks, period-16 sinks, etc. You may also have found period-3 sinks and orbits with seemingly erratic behaviour without showing any evidence of settling down into a regular pattern at all. In order to shed some light on all this, let us systematically plot the attractors of the map $f_a(x)$ against a as a is varied up to 4.

A period-3 sink occurs at $a = 3.83$.

The following Maple program plots the bifurcation diagram for the logistic map $f_a(x)$ within a specified interval for a. It contains a procedure, called `bifdiagram`, which takes the interval $a_1 \leq a \leq a_2$ and divides it into N slices of equal width. For each slice, it computes the attracting points and plots them. It does this by first iterating out the transients, i.e. that part of the orbit which depends on the initial value, which in this case is arbitrarily set at 0.6. It is assumed that after 100 iterations the orbit will converge to points sufficiently close to its attracting set. It then computes and plots the next 200 iterates. After this, the procedure moves on to the next slice in the a interval. The parameters a_1, a_2 and N are the arguments `a1`, `a2` and `N` of `bifdiagram`. A plot resulting from running the Maple program is shown in Figure 2.14.

```
>   restart:  with(plots):
>   bifdiagram := proc(a1,a2,N::posint)
>     local bifdiag,a,da,x,pts,j,cond1,cond2:
>     cond1 := style=point,symbol=point,view=[a1..a2,0..1],
                color=black:
>     cond2 := labels=["a","x*"],labelfont=[TIMES,ITALIC,18],
                axes=BOXED:
>     da := evalf((a2-a1)/N);
>     bifdiag := NULL:
>     for a from a1 to a2 by da do
>       x := 0.6;
>       for j from 1 to 100 do
>         x := evalf(a*x*(1-x));          # Removes transients
>       end do;
>       pts := NULL:
>       for j from 1 to 200 do
>         x := evalf(a*x*(1-x));        # Finds attracting point
>         pts := pts,[a,x];             # Appends attracting point
                                        # to attractor
>       end do;
>       bifdiag := bifdiag,plot([pts],cond1,cond2);
                    # Plots attractor at given a and appends plot
                    # of attractor to bifurcation diagram
>     end do:
>     display(bifdiag);
>   end proc:
>   bifdiagram(1,4,1000);
```

Note that when generating Figures 2.14 and 2.15, N was set at 1000 in the third argument of **bifdiagram**, which may require considerable computing time. If your computer appears too slow for this, try reducing N, starting at, say, $N = 100$.

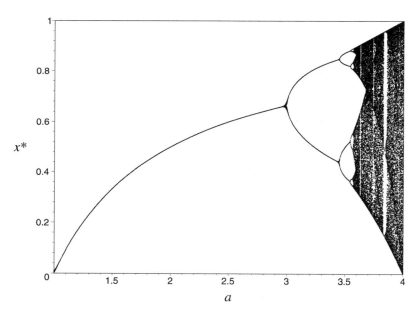

Figure 2.14   Bifurcation diagram for the logistic map $f_a(x) = ax(1 - x)$

Figure 2.14 shows the bifurcation diagram plotted for the full range of a for which the interval $[0, 1]$ is an invariant set *and* where the attractor is non-trivial (i.e. not just the origin, as would be the case for $0 \leq a \leq 1$). The part of the diagram for $1 \leq a \leq 3.449\,49$ should, of course, coincide with Figure 2.13. As with Figure 2.13, you can see, at $a = 3$, the period-doubling bifurcation from the period-1 sink to the period-2 sink. However, here one can now see the next bifurcation to the period-4 sink, at $a \simeq 3.449$, and a further bifurcation to a period-8 sink, after which the

Exercise 2.9 showed that $[0, 1]$ is an invariant set for $0 < a \leq 4$.

attractor rapidly starts to look very complicated and indeterminable. This part of the bifurcation diagram, i.e. with $1 + \sqrt{6} \leq a \leq 4$, is replotted in Figure 2.15 in order to show in more detail the interesting and strikingly intricate behaviour of the attractor for these values of a.

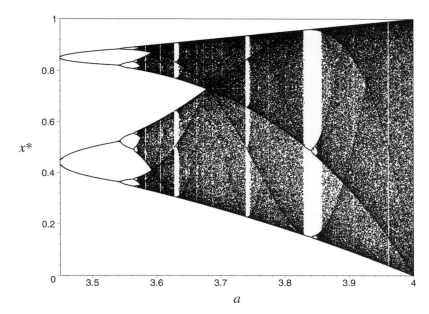

Figure 2.15   More detailed view of the bifurcation diagram for the logistic map $f_a(x) = ax(1 - x)$, for $1 + \sqrt{6} \leq a \leq 4$

As a increases from $a = 1$, a series of period-doubling bifurcations occurs to sinks of period 2^n, $n = 1, 2, 3, \ldots$, with the bifurcations getting closer together with increasing a. The period of these sinks diverges as a increases to a value of about 3.57, beyond which the orbits become **chaotic**. This period-doubling route to chaos is referred to as a **period-doubling cascade**.

Proceeding further, beyond this cascade, one notices 'windows' containing sinks with relatively low periods amongst high-period or chaotic attractors. Some of these windows are quite pronounced. For example, there is a period-5 window around $a = 3.74$, and a much wider period-3 window enclosing $a = 3.83$. Clearly, these sinks no longer fit the pattern of the period-2^n orbits emerging from period doubling. Figure 2.16 shows examples of orbits attracted to these sinks, i.e. period-5 and period-3 sinks. As before, the orbits were plotted with Maple using the `plotorbit` procedure.

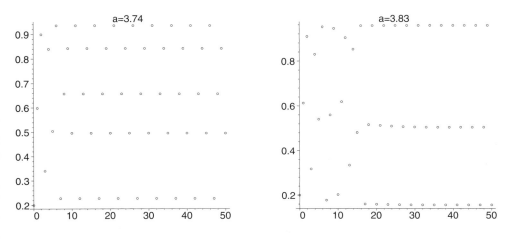

Figure 2.16   Maple plots of orbits generated under the logistic map $f_a(x)$, for $a = 3.74$ (period 5) and 3.83 (period 3). The abscissa is n.

89

2.3 Chaotic orbits and Lyapunov exponents

2.3.1 Sensitive dependence on initial conditions

As mentioned in the previous unit, chaotic orbits are characterized by their *extreme sensitivity* to initial conditions, which means that very small changes in the initial value, x_0, of the orbit will eventually lead to relatively large deviations in subsequent iterates, $x_n = f^n(x_0)$, for n large enough. This erratic behaviour makes the orbit appear 'random' although, of course, we know that it is *deterministic*. Although this is an important characteristic property of chaos, it is not adequate for a *precise* definition of a chaotic orbit, which will be given later in this section. However, in order to introduce the notion of chaotic orbits, let us illustrate this property (of extreme sensitivity to initial values) by turning again to the logistic map.

First we consider stable (i.e. non-chaotic) orbits under the logistic map, with a chosen such that the orbits converge to the sink at $x^* = 1 - \frac{1}{a}$, so that $1 < a < 3$ (we shall choose $a = 2.4$). You should have noticed, by experimenting with the procedures `orbit` and `plotorbit` in Subsection 2.2.1, that for this range of a the orbits converge to the sink x^* for all values of x_0 in the range $0 < x_0 < 1$. Let us now examine in more detail two such orbits with different x_0.

The procedure `orbit` is used to generate two orbits under the logistic map with $a = 2.4$, with one orbit having $x_0 = 0.2$ and the other $x_0 = 0.3$. These two orbits, assigned to `xorb1` and `xorb2`, respectively, are generated within Maple as follows:

```
>   xorb1 := orbit(0.2,2.4,30):          # Create orbit xorb1
>   xorb2 := orbit(0.3,2.4,30):          # Create orbit xorb2
```

Both orbits are then plotted on the same graph, using the Maple statement

```
>   plot([xorb1,xorb2],style=point,symbol=[circle,cross],
     color=[red,black],title="a=2.4",legend=["x0=0.2","x0=0.3"]);
```

with the result shown in Figure 2.17.

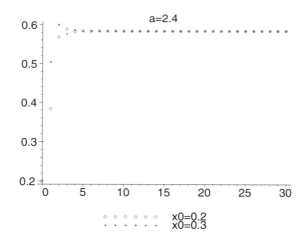

Figure 2.17 Maple plots of orbits generated under the logistic map $f_a(x)$, for $a = 2.4$. The abscissa is the iterate index n. The orbits start with different initial values x_0, with the orbit of $x_0 = 0.2$ shown as circles and that of $x_0 = 0.3$ shown as crosses.

90

As expected, the orbits rapidly get close together, with both converging to the same fixed point. How rapidly this process occurs can be assessed by examining the *absolute* difference of the two orbits as a function of the iterate index n. This quantity is generated using the Maple statement

```
>   absdifferorbit := [seq([xorb1[k,1],
    abs(xorb1[k,2]-xorb2[k,2])],k=1..nops(xorb1))]:
```

which is then plotted against n on a *linear* scale using

```
>   plot(absdifferorbit,style=point,symbol=circle,color=black);
```

and on a *logarithmic* scale using

```
>   plots[logplot](absdifferorbit,style=point,symbol=circle);
```

with the resulting plots shown in Figure 2.18.

logplot is a command in the plots package which creates a plot with the vertical axis given as a logarithmic scale (in base 10).

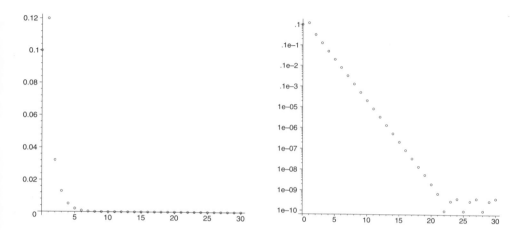

Figure 2.18   Maple plots of the absolute difference of the two orbits displayed in Figure 2.17. In the left graph, the vertical scale is linear, as usual, whereas that of the right is logarithmic. In both graphs, the abscissa is the iterate index n.

Note that for $n > 20$, the logplot result in Figure 2.18 shows values of the absolute difference of the two orbits fluctuating between 10^{-10} and 10^{-9}. This is due to numerical rounding errors; the limit of numerical precision has been exceeded for these values of n.

The plots again show how rapidly the two orbits approach one another, but the **logplot** result, the right panel in Figure 2.18, is particularly illuminating as it clearly shows a linear trend in the *logarithm* of the absolute separation of the iterates as a function of the iterate index n. This implies that the two orbits approach one another *exponentially* fast, a result consistent with the discussion following Theorem 2.1 in Subsection 2.1.4 where it was pointed out that, in general, orbits approach sinks exponentially fast with n.

We now turn to *chaotic* orbits. Again, the procedure **orbit** is used to generate two orbits under the logistic map, but now with a chosen such that the orbits are chaotic. In this case we set $a = 3.98$, and the initial values, **xint**, of the two orbits are chosen to be very close. The two orbits **xorb1** and **xorb2**, with initial values $0.200\,000\,00$ and $0.200\,000\,01$, respectively, are generated using the following Maple assignments:

```
>   xorb1:=orbit(0.20000000,3.98,60):      # Create orbit xorb1
>   xorb2:=orbit(0.20000001,3.98,60):      # Create orbit xorb2
```

Note that the separation in initial values, which is 10^{-8}, is *very* small. Again, we plot the two orbits on the same graph using the Maple statement

```
>   plot([xorb1,xorb2],style=point,symbol=[circle,cross],
    color=[red,black],title="a=3.98",
    legend=["x0=0.20000000","x0=0.20000001"]);
```

and the resulting plot is shown in Figure 2.19.

91

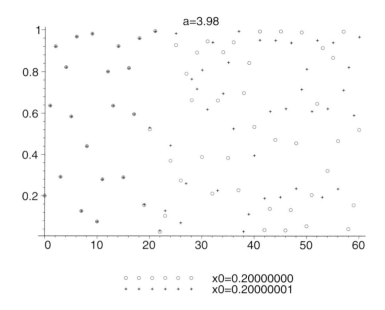

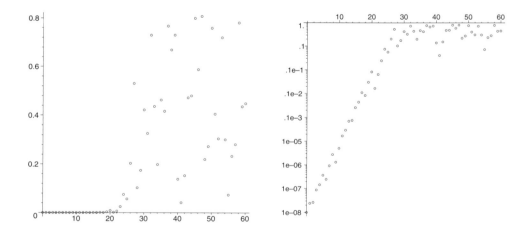

Figure 2.19   Maple plots of orbits generated under the logistic map $f_a(x)$, for $a = 3.98$. The abscissa is the iterate index n. The orbits start with slightly different initial values x_0, with the orbit of $x_0 = 0.200\,000\,00$ shown as circles and that of $x_0 = 0.200\,000\,01$ shown as crosses.

You will observe from Figure 2.19 that for quite some time, in fact for the first 22 iterates or so, the two orbits appear to stay very close together. Then, apparently quite abruptly, at about $n = 23$, the orbits begin to separate to a discernible degree. As before, another way of illustrating this is to determine the *absolute* differences of the two orbits at each iterate, assigned to `absdifferorbit`, exactly as with the previous case for $a = 2.4$ (the Maple statement being identical), and then plot `absdifferorbit` against the iterate number n, either on a *linear* scale, using `plot` (again, exactly as before), or on a *logarithmic* scale, using `plots[logplot]` (exactly as before). The resulting plots are shown in Figure 2.20.

Figure 2.20   Maple plots of the absolute difference of the two orbits displayed in Figure 2.19. In the left graph, the vertical scale is linear, as usual, whereas that of the right is logarithmic. In both graphs, the abscissa is the iterate index n.

The left plot in Figure 2.20 shows that the two orbits are barely distinguishable for the first 22 iterates, after which they appear to separate suddenly in a perceptible but seemingly unpredictable manner. The `logplot` result, shown on the right, is again more illuminating. On this plot you can see that for the first 30 iterates or so, the absolute separation in the orbits does vary perceptibly with n, the iterate index, and moreover, plotted this way, with a logarithmic vertical scale, the variation is approximately *linear* in n until n reaches about 30, after which the separation levels off and stays at around unity (although the orbits appear to get much closer again at about $n = 41$). Because the vertical scale is logarithmic, what this actually means is that the two nearby orbits initially separate in a way that is approximately *exponential* with n until n reaches a value where the separation is of the order of unity (which, in this case, happens at about $n \simeq 30$).

You should experiment a bit with the above procedures by varying the location of the initial values of the two orbits and their initial separations.

Exercise 2.19

Consider the map $f(x)$ applied to two initial values, x_0 and $x_0 + \delta x_0$, where δx_0 is small, i.e. the initial values are separated by a small distance $|\delta x_0|$. Assuming that Taylor's theorem applies to $f(x)$ at $x = x_0$, we have

$$f(x_0 + \delta x_0) \simeq f(x_0) + \delta x_0 \, f'(x_0) \qquad (2.30)$$

to a good approximation for sufficiently small δx_0.

(a) Given that $\{x_n\}_{n\geq 0} = \{f^n(x_0)\}_{n\geq 0}$, show that the distance separating the nth iterates of the two orbits can be approximated by

$$|f^n(x_0 + \delta x_0) - x_n| \simeq |\delta x_0| \, |f'(x_0)| \cdots |f'(x_{n-1})| \qquad (2.31)$$

for $n \geq 1$, provided that the right-hand side of approximation (2.31) stays sufficiently small.

(b) Apply (2.31) to the two orbits of the logistic map $f_a(x)$, for $a = 3.98$, given above and as displayed in Figures 2.19 and 2.20, and use Maple to plot the results on a logarithmic scale using `logplot`. Compare with the data plotted in Figure 2.20 (right-hand graph) by plotting both data sets on the same graph, and comment on the value of n for which the two data sets begin to deviate.

2.3.2 Lyapunov exponents

It should be clear from Exercise 2.19, and also from the discussions on the stability of fixed points and periodic points, that important information about the nature of orbits under the map $f(x)$ is obtained from the derivative $f'(x)$ evaluated at points in the orbit. So if the Taylor expansion (2.30) is valid for $f(x)$ at $x = x_0$, and we consider an orbit of x_0 under f and a second orbit with initial value sufficiently close to x_0, then (2.30) tells us that the distance separating the two orbits will change by a factor of $|f'(x_0)|$ after one iteration.

If we consider a fixed point x^* of the map $f(x)$, and again assume that (2.30) applies, then $|f'(x^*)|$ will determine the multiplicative factor by which the distance separating x^* from points initially close to x^* increases (if x^* is a source, since then $|f'(x^*)| > 1$) or decreases (if x^* is a sink, since then $|f'(x^*)| < 1$) after successive iterates of these points under f. As an example, consider the logistic map for $a = \frac{5}{2}$, i.e. $f_{5/2}(x) = \frac{5}{2}x(1 - x)$. In previous discussions of the logistic map (see, in particular, Exercise 2.10), we found that for $1 < a < 3$, there is a *source* at $x = 0$ and a *sink* at $x = 1 - \frac{1}{a}$. Thus for $a = \frac{5}{2}$, there is a source at $x = 0$ and a sink at $x = 1 - \frac{2}{5} = \frac{3}{5}$. Now, $f'_{5/2}(x) = \frac{5}{2}(1 - 2x)$, so for $x^* = 0$, $f'_{5/2}(x^*) = \frac{5}{2}$, and for $x^* = \frac{3}{5}$, $f'_{5/2}(x^*) = -\frac{1}{2}$. For both of these fixed points we shall determine $f^n_{5/2}(x^* + 0.0001) - x^*$ for $n = 1, 2, 3$ and compare the results with $0.0001 \times [f'_{5/2}(x^*)]^n$. So for the source $x^* = 0$ we have

$$f_{5/2}(0.0001) = 0.000\,249\,975 \qquad \text{versus} \quad 0.0001 \times \tfrac{5}{2} = 0.000\,25,$$
$$f^2_{5/2}(0.0001) = 0.000\,624\,781\ldots \quad \text{versus} \quad 0.0001 \times (\tfrac{5}{2})^2 = 0.000\,625,$$
$$f^3_{5/2}(0.0001) = 0.001\,560\,98\ldots \quad \text{versus} \quad 0.0001 \times (\tfrac{5}{2})^3 = 0.001\,562\,5,$$

and for the sink $x^* = \frac{3}{5} = 0.6$ we have

$$f_{5/2}(0.6001) - 0.6 = -0.000\,050\,025 \qquad \text{versus} \quad 0.0001 \times (-\tfrac{1}{2}) = -0.000\,05,$$
$$f^2_{5/2}(0.6001) - 0.6 = 0.000\,025\,006\ldots \quad \text{versus} \quad 0.0001 \times (-\tfrac{1}{2})^2 = 0.000\,025,$$
$$f^3_{5/2}(0.6001) - 0.6 = -0.000\,012\,505\ldots \quad \text{versus} \quad 0.0001 \times (-\tfrac{1}{2})^3 = -0.000\,012\,5.$$

You can check these results using Maple. Notice that for the source $x^* = 0$, the Taylor expansion approximation gets progressively worse with increasing n since the iterates are moving further away from the source. The opposite is true for the sink.

We can generalize these ideas to orbits starting *near* period-k orbits, with $k \geq 1$. Let $\{x^*_1, \ldots, x^*_k\}$ be a period-k orbit for the map $f(x)$. We can apply the Taylor expansion to $f^k(x)$ for x near to one of the points of the period-k orbit, say x^*_1, to determine the multiplicative factor by which the distance of this point from x^*_1 *rescales* after k iterations. This factor is given by $|(f^k)'(x^*_1)|$, which, as can be seen from Equation (2.20), would be the same if x^*_1 were replaced by any other point of the period-k orbit. But this gives the multiplicative factor after k iterations. What we would rather have is the *average* factor per iteration over the k period. This is given by the kth root of $|(f^k)'(x^*_1)|$, which, using Equation (2.20), can be expressed as

$$|(f^k)'(x^*_1)|^{1/k} = |(f^k)'(x^*_2)|^{1/k}$$
$$= \cdots = |(f^k)'(x^*_k)|^{1/k} = \left| \prod_{j=1}^{k} f'(x^*_j) \right|^{1/k}. \tag{2.32}$$

Given that $|f'(x^*_j)|$, for $j = 1, \ldots, k$, is the factor which determines how distances separating points infinitesimally close to x^*_j rescale after just *one* iteration, a way of putting Equation (2.32) into words is to say that the average rescaling factor per iteration across a complete k period of the period-k orbit is the **geometric mean** of the individual rescaling factors for each point making up the period-k orbit.

These ideas need not be confined to periodic orbits. As Equation (2.31) in Exercise 2.19 suggests, we could consider length rescalings of infinitesimal distances after n iterations (as given in approximation (2.31)), express the result as a geometric mean and then take the limit as $n \to \infty$. This leads to the following definitions for general orbits (not necessarily periodic).

Let $\{x_j\}_{j \geq 0} = \{f^j(x_0)\}_{j \geq 0}$ be the orbit of x_0 under the map $f(x)$. The **Lyapunov number**, $L(x_0)$, of the orbit is defined as

$$L(x_0) = \lim_{n \to \infty} \left| \prod_{j=0}^{n-1} f'(x_j) \right|^{1/n}, \tag{2.33}$$

Aleksandr Lyapunov (1857–1918) was a Russian mathematician whose fundamental contribution to the theory of stability of motion formed an important complement to the work of Poincaré. Lyapunov's work was first published in Russian in 1892; it became known to the wider mathematical community in 1907 when it appeared in French translation.

provided that this limit exists. The **Lyapunov exponent**, $h(x_0)$, of the orbit of x_0 under $f(x)$ is defined as

$$h(x_0) = \lim_{n \to \infty} \frac{1}{n} \sum_{j=0}^{n-1} \ln |f'(x_j)|, \tag{2.34}$$

provided that this limit exists. Note that if both of these limits exist and $L(x_0)$ is *non-zero*, then

$$h(x_0) = \ln L(x_0), \quad L(x_0) = e^{h(x_0)}, \tag{2.35}$$

and, moreover, $h(x_0)$ exists if and only if $L(x_0)$ exists. It follows from the definitions that $L(x_0)$ is the average-per-iterate local rescaling factor for points near the orbit of x_0 and that if $L(x_0) > 1$ or, equivalently, if $h(x_0) > 0$, local distances averaged across the orbit get *expanded*, whereas if $L(x_0) < 1$ or $h(x_0) < 0$, average local distances get *contracted*.

From the discussion in Subsection 2.3.1, one would expect $h(x_0) < 0$ for stable orbits (orbits converging to sinks) because in this case orbits approach one another exponentially fast. By contrast, for chaotic orbits the same discussion suggests that $h(x_0) > 0$ since in this case it was shown that initially nearby orbits begin to separate exponentially fast. It will turn out that positivity of Lyapunov exponents plays an important role in the determination of chaos.

Exercise 2.20

(a) If x^* is a fixed point of the map $f(x)$, show that the Lyapunov exponent $h(x^*)$ is given by

$$h(x^*) = \ln |f'(x^*)|, \tag{2.36}$$

and hence the Lyapunov number $L(x^*)$ is given by

$$L(x^*) = |f'(x^*)|. \tag{2.37}$$

(b) Similarly, if $\{x_1^*, \ldots, x_k^*\}$ is a period-k orbit of the map $f(x)$, show, by carefully considering the limit in Equation (2.34), that the Lyapunov exponents are given by

$$h(x_1^*) = h(x_2^*) = \cdots = h(x_k^*) = \frac{1}{k} \sum_{j=1}^{k} \ln |f'(x_j^*)|, \tag{2.38}$$

and the Lyapunov numbers are given by

$$L(x_1^*) = L(x_2^*) = \cdots = L(x_k^*) = \left| \prod_{j=1}^{k} f'(x_j^*) \right|^{1/k}. \tag{2.39}$$

Compare this last result with Equation (2.32).

Recall from the stability test for a sink, Theorem 2.1, that if $|f'(x^*)| < 1$, then x^* is a sink. Thus the result of Exercise 2.20(a), Equation (2.37), shows that if $L(x^*) < 1$, or, equivalently, $h(x^*) = \ln L(x^*) < 0$, then x^* is a sink. Similarly, for a period-k sink, $L(x_1^*) < 1$ and therefore $h(x_1^*) < 0$.

We now introduce the notion of an **asymptotically periodic** orbit. This is an orbit which converges to a periodic orbit as the iterate index n increases. It is important to note that the orbit to which an asymptotically periodic orbit converges need not be a period-k sink, though usually it is. One can find exceptional orbits which are taken to a period-k source after a finite number of iterates (and are therefore asymptotically periodic to a period-k source). We will discuss these exceptional orbits later.

Suppose that an orbit $\{x_n\}_{n\geq 0} = \{f^n(x_0)\}_{n\geq 0}$ of the smooth map f on $\mathbb{R}$, with $f'(x_n) \neq 0$ for all $n \geq 0$, is *asymptotically periodic* to the periodic orbit $\{x_1^*, x_2^*, \ldots\}$, and consider its Lyapunov exponent $h(x_0)$. In the definition of $h(x_0)$, Equation (2.34), the sum is dominated by the values of x_n for large n, since the limit $n \rightarrow \infty$ is taken, and these converge to the values on the periodic orbit, $x_1^*, x_2^*, \ldots$. Hence we have $h(x_0) = h(x_1^*)$, provided that both Lyapunov exponents exist. This is useful in the calculation of Lyapunov exponents for the case of asymptotically periodic orbits.

Let us apply this idea to the logistic map for a in the range $0 < a \leq 1 + \sqrt{6}$. We shall consider Lyapunov exponents for the logistic map $f_a(x) = ax(1-x)$, for orbits starting in the closed interval $[0, 1]$ which we know to be an invariant set for $0 < a \leq 4$. We shall consider three ranges of a in turn, and for each the Lyapunov exponent $h_a(x_0)$ for all $x_0 \in [0, 1]$ will be determined.

(a) $0 < a \leq 1$. For this range of a, the map has only one fixed point in the interval $[0, 1]$, which is the sink at $x = 0$. It is clearly a sink because $f_a'(x) = a(1 - 2x)$ and so $f_a'(0) = a$ which is less than 1 for this range of a (except at $a = 1$). Moreover, the orbits of x_0 under f_a *converge* to $x = 0$ for *all* $x_0 \in [0, 1]$ (you should sketch the cobweb plots to check this). This is even true of the case when $a = 1$, where $f_a'(0) = 1$, as an examination of the cobweb plot makes clear. Hence, applying $h_a(x_0) = h_a(x^*)$ for asymptotic periodicity, the Lyapunov exponent is given by

$$h_a(x_0) = h_a(0) = \ln|f_a'(0)| = \ln a \quad \text{for all } x_0 \in [0, 1].$$

Note that $h_a(x_0) < 0$ for $0 < a < 1$, so average-per-iteration local distances get contracted along the orbit of x_0. This reflects the fact that the orbits of x_0 are converging to a sink.

(b) $1 < a \leq 3$. Here, the fixed point at $x = 0$ becomes a *source*, but a second fixed point occurs in the interval $[0, 1]$ at $x^* = 1 - \frac{1}{a}$, which is a *sink* for this range of a (see Exercise 2.10). At this point, $f_a'(x^*) = 2 - a$, which implies that $h_a(x^*) = \ln|2 - a|$. But does $h_a(x_0)$ equate to this for all $x_0 \in [0, 1]$? The answer is no, since the orbit with $x_0 = 0$ *stays* at the source at $x = 0$, and the orbit with $x_0 = 1$ goes to the source at $x = 0$ immediately after one iteration. However, as an examination of the cobweb plots makes clear, all orbits of x_0 for $x_0 \in (0, 1)$ (i.e. the *open* interval) converge to the sink at $x^* = 1 - \frac{1}{a}$. So, by again applying $h_a(x_0) = h_a(x^*)$ for asymptotic periodicity, we have that

$$h_a(x_0) = \begin{cases} \ln|2 - a| & \text{if } x_0 \in (0, 1), \\ \ln a & \text{if } x_0 \in \{0\} \cup \{1\}. \end{cases} \tag{2.40}$$

Note that $h_a(x_0) < 0$ for $1 < a < 3$ for all $x_0 \in (0, 1)$, which again reflects the fact that all these orbits of x_0 are attracted to the sink, whereas $h_a(0) = h_a(1) > 0$, indicating that nearby orbits are repelled by the source at $x = 0$ and, therefore, average-per-iterate local distances get expanded.

(c) $3 < a \leq 1 + \sqrt{6}$. As explained in Subsection 2.2.3, particularly in Exercises 2.17 and 2.18, for this range of a there exists a period-2 sink $\{x_1^*, x_2^*\}$ with x_1^* and x_2^* given by Equations (2.25) and (2.26). Furthermore, the fixed point at $x^* = 1 - \frac{1}{a}$ becomes a source in addition to the source at $x = 0$. Now, an examination of the cobweb plots for $f_a(x)$ and $f_a^2(x)$ should convince you that *almost* all orbits of $x_0 \in (0, 1)$ will be asymptotically periodic to the period-2 sink $\{x_1^*, x_2^*\}$, with the exception of a countably infinite set of points, denoted S.

A countably infinite set has an infinite number of elements having a one-to-one correspondence with the set of positive integers.

This is the set of points which get taken to the source at $x^* = 1 - \frac{1}{a}$ after a finite number of iterates, and can be expressed as

$$S = \left\{ x \in (0,1) : f_a^n(x) = 1 - \frac{1}{a}, \ 0 \le n < \infty \right\}. \tag{2.41}$$

Now, for the period-2 sink,

$$h_a(x_1^*) = \tfrac{1}{2} \ln \left| f_a'(x_1^*) f_a'(x_2^*) \right| = \tfrac{1}{2} \ln \left| 5 - (a-1)^2 \right|,$$

using Equation (2.28). Hence, applying yet again $h_a(x_0) = h_a(x_1^*)$ for asymptotic periodicity, we have

$$h_a(x_0) = \begin{cases} \tfrac{1}{2} \ln \left| 5 - (a-1)^2 \right| & \text{for all } x_0 \in (0,1) \setminus S, \\ \ln |a-2| & \text{for all } x_0 \in S, \\ \ln a & \text{for } x_0 \in \{0\} \cup \{1\}. \end{cases} \tag{2.42}$$

Finally, note that for $3 < a < 1 + \sqrt{6}$, $h_a(x_0) < 0$ for $x_0 \in (0,1) \setminus S$ (reflecting the fact that such orbits of x_0 are converging to the period-2 sink); $h_a(x_0) > 0$ for $x_0 \in S$ (due to nearby points being repelled by the source at $x^* = 1 - \frac{1}{a}$); and, again, $h_a(x_0) > 0$ for $x_0 \in \{0\} \cup \{1\}$ (nearby points are repelled by the source at $x = 0$).

Exercise 2.21

Consider the countably infinite set S in Equation (2.41) for $a > 2$.

(a) Show that S is an *invariant set* under the map f_a.

(b) Clearly, the source $x^* = 1 - \frac{1}{a}$ is a member of S. Give explicit expressions, in terms of a, for *three* other members of S.

We finish this subsection with a few general remarks about some features of the Lyapunov exponent.

1. If x_0 is asymptotically periodic to a period-k sink ($k \ge 1$) $\{x_1^*, \ldots, x_k^*\}$, then $h(x_0) = h(x_1^*) < 0$, i.e. its Lyapunov exponent is negative. This follows from the stability condition

$$\left| \prod_{j=1}^{k} f'(x_j^*) \right| < 1$$

for a period-k sink and therefore, from Equation (2.39),

$$L(x_1^*) = \left| \prod_{j=1}^{k} f'(x_j^*) \right|^{1/k} < 1,$$

so $h(x_0) = h(x_1^*) = \ln L(x_1^*) < 0$. Thus, when $h(x_0) < 0$, the orbit of x_0 is asymptotic to a stable periodic orbit.

2. It is possible to have $h(x_0) = 0$. This happens when the orbit of x_0 under the map $f(x)$ is asymptotically periodic to a period-k orbit $\{x_1^*, \ldots, x_k^*\}$ with the property

$$\left| \prod_{j=1}^{k} f'(x_j^*) \right| = 1,$$

as would be the case if the period-k orbit were on the threshold of a change in stability. In the example above for the logistic map f_a, you can see that for all $x_0 \in [0,1]$, $h_a(x_0) = 0$ at $a = 1$ because at this value of a the fixed point at $x = 0$ becomes unstable in favour of the sink starting to appear at $x^* = 1 - \frac{1}{a}$. As a increases further, one finds that, for all $x_0 \in (0,1)$, $h_a(x_0) = 0$ at $a = 3$, which is due to the *bifurcation* of the fixed point at $x^* = 1 - \frac{1}{a}$ into the period-2 sink. Increasing a yet further, one finds that for all $x_0 \in (0,1) \setminus S$, $h_a(x_0) = 0$ at $a = 1 + \sqrt{6}$, which is where the period-2 sink bifurcates into a period-4 sink. (Recall the discussion following Exercise 2.18.) So, for a range of $a > 1$, the zeros of $h_a(x_0)$ correspond to bifurcations of periodic sinks.

3. It can happen that $h(x_0) \to -\infty$ as certain points are approached; specifically, points where the orbit of x_0 is asymptotically periodic to a period-k sink $\{x_1^*, \ldots, x_k^*\}$, with $f'(x_j^*) = 0$ for at least one point in the period-k sink. For the case $k = 1$, such a point has been met before: it is a *superstable* sink, a point to which orbits converge *faster* than any exponential. This notion generalizes to a superstable period-k sink. In the above example for the logistic map, one finds that for all $x_0 \in (0,1)$, $h_a(x_0) \to -\infty$ as $a \to 2$, due to the superstable sink at $x^* = \frac{1}{2}$ (see the example just before Exercise 2.6 and Figure 2.6), and for all $x_0 \in (0,1) \setminus S$, $h_a(x_0) \to -\infty$ as $a \to 1 + \sqrt{5}$, where the period-2 sink becomes superstable.

2.3.3 Chaotic orbits

The analysis of the logistic map in the previous subsection shows that some important properties of an orbit are manifest in the value of its Lyapunov exponent. We have been able to explore the range of values of the Lyapunov exponent $h_a(x_0)$ for the logistic map $f_a(x)$, for values of a satisfying $0 < a \le 1 + \sqrt{6}$. One aspect of $h_a(x_0)$ for these values of a which is worth noting is that for *almost all* $x_0 \in (0,1)$, $h_a(x_0) \le 0$ (with equality to zero *only* for a corresponding to bifurcation points or points where a new sink stabilizes). The very exceptional values of x_0 where $h_a(x_0) > 0$ are for orbits which are asymptotic to periodic *sources*.

We would like to explore $h_a(x_0)$ for values of a satisfying $1 + \sqrt{6} < a \le 4$ where the bifurcation diagram, Figures 2.14 and 2.15, indicates some interesting and complicated behaviour, as do the orbits featured in Figures 2.19 and 2.20 where $a = 3.98$. However, as with the bifurcation diagram, we will need to use numerical methods, with the help of Maple, to proceed further. Enter the following *procedure* into a Maple worksheet.

```
> restart:  with(plots):
> lypt := proc(a1,a2,xint,M::posint,N::posint)
>    local x,a,da,h,j,pts,cond1,cond2,P1,P2;
>    cond1 := color=black,
          title="Lyapunov Exponent h vs a for the Logistic Map";
>    cond2 := labels=["a","h"],labelfont=[TIMES,ITALIC,18],
             axes=BOXED;
>    da := evalf((a2-a1)/M);
>    pts := NULL;
>    for a from a1 to a2 by da do
>       h := 0;
>       x := xint;
>       for j from 1 to 100 do            # Removes transients
>          x := evalf(a*x*(1-x));
>       end do:
```

```
>        for j from 1 to N do
>            x := evalf(a*x*(1-x));
>            h := evalf(h+ln(abs(1-2*x)));
>        end do:
>        h := evalf(ln(abs(a))+(h/N));
>        pts := pts,[a,h];
>      end do;
>      P1 := plot([pts],cond1);
>      P2 := plot(0,xaxis=a1..a2,color=black);
>      display({P1,P2},cond2);
>    end proc:
```

The procedure `lypt` takes the interval $a_1 < a < a_2$ (a_1 and a_2 being the first two arguments of `lypt`), divides it into M slices (where M is the fourth argument of `lypt`) and computes $h_a(x_0)$ at each slice (x_0 being the third argument of `lypt`). It approximates $h_a(x_0)$ by replacing the infinite limit in Equation (2.34) by a finite sum with N terms (where N is the fifth argument of `lypt`), where N is taken to be large. Figure 2.21 was generated by entering the statement

```
>  lypt(1,4,0.4,1000,200);
```

at the bottom of the worksheet. This plot corresponds to the bifurcation diagram displayed in Figure 2.14.

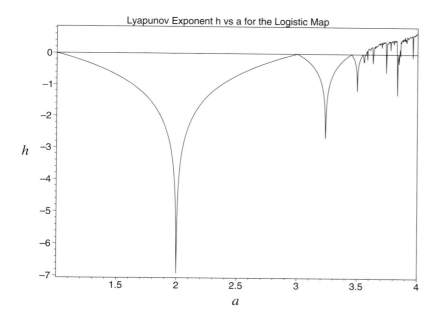

Figure 2.21   Maple generated plot of the Lyapunov exponent $h_a(x_0)$ for the logistic map $f_a(x) = ax(1-x)$, plotted as a function of a for $1 \leq a \leq 4$

Note that, to generate this plot, we set $x_0 = 0.4$. You should check that changing this value of x_0 (but always keeping $0 < x_0 < 1$) has no discernible effect on this plot. In fact, it holds for almost all $x_0 \in (0,1)$.

The part of the plot for which $1 \leq a \leq 1 + \sqrt{6}$ coincides with the explicit expressions given by Equations (2.40) and (2.42) (i.e. the cases in these equations holding for almost all $x_0 \in (0,1)$ where $h_a(x_0) \leq 0$). Notice how the numerical plots of $h_a(x_0)$ form distinct spikes which point down in the direction of negative h_a. These spikes, the tips of which occur at values of a where *superstable* orbits are found, are the numerical approximations to the *logarithmic* divergence to $-\infty$ of the Lyapunov exponents which results from superstable period-k sinks (as we argued in Remark 3 on page 98).

The plot starts to look more interesting in the region where $1 + \sqrt{6} < a \leq 4$, and a more detailed view of this portion is shown in Figure 2.22, which corresponds to the detail of the bifurcation diagram displayed in Figure 2.15. It was generated using the Maple statement

```
> lypt(evalf(1+sqrt(6)),4,0.4,1000,200);
```

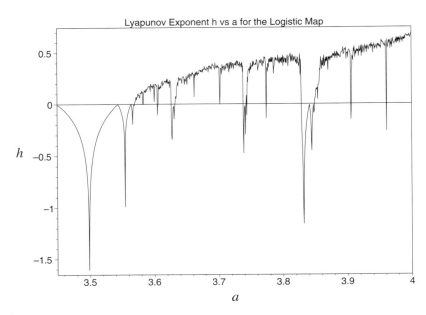

Figure 2.22   Maple generated plot of the Lyapunov exponent $h_a(x_0)$ for the logistic map $f_a(x)$, plotted as a function of a for $1 + \sqrt{6} \leq a \leq 4$

By comparing the plots of $h_a(x_0)$ (Figures 2.21 and 2.22) with the respective bifurcation diagrams (Figures 2.14 and 2.15), we can see that $h_a(x_0)$ appears to be positive *only* for those values of a where highly complicated behaviour is found in the corresponding bifurcation diagram. In fact, as a increases from 1, it first becomes positive at $a = 3.570$, where the period-doubling cascade becomes chaotic. For period-k sinks, $h_a(x_0)$ takes negative or zero values (recall Remark 1 on page 97, which argued that negative Lyapunov exponents are an indicator of stability); notice, for instance, the so-called period-3 window enclosing $a = 3.83$. We have already argued that $h_a(x_0)$ is positive for orbits asymptotically periodic to a *source* (actually, these orbits of x_0 land on the period-k source after a finite number of iterations). However, this occurs *only* at very *rare* isolated values of x_0. For almost all $x_0 \in (0, 1)$, other behaviour is found. So regions in Figures 2.21 and 2.22 showing positive $h_a(x_0)$ *cannot* be explained away as being due to the rare orbits that land on sources. In fact, they are due to the orbits of x_0 under f_a being *chaotic*, and the positive Lyapunov exponents are a manifestation of the extreme sensitivity to initial conditions characteristic of chaotic orbits. Subsection 2.3.1 illustrated the role of sensitive dependence on initial conditions, and Figure 2.20 together with Exercise 2.19 strongly suggests that a positive Lyapunov exponent lies behind this phenomenon.

We are now ready to give a *precise* definition of a chaotic orbit. The orbit $\{x_n\}_{n \geq 0}$ of x_0 under the map f is *chaotic* if the following three conditions hold:

1. $\{x_n\}_{n \geq 0}$ is bounded;
2. $\{x_n\}_{n \geq 0}$ is *not* asymptotically periodic;
3. $h(x_0) > 0$ for the Lyapunov exponent $h(x_0)$.

It is necessary to include Condition 1 in order to exclude orbits that diverge to infinity, and are therefore not asymptotically periodic, with positive Lyapunov exponent. An example of one of these orbits is that of $x_0 \neq 0$ under the linear map $f(x) = bx$, with $|b| > 1$. This orbit clearly does not exhibit the interesting properties inherent in chaos. Condition 2 is needed so as to exclude those special orbits which are asymptotically periodic to a periodic source as discussed above for the logistic map (e.g. orbits of $x_0 \in S$ in Equation (2.40) for $a > 3$). Condition 3 is needed because it encapsulates the sensitive dependence on initial conditions. Thus a chaotic orbit has expanding average-per-iterate local distances across its entire non-asymptotically-periodic bounded orbit.

2.4   The tent map

We finish this unit by *proving* (i.e. explicitly showing without numerics) the existence of chaotic orbits under the logistic map at $a = 4$.

2.4.1   Introduction to the tent map

The **tent map** is given by

$$x_{n+1} = T_c(x_n),$$

where

$$T_c(x) = c\min(x, 1-x) = \begin{cases} cx & \text{if } x \leq \frac{1}{2}, \\ c(1-x) & \text{if } x > \frac{1}{2}, \end{cases} \qquad (2.43)$$

and $c > 0$. The map $T_c(x)$, for $0 \leq x \leq 1$ and $c > 1$, is plotted in Figure 2.23.

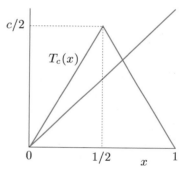

Figure 2.23   Tent map $T_c(x)$ for $c > 1$ plotted on $0 \leq x \leq 1$. The line $y = x$ is also plotted to locate the fixed points.

Note that this map is similar to the logistic map, $f_a(x)$, in that it is symmetrical about $x = \frac{1}{2}$ and peaked at this point, and takes positive values only for $0 < x < 1$. However, in general, the behaviour of its orbits will be shown to be quite different.

Exercise 2.22

Show that the interval $[0, 1]$ is an invariant set under $T_c(x)$ for all $0 < c \leq 2$.

Exercise 2.23

(a) Show that for $0 < c < 1$, the tent map has a sink at the origin with the whole of $[0, 1]$ being in its basin of attraction.

(b) Show that for $c > 1$, the origin becomes a source, and show that there exists another fixed point which is also a source. Locate this source.

(c) Show that the Lyapunov exponent $h_c(x_0)$ for the tent map for all x_0 is

$$h_c(x_0) = \ln c. \qquad (2.44)$$

These two exercises reveal some interesting features. First, just as $[0, 1]$ was an invariant set under the logistic map $f_a(x)$ for $0 < a \leq 4$, so it is under the tent map $T_c(x)$ for $0 < c \leq 2$. Henceforth, we shall confine c to $0 < c \leq 2$ so that all orbits will be bounded within $[0, 1]$. Second, for $0 < c < 1$, all orbits of $x_0 \in [0, 1]$ converge to a sink at the origin. However, for $1 < c \leq 2$, there are no sinks but instead two sources. Finally, for $1 < c \leq 2$, the Lyapunov exponent is $h_c(x_0) = \ln c > 0$ and, since all orbits are bounded, this implies that almost all orbits are chaotic, the exceptions being the relatively few asymptotically periodic orbits.

Exercise 2.24

Consider the infinite set of points $\{y_n^{\pm}, n = 0, 1, 2, \ldots\}$, where

$$y_n^- = \frac{1}{(c + 1)c^n}, \qquad y_n^+ = 1 - y_n^-.$$

For $c > 1$, show that orbits of these points under the tent map $T_c(x)$ are asymptotic to the period-1 source found in Exercise 2.23(b).

Exercise 2.25

Show that *all* period-k orbits of $T_c(x)$ are *sources* when $c > 1$. Assume that these orbits avoid the point $x = \frac{1}{2}$.

Some insight into the chaotic nature of the tent map for $1 < c \leq 2$ can be gained by inspecting its bifurcation diagram. This can be generated within Maple by making the appropriate modification to the procedure `bifdiagram` introduced in Subsection 2.2.4 for the logistic map. The resulting plot is shown in Figure 2.24.

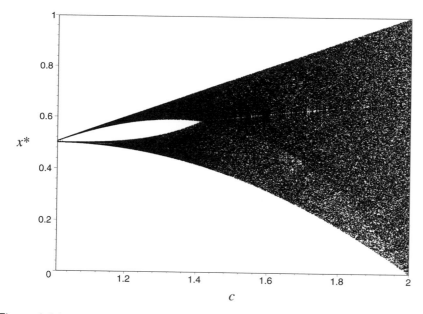

Figure 2.24   Bifurcation diagram for the tent map $T_c(x)$ for $1 < c \leq 2$

In contrast to the logistic map, notice the absence of windows corresponding to periodic sinks.

By making changes to the Maple procedure `bifdiagram` appropriate to the tent map, generate the bifurcation diagram shown in Figure 2.24.

2.4.2 Binary numbers and the connection with the logistic map

So far in this unit we have had to rely on numerical work to see evidence of chaotic orbits: we have not been able to *prove* that chaos exists; we have just been able to make reasonable inferences based on what the computer generates. This subsection will culminate with an explicit demonstration that chaotic orbits really do exist in the logistic map, at least for $a = 4$. To this end, we start by noting that the dynamics of the tent map $T_c(x)$ become particularly transparent when $c = 2$. This is because when representing x in **binary** form, i.e. as a fraction expressed in base 2, the map $T_2(x)$ simply performs a shifting operation on the binary digits. Moreover, it turns out that $T_2(x)$ is *equivalent* to the logistic map $f_a(x)$ for $a = 4$. We can then show the existence of chaotic orbits for these maps *explicitly* without having to rely on numerical computation.

Bicimals

We usually write numerals in what is called the decimal (or base 10) place-value system. This means that where you place a numeral determines its value. We call a decimal number between 0 and 1 a decimal fraction and write it as $0.d_1 d_2 d_3 \ldots$, where d_j is a base-10 digit taking values $0, 1, 2, \ldots, 9$. We express a decimal fraction in terms of place value as follows:

$$0.d_1 d_2 d_3 \ldots = \frac{d_1}{10} + \frac{d_2}{10^2} + \frac{d_3}{10^3} + \cdots.$$

This idea can be extended to any base and in particular base 2. Fractions expressed in base 2 are called **bicimals**, with the decimal point replaced by the **bicimal point**. Thus a bicimal number between 0 and 1 is written in terms of binary digits, $b_j = 0, 1$, as follows:

$$0.b_1 b_2 b_3 \ldots = \frac{b_1}{2} + \frac{b_2}{2^2} + \frac{b_3}{2^3} + \cdots = \sum_{j=1}^{\infty} \frac{b_j}{2^j}. \tag{2.45}$$

We stress that each b_j takes one of two values, 0 or 1. Note that the bicimal representation of 1 is $0.11111 \ldots$, just as in decimal notation $1 = 0.999999 \ldots$. Some other examples of numbers written in bicimal form are

$$\tfrac{1}{2} = 0.1, \quad \tfrac{1}{4} = 0.01, \quad \tfrac{3}{16} = 0.0011, \quad \tfrac{11}{16} = 0.1011. \tag{2.46}$$

Notice that all these fractions have a denominator which is a power of 2, and it is for this reason that their bicimal representations terminate. One can also find *repeating* or *recurring* bicimals, for example

$$\tfrac{1}{3} = 0.01010101 \ldots, \quad \tfrac{2}{3} = 0.10101010 \ldots, \tag{2.47}$$

with the pattern repeating after the ellipsis.

Exercise 2.27

Show that the fractions $\frac{1}{3}$ and $\frac{2}{3}$ have the bicimal forms given in Equations (2.47). [*Hint*: Note that $\frac{1}{3}$ can be expressed as $\frac{1}{4}/(1-\frac{1}{4})$.]

In summary, all *rational* numbers when written in bicimal form either terminate, such as those in Equations (2.46), or contain a repeating pattern, such as those in Equations (2.47). All other numbers are *irrational*, and these have bicimal representations which are neither terminating nor repeating.

Tent map at c = 2

Here we investigate the tent map $T_2(x)$ (i.e. $T_c(x)$ with $c=2$) when applied to x written in bicimal form. In order to do this, recall from Equation (2.43) that we need to know whether x is greater or less than $\frac{1}{2}$. This follows easily from observing the first bicimal place of x, so that

$$0.b_1b_2b_3\ldots \begin{cases} \leq \frac{1}{2} & \text{if } b_1 = 0, \\ \geq \frac{1}{2} & \text{if } b_1 = 1. \end{cases}$$

So if $b_1 = 0$, then from the definition of $T_2(x)$ (Equation (2.43) for $c=2$),

$$T_2(0.0b_2b_3\ldots) = 2\left(\frac{b_2}{2^2} + \frac{b_3}{2^3} + \frac{b_4}{2^4} + \cdots\right)$$
$$= \frac{b_2}{2} + \frac{b_3}{2^2} + \frac{b_4}{2^3} + \cdots$$
$$= 0.b_2b_3b_4\ldots,$$

i.e. $T_2(x)$ shifts the bicimal digits one place to the left. On the other hand, if $b_1 = 1$, then applying Equation (2.43) for $x > \frac{1}{2}$ gives

$$T_2(0.1b_2b_3\ldots) = 2(1 - 0.1b_2b_3\ldots)$$
$$= 2 \times 0.0\bar{b}_2\bar{b}_3\bar{b}_4\ldots$$
$$= 2\left(\frac{\bar{b}_2}{2^2} + \frac{\bar{b}_3}{2^3} + \frac{\bar{b}_4}{2^4} + \cdots\right)$$
$$= \frac{\bar{b}_2}{2} + \frac{\bar{b}_3}{2^2} + \frac{\bar{b}_4}{2^3} + \cdots$$
$$= 0.\bar{b}_2\bar{b}_3\bar{b}_4\ldots,$$

where we have introduced the bar notation

$$\bar{b}_j = 1 - b_j,$$

so that $\bar{0} = 1$ and $\bar{1} = 0$. Also, in the second equality of the above calculation, use has been made of the fact that $1 = 0.11111\ldots$, which is why the bars appear when they do. Thus, for this case, $T_2(x)$ flips all the 0s to 1s and 1s to 0s, and then shifts the resulting bicimal digits one place to the left. The action of $T_2(x)$ on bicimals can be summarized as follows:

$$T_2(0.b_1b_2b_3\ldots) = \begin{cases} 0.b_2b_3b_4\ldots & \text{if } b_1 = 0, \\ 0.\bar{b}_2\bar{b}_3\bar{b}_4\ldots & \text{if } b_1 = 1. \end{cases} \tag{2.48}$$

Equation (2.48) allows us to follow the progress of orbits of initial value $x_0 \in [0,1]$ by taking into account their bicimal representation.

Since $[0,1]$ is an invariant set under $T_2(x)$, clearly orbits of $x_0 \in [0,1]$ are bounded. Also, we know that the Lyapunov exponent $h_2(x_0) = \ln 2 > 0$ is positive. However, in order for the orbit of x_0 to be chaotic, it needs to satisfy the remaining condition, that of the absence of asymptotic periodicity. If x_0 is a rational number that has a terminating bicimal representation, then the shifting action expressed in Equation (2.48) shows that its orbit will eventually be taken to the source at $x = 0$ after a finite number of steps; iterations under $T_2(x)$ will eventually shift all the bicimal digits to the left so that only zero remains. If x_0 is a rational number that has a recurring (i.e. repeating) bicimal representation, then the shifting action of $T_2(x)$ will take its iterates to a period-k source, including possibly the period-1 source at non-zero x found in Exercise 2.23(b) with $c = 2$, but there are others with $k > 1$. So the orbits of *rational* x_0 are asymptotically periodic and therefore non-chaotic. This is not the case if x_0 is *irrational*, since the bicimal representations of irrational numbers are neither terminating nor repeating. Thus the orbits of irrational x_0 under the tent map $T_2(x)$ are *chaotic* under all conditions set out at the end of Subsection 2.3.3. Since almost all *real* numbers are irrational, this means that the orbits of almost all $x_0 \in [0, 1]$ are chaotic. We emphasize that this observation is not based on numerical evidence at all.

Logistic map at a = 4 and the tent map

Given that it has been established that the tent map $T_2(x)$ has chaotic orbits, we now finish this section by showing how this relates to chaos in the logistic map. Specifically, we show that the tent map for $c = 2$, $T_2(x)$, is *equivalent* to the logistic map for $a = 4$, which is given by

$$x_{n+1} = f_4(x_n) = 4x_n(1 - x_n).\tag{2.49}$$

This is done through a change of variable as follows:

$$x = C(u) = \sin^2\left(\tfrac{1}{2}\pi u\right),$$

that is, the variable u is mapped to x through the function $C(u)$, which is plotted in Figure 2.25. Note that $C(u)$ maps the interval $[0, 1]$ onto itself and that there is a one-to-one correspondence between u and x in this domain, i.e. each $x \in [0, 1]$ comes from a unique $u \in [0, 1]$. Moreover, the inverse $u = C^{-1}(x)$ exists provided that we keep $x \in [0, 1]$ and $u \in [0, 1]$. We now change variables from x_n to u_n (with $x_n = C(u_n)$), and investigate the mapping $x_n \longmapsto x_{n+1} = f_4(x_n)$ when expressed in terms of u_n, and so determine the equivalent mapping $u_n \longmapsto u_{n+1}$. Thus substituting $x_n = C(u_n)$ into Equation (2.49) leads to

$$
\begin{aligned}
C(u_{n+1}) &= 4C(u_n)\left(1 - C(u_n)\right)\\
&= 4\sin^2\left(\tfrac{1}{2}\pi u_n\right)\left(1 - \sin^2\left(\tfrac{1}{2}\pi u_n\right)\right)\\
&= 4\sin^2\left(\tfrac{1}{2}\pi u_n\right)\cos^2\left(\tfrac{1}{2}\pi u_n\right)\\
&= \left(2\sin\left(\tfrac{1}{2}\pi u_n\right)\cos\left(\tfrac{1}{2}\pi u_n\right)\right)^2\\
&= \sin^2(\pi u_n),
\end{aligned}\tag{2.50}
$$

where the third equality used the identity $\cos^2\theta = 1 - \sin^2\theta$, and the final equality used the double-angle formula $\sin 2\theta = 2\sin\theta\cos\theta$. Note also, from the definition of $C(u)$, that

$$C(u_{n+1}) = \sin^2\left(\tfrac{1}{2}\pi u_{n+1}\right),$$

and equating this with Equation (2.50) yields

$$\sin^2\left(\tfrac{1}{2}\pi u_{n+1}\right) = \sin^2(\pi u_n) = \sin^2(\pi(1 - u_n)),\tag{2.51}$$

where the second equality follows from the formula $\sin(\pi - \theta) = \sin\theta$. It is important to recall the restriction $0 \le u_n \le 1$ for all n, in order to preserve the one-to-one correspondence with x_n. So for $0 \le u_n \le \tfrac{1}{2}$, the first equality in Equation (2.51) shows that $u_{n+1} = 2u_n$. But for $\tfrac{1}{2} < u_n \le 1$, the second equality in Equation (2.51) must be used, in order to keep $0 \le u_{n+1} \le 1$, implying that $u_{n+1} = 2(1 - u_n)$. Thus, combining these two

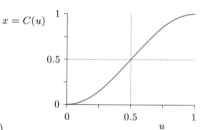

Figure 2.25   The function $x = C(u) = \sin^2\left(\tfrac{1}{2}\pi u\right)$ plotted against u

A map such as $C(u)$ is an example of a **bijection**, i.e. a one-to-one onto map.

The trigonometric identities and formulae used here, along with many others, can be found in the course *Handbook*.

105

cases, we have the following map for $u_n \longmapsto u_{n+1}$:

$$u_{n+1} = \begin{cases} 2u_n & \text{if } 0 \le u_n \le \frac{1}{2}, \\ 2(1 - u_n) & \text{if } \frac{1}{2} < u_n \le 1, \end{cases}$$

which is the tent map for $c = 2$. Therefore we have shown that the logistic map for $a = 4$ is equivalent to the tent map for $c = 2$, and that there is a one-to-one correspondence between orbits of these two maps. Since we have *proven* that almost all orbits of the tent map for $c = 2$ are chaotic, it must follow that almost all orbits of the logistic map for $a = 4$ are chaotic. Again, this conclusion does not rely on numerical observation.

2.5   Universality

At the start of Section 2.2, it was pointed out that many of the general properties of the logistic map hold for general *unimodal* maps, that is, smooth maps shaped like that shown in Figure 2.7 on page 77, with a single maximum. The logistic map $f_a(x) = ax(1 - x)$ is possibly the simplest such map, being just a quadratic function. In order to substantiate this claim of universality, consider another unimodal map, namely the so-called **sine map**, given by

$$x_{n+1} = S_a(x_n),$$

where

$$S_a(x) = a \sin(\pi x),$$

with a being an adjustable parameter playing a similar role to that of the parameter of the logistic map. A plot of $S_a(x)$ is shown in Figure 2.26; note that its shape is similar to that of the logistic map. But the similarities run much deeper. We shall investigate the behaviour of $S_a(x)$ for $0 < a \le 1$, where the interval $[0, 1]$ is invariant.

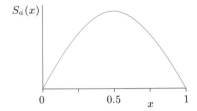

Figure 2.26   Sine map $S_a(x) = a \sin(\pi x)$ plotted for $0 \le x \le 1$

Exercise 2.28

Show that the interval $[0, 1]$ is an invariant set under $S_a(x)$ for all $0 < a \le 1$.

It turns out that the sine map has sinks and period-k sinks, similar to the logistic map, and bifurcations to chaos. To see this, we plot the bifurcation diagram for the sine map. This is obtained by modifying the procedure `bifdiagram` as appropriate for the sine map, resulting in the plot shown in Figure 2.27 for the range $0.32 \le a \le 1.0$. The more interesting features occur for $0.83 \le a \le 1.0$, and this part has been enlarged in Figure 2.28. Note the close similarities with the corresponding plots for the logistic map in Subsection 2.2.4. For lower values of a there is a single sink which, on increasing a, undergoes a series of period-doubling bifurcations to what appears to be chaos. For higher values of a one finds pronounced windows corresponding to orbits such as period-3 and period-5, just as for the logistic map, and these windows appear in the same order, although the windows and the bifurcation points occur for different values of a.

The modification simply entails substituting `a*x*(1-x)`, where it occurs in `bifdiagram`, with `a*sin(Pi*x)`.

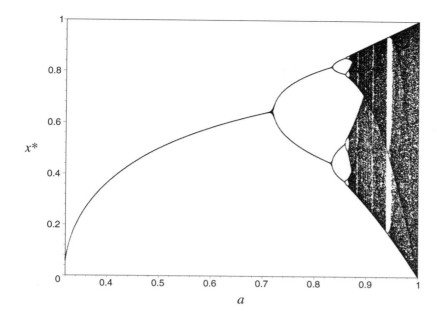

Figure 2.27   Bifurcation diagram for the sine map $S_a(x)$ with $0.32 \le a \le 1.0$

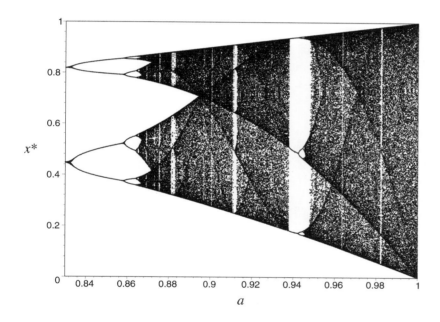

Figure 2.28   Bifurcation diagram for the sine map $S_a(x)$ with $0.83 \le a \le 1.0$

So, although there are *quantitative* differences between the bifurcation diagrams of the logistic and sine maps, there are strong *qualitative* similarities. However, it is possible to extract a *universal constant* related to the period-doubling route to chaos, i.e. the period-doubling cascade, common to *all* unimodal maps. This number, expressing quantitative universality, is called **Feigenbaum's constant** after its discoverer Mitchell Feigenbaum (1944–) whose work on this was published in 1978 and 1979.

To introduce the idea behind Feigenbaum's approach, consider the *schematic* depiction of a period-doubling cascade shown in Figure 2.29, i.e. that part of the bifurcation diagram close to a period-doubling cascade.

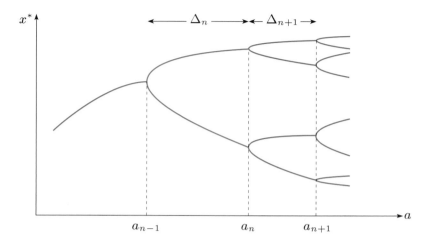

Figure 2.29 Schematic illustration of a period-doubling cascade showing the location of the period-2^n sinks as a function of the map parameter a

The horizontal direction has been 'stretched' for clarity in this figure, so that the bifurcation points a_n are clearly shown. The horizontal axis is the map parameter a, and the vertical axis indicates the location of the periodic sink in x. In fact, a_n is the threshold where the period-2^n sink first appears, and the gap between succeeding bifurcations,

$$\Delta_n = a_n - a_{n-1},$$

gets vanishingly small as n increases, i.e. $\Delta_n \to 0$ as $n \to \infty$, at which point, $a = a_\infty$, chaos first appears. This period-doubling cascade was described for the logistic map at the end of Subsection 2.2.4, where it was pointed out that $a_\infty = 3.570\ldots$ (for the sine map, $a_\infty \simeq 0.87$). In order to extract the universal Feigenbaum's constant, we consider ratios of succeeding gaps, Δ_n/Δ_{n+1}, as n gets large. Feigenbaum's constant, δ, is then defined as the limit

$$\delta = \lim_{n \to \infty} \frac{\Delta_n}{\Delta_{n+1}} = \lim_{n \to \infty} \frac{a_n - a_{n-1}}{a_{n+1} - a_n}. \tag{2.52}$$

This implies that as n gets large, a_n approaches a_∞ in the following way:

$$a_n \simeq a_\infty - \frac{K}{\delta^n} \quad \text{as } n \to \infty,$$

where the constant K depends on the map, but δ is a universal constant common to *all* unimodal maps. It is now known that δ takes the value

$$\delta = 4.669\,201\,609\ldots$$

which has also been confirmed in many physical experiments (subject to experimental error), particularly in hydrodynamics and electronics.

To solve $\dfrac{a_n - a_{n-1}}{a_{n+1} - a_n} \simeq \delta$ for large n, try $a_n = a_\infty - K\alpha^n$ (where $|\alpha| < 1$) and determine α by substitution, which implies that $\alpha = 1/\delta$.

2.6 End of unit exercises

These questions concern the tent map $T_c(x)$, discussed in Section 2.4.

Exercise 2.29

(a) Express $T_c^2(x)$ for $0 < c \le 1$, and show that for $1 < c \le 2$ it is given by

$$T_c^2(x) = \begin{cases} c^2 x & \text{if } 0 \le x \le \frac{1}{2c}, \\ c - c^2 x & \text{if } \frac{1}{2c} \le x \le \frac{1}{2}, \\ c - c^2 + c^2 x & \text{if } \frac{1}{2} \le x \le 1 - \frac{1}{2c}, \\ c^2(1 - x) & \text{if } 1 - \frac{1}{2c} \le x \le 1. \end{cases}$$

(b) Use the results of part (a) to find all the fixed points of $T_c^2(x)$ for $1 < c \le 2$. Identify the period-2 orbit $\{x_1^*, x_2^*\}$, and verify explicitly that $T_c(x_1^*) = x_2^*$ and $T_c(x_2^*) = x_1^*$.

Exercise 2.30

Consider the tent map for $c = 2$, i.e. $T_2(x)$.

(a) Show that the following are period-3 orbits under $T_2(x)$:

   (i) $\{\frac{2}{7}, \frac{4}{7}, \frac{6}{7}\}$,   (ii) $\{\frac{2}{9}, \frac{4}{9}, \frac{8}{9}\}$.

(b) Express $\frac{1}{7}$ and $\frac{2}{7}$ in bicimal form. Hence show, in terms of the shifting operation on binary digits, that $\frac{2}{7}$ is on a period-3 orbit under $T_2(x)$. [*Hint:* Note that $\frac{1}{7} = 1/(8 - 1)$.]

Learning outcomes

After studying this unit you should be able to:
- locate fixed points of one-dimensional maps and determine their stability;
- construct cobweb plots;
- understand the concept of an invariant set;
- locate and determine the stability of periodic orbits;
- construct bifurcation diagrams;
- understand the period-doubling route to chaos;
- calculate Lyapunov numbers and Lyapunov exponents;
- understand the precise definition of a chaotic orbit in a one-dimensional map;
- use binary numbers to identify periodic and chaotic orbits in the tent map, and understand how this relates to the logistic map;
- appreciate some of the universal aspects of period-doubling cascades such as that leading to Feigenbaum's constant.

Solutions to Exercises

Solution 2.1

The map is

$$x_{n+1} = a + bx_n. \tag{2.53}$$

Following the hint, put $x_n = u_n + \alpha$, so that Equation (2.53) becomes

$$u_{n+1} + \alpha = a + b(u_n + \alpha)$$
$$= bu_n + a + b\alpha,$$

which can be expressed as

$$u_{n+1} = a + (b-1)\alpha + bu_n. \tag{2.54}$$

We first proceed for the case where $b \neq 1$. Putting $\alpha = a/(1-b)$ in Equation (2.54) gives $u_{n+1} = bu_n$ which, following the argument after Equation (2.2), generates the orbit $u_n = b^n u_0$. Converting back to x_n leads to

$$u_n = x_n - \frac{a}{1-b} = b^n u_0 = b^n\left(x_0 - \frac{a}{1-b}\right),$$

which can be rearranged to give

$$x_n = b^n x_0 + \frac{(1-b^n)\,a}{1-b}, \tag{2.55}$$

as required. For $b = 1$, the map in Equation (2.53) becomes $x_{n+1} = a + x_n$. Thus

$$x_n = a + x_{n-1}$$
$$= 2a + x_{n-2}$$
$$= na + x_0,$$

giving the required map for the case where $b = 1$. Note that this also follows from Equation (2.55) by putting $b = 1 + \delta$ into this equation and then letting $\delta \to 0$.

Solution 2.2

The cobweb plot is constructed by following repeatedly the steps described on page 69, and the result is shown in Figure 2.30.

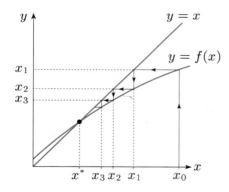

Figure 2.30   Cobweb plot for the orbit of x_0 under f with $0 < f'(x^*) < 1$ for $x_0 > x^*$

Solution 2.3

(a) The fixed point is given by $f(x^*) = x^*$, so with $f(x) = a + bx$, x^* satisfies

$$x^* = a + bx^*,$$

so

$$x^* = \frac{a}{1-b}.$$

(b) For $0 < b < 1$, the cobweb plot is shown in Figure 2.31.

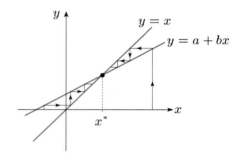

Figure 2.31   Cobweb plot of two orbits (one with $x_0 < x^*$ and the other with $x_0 > x^*$) under $f(x) = a + bx$ with $a > 0$ and $0 < b < 1$

For $b > 1$, the cobweb plot is shown in Figure 2.32.

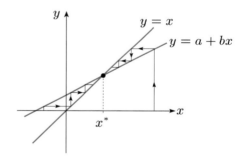

Figure 2.32   Cobweb plot of two orbits (one with $x_0 < x^*$ and the other with $x_0 > x^*$) under $f(x) = a + bx$ with $a > 0$ and $b > 1$

For $b = 1$, there is no fixed point since there is no solution of the equation $f(x^*) = x^*$. This can also be seen graphically by considering the cobweb plot when $b = 1$. This is shown in Figure 2.33 where the orbit is represented by the staircase of arrowed lines with *regularly* spaced steps. This regular spacing between the iterates of the orbit $(x_{n+1} - x_n = a)$ is consistent with the solution to Exercise 2.1 for $b = 1$.

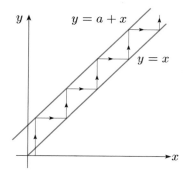

Figure 2.33 Cobweb plot of an orbit under $f(x) = a + x$ with $a > 0$

From the solution to part (a) (and also by looking at the cobweb plots) we can see that as $b \uparrow 1$, $x^* \to +\infty$, and as $b \downarrow 1$, $x^* \to -\infty$.

Solution 2.4

From the solution to Exercise 2.3 we have $x^* = a/(1 - b)$. For $b > 0$ and $b \neq 1$, examining the cobweb plots in the solution to Exercise 2.3, we find three elementary invariant sets, namely $(-\infty, x^*)$, $\{x^*\}$ and (x^*, ∞). For $b = 1$, there is only *one* elementary invariant set, namely $\mathbb{R}$. For $b < 0$, the cobweb plots are similar to those shown in Figure 2.4 with the origin shifted to x^*. Hence for this case there are two elementary invariant sets, namely $\{x^*\}$ and $\mathbb{R} \setminus \{x^*\} = (-\infty, x^*) \cup (x^*, \infty)$.

Solution 2.5

For the fixed point x^* to be superstable, we must have $F'(x^*) = 0$. To show this, note that
$$F'(x) = 1 - \frac{(f'(x))^2 - f(x)f''(x)}{(f'(x))^2} = \frac{f(x)f''(x)}{(f'(x))^2},$$
where the first equality uses the quotient rule for differentiation. The fixed point is at $x^* = x_s$, therefore $f(x^*) = f(x_s) = 0$, and substituting this into the equation above implies that $F'(x^*) = 0$ provided that $f'(x_s) \neq 0$, as required. Note that for the Newton–Raphson method to be applicable, one must have $f'(x_s) \neq 0$.

Solution 2.6

The cobweb plot for $f(x) = x^2$ is shown in Figure 2.34, from which we can see the following. Orbits starting in the interval $(0, 1)$ converge to the origin. Orbits starting in $(-1, 0)$ jump to $(0, 1)$ in the first iteration, and then proceed to converge to the origin. Orbits starting in $(1, \infty)$ diverge to ∞. Orbits starting in $(-\infty, -1)$ jump to $(1, \infty)$ in the first iteration, and then proceed to diverge to ∞. Orbits starting at $x = 1$ stay at this fixed point, and orbits starting at $x = -1$ jump to $x = 1$ in the first iteration and then stay at this fixed point. Putting all this together implies that the basin of attraction of the sink at the origin is the open interval $(-1, 1)$.

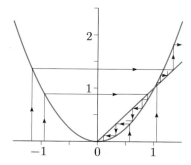

Figure 2.34 Cobweb plot for the orbits under $f(x) = x^2$ with various x_0

Solution 2.7

(a) The fixed points are determined by $f(x) = x$ with $f(x) = x(3 - x^2)/2$ and are therefore solutions of
$$x(3 - x^2) = 2x.$$
One of these solutions is at $x = 0$. The others solve $3 - x^2 = 2$, that is, $x^2 = 1$, so the remaining fixed points are at $x = \pm 1$. Noting that
$$f'(x) = \tfrac{3}{2} - \tfrac{3}{2}x^2,$$
we have $f'(0) = \tfrac{3}{2} > 1$, so the fixed point at $x = 0$ is a source, and $f'(\pm 1) = 0$, so the fixed points at $x = \pm 1$ are superstable sinks.

(b) The cobweb plot for $f(x) = x(3 - x^2)/2$ is shown in Figure 2.35, from which we can see that orbits starting in the open interval $(0, \sqrt{3})$ converge to the sink at $x = 1$ (two of them are shown in the figure), so $(0, \sqrt{3})$ is part of the basin of attraction for the sink at $x = 1$. Note that $\sqrt{3}$ maps to the source at $x = 0$ in one iteration and is therefore not part of the basin of attraction of the sink at $x = 1$.

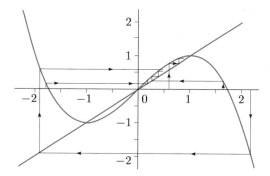

Figure 2.35 Cobweb plot for the orbits under $f(x) = x(3 - x^2)/2$ with various x_0. The zeros of $f(x)$ are at $x = 0, \pm\sqrt{3}$.

We can also see from Figure 2.35 that orbits starting in the semi-open interval $[-2, -\sqrt{3})$ (note that $f(-2) = 1$) map to the interval $(0, 1]$ in one iteration, and since $(0, 1]$ is part of the basin of attraction for $x = 1$, so too is $[-2, -\sqrt{3})$. Therefore the basin of attraction of the sink at $x = 1$ includes the set $[-2, -\sqrt{3}) \cup (0, \sqrt{3})$. But there is more. Figure 2.35 also shows that there is an interval somewhere to the right of $x = 2$ which maps to $[-2, -\sqrt{3})$ in one iteration, so this interval is also part of the basin of attraction of $x = 1$. This process continues *ad infinitum* to produce, as the basin of attraction for $x = 1$, a complicated set consisting of a union of non-overlapping intervals.

Solution 2.8

For each map in this question, we have $f'(0) = 1$, so Theorem 2.1 does not determine the stability of the fixed point at $x = 0$. Examine instead the cobweb plots.

(a) The cobweb plot is shown in Figure 2.36. From this you can see that orbits starting in $(0, \infty)$ diverge to $+\infty$, whereas orbits starting anywhere in the interval $(-1, 0)$ converge to $x = 0$. Orbits starting in $(-\infty, -1)$ map to $(0, \infty)$ in the first iteration. Therefore the fixed point at the origin does not satisfy the conditions defining either a sink or a source, so it is neither a sink nor a source (it attracts from the left and repels from the right).

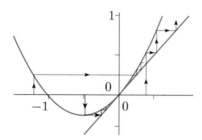

Figure 2.36   Cobweb plot for the orbits under $f(x) = x + x^2$ with various x_0

(b) The cobweb plot is shown in Figure 2.37. From this you can see that orbits starting anywhere in the interval $(0, 1)$ converge to the origin, whereas orbits starting in $(-\infty, 0)$ diverge to $-\infty$. Orbits starting in $(1, \infty)$ map to $(-\infty, 0)$ in the first iteration. Therefore the fixed point at the origin does not satisfy the conditions defining either a sink or a source, so it is neither a sink nor a source (it attracts from the right and repels from the left).

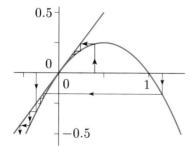

Figure 2.37   Cobweb plot for the orbits under $f(x) = x - x^2$ with various x_0

(c) The cobweb plot is shown in Figure 2.38, from which you can see that the origin is a repelling fixed point, i.e. a source.

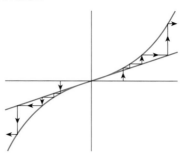

Figure 2.38   Cobweb plot for the orbits under $f(x) = x + x^3$ for two different x_0

(d) The cobweb plot is shown in Figure 2.39, from which you can see that the origin is an attracting fixed point, i.e. a sink.

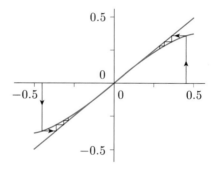

Figure 2.39   Cobweb plot for the orbits under $f(x) = x - x^3$ for two different x_0

Solution 2.9

For $[0, 1]$ to be invariant under f_a, it is required that $a > 0$, because if $a < 0$ then for all $0 < x < 1$ we find that $f_a(x) < 0$ so $f_a(x) \notin [0, 1]$. From the partial cobweb plot shown in Figure 2.40, we see that *provided* that the maximum value of $f_a(x)$ satisfies $f_a(x) \leq 1$, then $f_a(x) \in [0, 1]$ for all $x \in [0, 1]$.

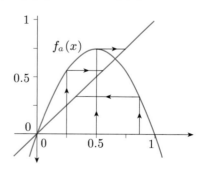

Figure 2.40   Cobweb plot for the orbits under $f_a(x)$ for some $a < 4$

To find the maximum of $f_a(x)$, note that
$$f_a'(x) = a(1 - 2x), \tag{2.56}$$
which is zero at $x = \frac{1}{2}$ and therefore $\max f_a(x) = f_a(\frac{1}{2}) = a/4$. Therefore $\max f_a(x) \leq 1$ provided that $a \leq 4$. Hence $[0, 1]$ is an invariant set under f_a provided that $0 < a \leq 4$.

Solution 2.10

To determine the stability of the fixed point, we need to find $f_a'(x)$, which is given by Equation (2.56) in the solution to Exercise 2.9. Hence, for the fixed point at the origin, $f_a'(0) = a$ so $|f_a'(0)| = |a|$. Therefore, by applying Theorem 2.1, the fixed point at the origin is a sink for $|a| < 1$ and a source for $|a| > 1$.

To determine the other fixed point, we need to find the non-zero solution of the equation $f_a(x^*) = x^*$, that is,

$$ax^*(1 - x^*) = x^*,$$

and since $x^* \neq 0$, we can divide through by x^* to give $a(1 - x^*) = 1$, which can be rearranged to yield the answer

$$x^* = 1 - \frac{1}{a}.$$

To determine the stability of x^*, we note that

$$f_a'(x^*) = a\left(1 - 2 + \tfrac{2}{a}\right) = 2 - a. \qquad (2.57)$$

By again applying Theorem 2.1, we see that x^* is a sink if $|2 - a| < 1$ and a source if $|2 - a| > 1$. The condition $|2 - a| < 1$ is equivalent to $1 < a < 3$, and $|2 - a| > 1$ is equivalent to $a > 3$ or $a < 1$.

Solution 2.11

In order to investigate how rapidly orbits for the map $x_{n+1} = f_a(x_n)$ converge to the sink x^*, we linearize the map about this sink. Thus, writing $x_n = x^* + u_n$, with u_n small, and Taylor expanding, we have

$$\begin{aligned}
x_{n+1} &= x^* + u_{n+1} \\
&= f_a(x^* + u_n) \\
&\simeq f_a(x^*) + f_a'(x^*)\, u_n \\
&= x^* + f_a'(x^*)\, u_n,
\end{aligned}$$

which reduces to the linear map $u_{n+1} \simeq f_a'(x^*)\, u_n$. By recalling the properties of linear maps, as set out in Subsection 2.1.1 (see Equations (2.3) and (2.4) with $b = f_a'(x^*)$), we can see that the closer the value of $|f_a'(x^*)|$ is to 1, the more slowly u_n converges to 0 (i.e. x_n converges to x^*). By applying Equation (2.57), we find that $f_a'(2.4) = -0.4$ and $f_a'(2.8) = -0.8$, and therefore $|f_a'(2.8)|$ is closer to 1 than $|f_a'(2.4)|$ is.

Solution 2.12

(a) From Equation (2.16) (for $j = 1$) we have that $f(x_1^*) = x_2^*$. Therefore

$$f^2(x_1^*) = f(x_2^*) = x_3^*,$$

where Equation (2.16) was again used in the last equality. Continuing in this way,

$$f^3(x_1^*) = f(x_3^*) = x_4^*,$$

so that in general (following simply by induction) $f^{j-1}(x_1^*) = x_j^*$ for $2 \leq j \leq k$, as required.

(b) From Equation (2.16) (for $j = 2$) we have that $f(x_2^*) = x_3^*$. Applying f to this and using (2.16) again gives

$$f^2(x_2^*) = f(x_3^*) = x_4^*,$$

and continuing gives

$$f^3(x_2^*) = f(x_4^*) = x_5^*,$$

so that in general $f^{j-2}(x_2^*) = x_j^*$ for $3 \leq j \leq k$, as required. In order to complete the question we need to consider the case where $j = 1$. For this, consider the already derived result for $j = k$, $x_k^* = f^{k-2}(x_2^*)$. Applying f to this and using Equation (2.16) for $j = k$ gives

$$f^{k-1}(x_2^*) = f(x_k^*) = x_1^*,$$

which completes the exercise.

Solution 2.13

From the chain rule, Equation (2.18), we have

$$(f^2)'(x) = f'(x)\, f'(f(x)), \qquad (2.58)$$

and since $\{x_1^*, x_2^*\}$ is a period-2 orbit, we have (from Equation (2.14)) $f(x_1^*) = x_2^*$ and $f(x_2^*) = x_1^*$. Substituting these relations into Equation (2.58) yields

$$\begin{aligned}
(f^2)'(x_1^*) &= f'(x_1^*)f'(x_2^*), \\
(f^2)'(x_2^*) &= f'(x_2^*)f'(x_1^*),
\end{aligned}$$

as required.

Solution 2.14

Following the hint, writing $f^k = f \circ f^{k-1}$ and applying the chain rule, gives

$$(f^k)'(x) = (f^{k-1})'(x)\, f'(f^{k-1}(x)).$$

Applying this result to f^{k-1} gives

$$(f^{k-1})'(x) = (f^{k-2})'(x)\, f'(f^{k-2}(x)),$$

and substituting this back into the first equation leads to

$$(f^k)'(x) = f'(f^{k-1}(x))\, f'(f^{k-2}(x))\, (f^{k-2})'(x).$$

Continuing in this way, successively eliminating derivatives of the higher compositions of f, yields

$$\begin{aligned}
(f^k)'(x) = {}& f'(x)\, f'(f(x))\, f'(f^2(x)) \\
& \cdots f'(f^{k-1}(x)). \qquad (2.59)
\end{aligned}$$

Substituting $x = x_1^*$ into this, and noting the result of Exercise 2.12(a), leads immediately to Equation (2.20) for $(f^k)'(x_1^*)$. Substituting $x = x_2^*$ and noting Exercise 2.12(b) leads explicitly to Equation (2.20) for $(f^k)'(x_2^*)$, but considerations based on the periodicity property in Equation (2.16) imply that the same result must hold for general $(f^k)'(x_j^*)$, as required.

Solution 2.15

(a) Applying the chain rule to $f^2 = f \circ f$ gives

$$(f^2)'(x) = (f \circ f)'(x) = f'(x)\, f'(f(x)).$$

Substituting $x = x^*$ into this and using $f(x^*) = x^*$ implies

$$(f^2)'(x^*) = (f'(x^*))^2 \geq 0,$$

as required.

(b) By the definition of a fixed point, if x^* is a fixed point of $f(x)$, then $f^k(x^*) = x^*$ for all $k \geq 1$. Therefore if x^* is a fixed point of $f(x)$, it is a fixed point of $f^k(x)$ for all $k \geq 1$. Now, Equation (2.59), in the solution to Exercise 2.14, together with $f^k(x^*) = x^*$ for all $k \geq 1$, implies that $(f^k)'(x^*) = (f'(x^*))^k$ and therefore

$$\left|(f^k)'(x^*)\right| = |f'(x^*)|^k. \qquad (2.60)$$

Now, for all $k \geq 1$, $|y|^k < 1$ (respectively > 1) if and only if $|y| < 1$ (respectively > 1). Using this, together with Equation (2.60), we have, for all $k \geq 1$,

$$\left|(f^k)'(x^*)\right| = |f'(x^*)|^k < 1 \quad \text{(respectively } > 1)$$

if and only if $|f'(x^*)| < 1$ (respectively > 1). Hence, by the stability test for fixed points of f and f^k, we have the required result.

Solution 2.16

(a) Equation (2.59), in the solution to Exercise 2.14, takes the following form for $k = 4$:

$$(f^4)'(x) = f'(x)\, f'(f(x))\, f'(f^2(x))\, f'(f^3(x)). \quad (2.61)$$

Since $\{x_1^*, x_2^*\}$ is a period-2 orbit of $f(x)$, Equation (2.14) holds and therefore

$$f(x_1^*) = x_2^*, \quad f(x_2^*) = x_1^*,$$
$$f^2(x_1^*) = x_1^*, \quad f^2(x_2^*) = x_2^*,$$
$$f^3(x_1^*) = x_2^*, \quad f^3(x_2^*) = x_1^*,$$

and substituting these into Equation (2.61) implies

$$(f^4)'(x_1^*) = (f^4)'(x_2^*) = (f'(x_1^*)\, f'(x_2^*))^2 \geq 0, \quad (2.62)$$

giving the required result.

(b) Equation (2.62) implies that

$$\left|(f^4)'(x_1^*)\right| = \left|(f^4)'(x_2^*)\right| < 1$$
$$\text{(respectively } > 1) \quad (2.63)$$

if and only if

$$|f'(x_1^*)\, f'(x_2^*)| < 1 \quad \text{(respectively } > 1). \quad (2.64)$$

Expression (2.63) is the stability test for fixed points of $f^4(x)$, and Expression (2.64) is the stability test for period-2 orbits of $f(x)$. This completes the solution.

Solution 2.17

(a)
$$\begin{aligned} f_a^2(x) &= a^2 x(1-x)\,(1 - ax(1-x)) \\ &= a^2 x(1-x)\,(ax^2 - ax + 1) \\ &= a^2 x\,(-ax^3 + 2ax^2 - (1+a)x + 1). \end{aligned}$$

(b) Equating $f_a^2(x) = x$ and using the solution to the first part of the exercise gives

$$a^2 x\,(-ax^3 + 2ax^2 - (1+a)x + 1) = x,$$

and dividing through by x (which is permitted since we are seeking non-zero solutions) and rearranging leads to the required cubic equation:

$$a^3 x^3 - 2a^3 x^2 + a^2(1+a)x + 1 - a^2 = 0. \quad (2.65)$$

(c) We know that the equation $f_a^2(x) = x$ has four solutions: the trivial solution, $x = 0$; the fixed point of $f_a(x)$, $x^* = 1 - \frac{1}{a}$; and the points x_1^* and x_2^*. The trivial solution was eliminated in the derivation of Equation (2.65), so the remaining three solutions, x^*, x_1^*, x_2^*, are the roots of this cubic. Since x^* is a root, the left-hand side of Equation (2.65) must factorize with a factor

$$x - x^* = x - \left(1 - \tfrac{1}{a}\right) = \tfrac{1}{a}\,(ax - a + 1).$$

Given that we anticipate that the left-hand side of Equation (2.65) must contain the factor $(ax - a + 1)$, the other factor can be deduced so that Equation (2.65) becomes

$$(ax - a + 1)\,(a^2 x^2 - a(1+a)x + 1 + a) = 0,$$

and the solutions x_1^* and x_2^* must be the roots of the quadratic equation from the second factor.

Solution 2.18

First, we consider the implications of the condition

$$4 + 2a - a^2 > -1,$$

which can be rearranged to

$$a^2 - 2a - 5 < 0.$$

This is satisfied by $a_- < a < a_+$, where $a_\pm$ are the roots of the quadratic

$$a^2 - 2a - 5 = 0,$$

which are $a_\pm = 1 \pm \sqrt{6}$.

Now we consider the second condition,

$$4 + 2a - a^2 < 1,$$

which can be rearranged to

$$a^2 - 2a - 3 > 0.$$

This is satisfied by $a < a_-'$ and $a > a_+'$ where $a_\pm'$ are the roots of

$$a^2 - 2a - 3 = 0,$$

which are $a_-' = -1$ and $a_+' = 3$.

Combining all these conditions together means that we require that either $a_- < a < a_-'$ or $a_+' < a < a_+$, but only the second bound is relevant since we require that a be non-negative.

Solution 2.19

(a) Note that the Taylor expansion, Equation (2.30), can be written as

$$f(x_0 + \delta x_0) \simeq f(x_0) + \delta x_0 f'(x_0) = x_1 + \delta x_0 f'(x_0),$$

so

$$\begin{aligned} f^2(x_0 + \delta x_0) &\simeq f(x_1 + \delta x_0 f'(x_0)) \\ &\simeq f(x_1) + \delta x_0 f'(x_0) f'(x_1) \\ &= x_2 + \delta x_0 f'(x_0) f'(x_1), \end{aligned}$$

where Taylor's approximation was again used in the second line. Similarly, for $f^3(x_0 + \delta x_0)$,

$$\begin{aligned} f^3(x_0 + \delta x_0) &\simeq f(x_2 + \delta x_0 f'(x_0) f'(x_1)) \\ &\simeq f(x_2) + \delta x_0 f'(x_0) f'(x_1) f'(x_2) \\ &= x_3 + \delta x_0 f'(x_0) f'(x_1) f'(x_2), \end{aligned}$$

so we can identify the general expression

$$f^n(x_0 + \delta x_0) \simeq x_n + \delta x_0 f'(x_0) f'(x_1) \cdots f'(x_{n-1}),$$

which can be substantiated inductively. Hence the expression for $|f^n(x_0 + \delta x_0) - x_n|$, as given by Equation (2.31), immediately follows.

(b) The evaluation of Equation (2.31) for the logistic map $f_a(x)$ involves the function $|f_a'(x)| = |a(1-2x)|$. In order to evaluate this repeatedly within Maple, it is useful to introduce the Maple function g(x):

```
>  g := x->abs(a*(1-2*x));
```
$$g := x \rightarrow |a(1-2x)|$$

We now apply Equation (2.31) to the two orbits plotted in Figure 2.19, which were generated in xorb1 and xorb2. This can be done by constructing the list Taylorapprox as follows:

```
>  a := 3.98:
>  Taylorapprox := [seq([xorb1[k,1],
   absdifferorbit[1,2]*mul(g(xorb1[j,2]),
   j=1..k-1)],k=1..30)]:
```

using the same list absdifferorbit as in the main text. Note that absdifferorbit[1,2] is equal to δx_0. The data are then plotted on the same logarithmic plot with those given before in absdifferorbit via

```
>  plots[logplot]([absdifferorbit,
   Taylorapprox],style=point,
   symbol=[circle,cross],color=[red,black],
   legend=["Actual absolute difference",
   "Taylor expansion approx"]);
```

which gives the plot shown in Figure 2.41.

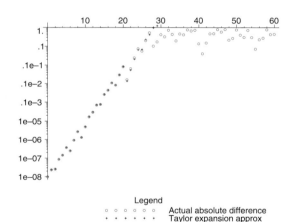

Figure 2.41 Maple logarithmic plot of the actual differences between the two orbits compared to the Taylor approximation for them

As can be seen from the plot, the two data sets begin to deviate appreciably for values of n in excess of about 20.

Solution 2.20

(a) If $x_0 = x^*$, then $x_j = f^j(x_0) = x^*$ for all $j \geq 0$. Therefore
$$\sum_{j=0}^{n-1} \ln|f'(x_j)| = n\ln|f'(x^*)|.$$

Substituting this into Equation (2.34) gives
$$h(x_0) = h(x^*) = \ln|f'(x^*)|,$$
as required, and $L(x^*) = |f'(x^*)|$ follows immediately from Equation (2.35).

(b) If $x_0 \in \{x_1^*, \ldots, x_k^*\}$, then by the defining property of period-k orbits, Equation (2.16), we have
$$S_1 = \sum_{j=0}^{k-1} \ln|f'(x_j)| = \sum_{j=1}^{k} \ln|f'(x_j^*)|.$$

Now, for n sufficiently large, we can write $n = n_1 k + n_2$, whilst keeping $0 \leq n_2 < k$, so that $n_1 \rightarrow \infty$ as $n \rightarrow \infty$. Using this, we have
$$\sum_{j=0}^{n-1} \ln|f'(x_j)| = n_1 S_1 + S_2,$$
where
$$S_2 = \sum_{j=n_1 k}^{n_1 k + n_2 - 1} \ln|f'(x_j)|.$$

Assuming that $f'(x_j) \neq 0$, S_2 is the sum of n_2 finite terms and therefore stays bounded as $n_1 \rightarrow \infty$. Therefore
$$\frac{1}{n}\sum_{j=0}^{n-1} \ln|f'(x_j)| = \frac{n_1 S_1}{n_1 k + n_2} + \frac{S_2}{n_1 k + n_2},$$
from which it follows that
$$h(x_0) = \lim_{n\rightarrow\infty} \frac{1}{n}\sum_{j=0}^{n-1} \ln|f'(x_j)|$$
$$= \lim_{n_1\rightarrow\infty}\left(\frac{n_1 S_1}{n_1 k + n_2} + \frac{S_2}{n_1 k + n_2}\right)$$
$$= S_1/k,$$

leading to Equation (2.38). Equation (2.39) follows immediately from substituting this into Equation (2.35). The Lyapunov number given in Equation (2.39) is identical to the right-hand side of Equation (2.32), i.e. the average-per-iterate multiplicative factor by which distances separating points close to a period-k orbit rescale over a complete k period.

Solution 2.21

(a) For all $x \in S$, $f_a^n(x) = 1 - \frac{1}{a}$ for some $0 \leq n < \infty$, so if $y = f_a(x)$, then
$$f_a^n(y) = f_a^{n+1}(x) = f_a\left(1 - \frac{1}{a}\right) = 1 - \frac{1}{a},$$
implying that $y = f_a(x) \in S$, and hence S is an invariant set under f_a.

(b) Three additional members of S are indicated in Figure 2.42 as y_0 and $y_\pm$.

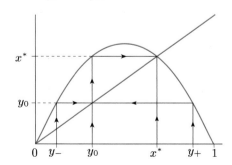

Figure 2.42 Cobweb plot showing orbits under $f_a(x)$ of the points x^*, y_0 and $y_\pm$, all being members of S since they reach $x^* = 1 - \frac{1}{a}$ in a finite number of iterations

Note that y_0 satisfies $f_a(y_0) = x^*$ such that $y_0 \neq x^*$, and $y_\pm$ are given by $f_a^2(y_\pm) = x^*$ and, as you can see from Figure 2.42, satisfy $f_a(y_\pm) = y_0$. So y_0 is a root of the quadratic equation $f_a(x) = ax(1-x) = x^*$, the other root being x^* itself. This quadratic equation can be expressed as

$$ax^2 - ax + 1 - \frac{1}{a} = 0,$$

which has roots $x^* = 1 - \frac{1}{a}$ and $y_0 = \frac{1}{a}$. Alternatively, note that y_0 can be more easily obtained from symmetry, since you can see from the figure that

$$\frac{1}{2} - y_0 = x^* - \frac{1}{2},$$

so $y_0 = 1 - x^* = \frac{1}{a}$. Since y_0 has been found, $y_\pm$ can now be obtained, as these solve the quadratic equation $f_a(x) = ax(1-x) = y_0$, which we write as

$$ax^2 - ax + \frac{1}{a} = 0.$$

This equation has roots

$$y_\pm = \frac{1}{2a}\left(a \pm \sqrt{a^2 - 4}\right),$$

which are real since $a > 2$.

Thus we have found three members of S, other than x^*, which are given by y_0 and $y_\pm$.

Solution 2.22

The argument is similar to that for Exercise 2.9. Provided that $\max T_c(x) \leq 1$, we have $T_c(x) \in [0,1]$ for all $x \in [0,1]$. But $\max T_c(x) = c/2$, so having $0 < c \leq 2$ ensures that $[0,1]$ is an invariant set.

Solution 2.23

(a) The origin is a fixed point since $T_c(0) = 0$. Note that $|T_c'(x)| = c$ *for all* x, including any fixed points. Thus, for $0 < c < 1$, $|T_c'(0)| < 1$, so from the stability test, Theorem 2.1, the fixed point at the origin is a sink. From the cobweb plot in Figure 2.43, we can see that orbits of all points in $[0,1]$ converge to the origin (for $0 \leq x \leq \frac{1}{2}$ as well as $\frac{1}{2} \leq x \leq 1$). Hence $[0,1]$ is in the basin of attraction of the sink at $x = 0$.

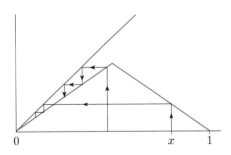

Figure 2.43   Cobweb plot showing orbits under $T_c(x)$ for $0 < c < 1$

(b) $|T_c'(x)| = c > 1$ for all x, including the fixed points, so from the stability test, Theorem 2.1, all fixed points are sources. So the origin is a source for $c > 1$.

The other fixed point, $x = x^* > 0$, is given by $T_c(x^*) = x^*$. We can see from Figure 2.23 that $\frac{1}{2} < x^* < 1$ and therefore $T_c(x^*) = c(1 - x^*) = x^*$. Solving for x^* gives

$$x^* = \frac{c}{c+1}, \tag{2.66}$$

which is also a source.

(c) Since $|T_c'(x)| = c$ for all x, we have

$$\sum_{j=0}^{n-1} \ln|T_c'(x_j)| = n \ln c,$$

and substituting this into the definition of the Lyapunov exponent, Equation (2.34), gives the required result.

Solution 2.24

Since $c > 1$, $0 < y_n^- < \frac{1}{2}$ for all $n \geq 0$. Therefore

$$T_c^{n+1}(y_n^-) = c^{n+1}y_n^- = \frac{c}{c+1} = x^*,$$

as required, where x^* is the source found in Exercise 2.23(b) as given by Equation (2.66). Since $0 < y_n^- < \frac{1}{2}$, we have $\frac{1}{2} < y_n^+ < 1$. Therefore, for all $n \geq 1$,

$$T_c(y_n^+) = c(1 - y_n^+) = cy_n^- = y_{n-1}^-,$$

so

$$T_c^{n+1}(y_n^+) = T_c^n(y_{n-1}^-) = c^n y_{n-1}^- = x^*,$$

as required. Finally, note that for y_n^+, the case $n = 0$ need not be considered since $y_0^+ = x^*$.

Solution 2.25

In order to test the stability of a period-k orbit, we need to determine

$$\prod_{j=1}^{k} |T_c'(x_j^*)|.$$

Since $x_j^* \neq \frac{1}{2}$, we have $|T_c'(x_j^*)| = c > 1$ for all $1 \leq j \leq k$. Therefore

$$\prod_{j=1}^{k} |T_c'(x_j^*)| = c^k > 1,$$

so, from the usual stability test, the periodic orbit is a period-k source.

Solution 2.26

In order to modify the procedure `bifdiagram`, used for the logistic map in Subsection 2.2.4, so that it can be used for the tent map, simply replace each of the two occurrences of `x:=evalf(a*x*(1-x))` by `x:=evalf(c*min(x,1-x))`. Also, in order to keep notation consistent, replace `a1`, `a2`, `a` and `da` by `c1`, `c2`, `c` and `dc`, respectively. Finally, the arguments in the `bifdiagram` statement, which generates the bifurcation diagram, are changed from `bifdiagram(1,4,1000)` to `bifdiagram(1.01,2,1000)`, and note that `c1` has been set to 1.01 so as to keep $c > 1$.

Solution 2.27

Following the hint:

$$\frac{\frac{1}{4}}{1 - \frac{1}{4}} = \frac{1}{4}\left(1 + \frac{1}{4} + \frac{1}{4^2} + \cdots\right)$$

$$= \frac{1}{4} + \frac{1}{4^2} + \frac{1}{4^3} + \cdots$$

$$= \frac{1}{2^2} + \frac{1}{2^4} + \frac{1}{2^6} + \cdots$$

$$= 0.010101\ldots,$$

where for the first equality the left-hand side was expanded as a geometric series, and the last equality made use of Equation (2.45) to express the result in bicimal form. For $\frac{2}{3}$ note that $\frac{2}{3} = 2 \times \frac{1}{3}$ and use the above expression to obtain

$$\frac{2}{3} = 2 \times \left(\frac{1}{2^2} + \frac{1}{2^4} + \frac{1}{2^6} + \cdots\right)$$

$$= \frac{1}{2} + \frac{1}{2^3} + \frac{1}{2^5} + \cdots$$

$$= 0.101010\ldots,$$

where, again, Equation (2.45) was used for the last equality.

Solution 2.28

The argument is similar to that used for previous maps. Provided that $\max S_a(x) \leq 1$, we have $S_a(x) \in [0, 1]$ for all $x \in [0, 1]$. But $\max S_a(x) = a$ (at $x = \frac{1}{2}$), so having $0 < a \leq 1$ ensures that $[0, 1]$ is an invariant set.

Solution 2.29

(a) Using the definition of the tent map given by Equation (2.43), we obtain

$$T_c^2(x) = T_c(T_c(x))$$

$$= \begin{cases} c\,T_c(x) & \text{if } 0 \leq T_c(x) \leq \frac{1}{2}, \\ c(1 - T_c(x)) & \text{if } \frac{1}{2} < T_c(x) \leq 1. \end{cases} \quad (2.67)$$

For $0 < c \leq 1$, it follows that $0 \leq T_c(x) \leq \frac{1}{2}$ for all $x \in [0, 1]$. Hence for all $x \in [0, 1]$ we have

$$T_c^2(x) = c\,T_c(x) = c^2 \min(x, 1 - x).$$

For $1 < c \leq 2$, we need to find the values of x for which $T_c(x) = \frac{1}{2}$ in order to determine when $T_c(x) < \frac{1}{2}$ and $T_c(x) > \frac{1}{2}$. But $T_c(x) = \frac{1}{2}$ when

$$cx = \frac{1}{2} \quad \text{and} \quad c(1 - x) = \frac{1}{2},$$

the first equality implying $x = 1/2c$ and the second implying $x = 1 - 1/2c$. From the plot of $T_c(x)$, Figure 2.23, it is clear that $T_c(x) < \frac{1}{2}$ for both $0 \leq x < 1/2c$ and $1 - 1/2c < x \leq 1$, and $T_c(x) > \frac{1}{2}$ for $1/2c < x < 1 - 1/2c$. Thus Equation (2.67) can be expanded further to yield

$$T_c^2(x) = \begin{cases} c\,T_c(x) & \text{if } 0 \leq x < \frac{1}{2c}, \\ c(1 - T_c(x)) & \text{if } \frac{1}{2c} \leq x \leq 1 - \frac{1}{2c}, \\ c\,T_c(x) & \text{if } 1 - \frac{1}{2c} < x \leq 1, \end{cases}$$

$$= \begin{cases} c^2 x & \text{if } 0 \leq x < \frac{1}{2c}, \\ c(1 - cx) & \text{if } \frac{1}{2c} \leq x \leq \frac{1}{2}, \\ c(1 - c(1 - x)) & \text{if } \frac{1}{2} \leq x \leq 1 - \frac{1}{2c}, \\ c^2(1 - x) & \text{if } 1 - \frac{1}{2c} < x \leq 1, \end{cases}$$

as required.

(b) The fixed points satisfy $T_c^2(x^*) = x^*$. Clearly, there is the trivial fixed point at $x^* = 0$; the others are indicated in Figure 2.44, which shows plots of $y = T_c^2(x)$ and $y = x$.

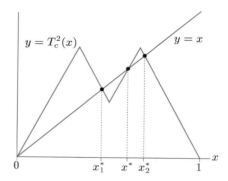

Figure 2.44 Plots of $y = T_c^2(x)$ and $y = x$ with fixed points located at x_1^*, x^* and x_2^*

To determine the solutions of $T_c^2(x^*) = x^*$ we consider each piece of $T_c^2(x)$ in turn (Figure 2.44 indicates that the curve $y = x$ intersects all four pieces).

For the first piece, we seek the solution of

$$c^2 x^* = x^*,$$

which occurs only at the origin $x^* = 0$.

For the second piece, we seek the solution of

$$c - c^2 x^* = x^*,$$

which is

$$x^* = x_1^* = \frac{c}{c^2 + 1}$$

(indicated by x_1^* in Figure 2.44).

For the third piece, we seek the solution of

$$c - c^2 + c^2 x^* = x^*,$$

which is

$$x^* = \frac{c(c - 1)}{c^2 - 1} = \frac{c(c - 1)}{(c + 1)(c - 1)} = \frac{c}{c + 1}.$$

This is the non-zero fixed point of $T_c(x)$ found in Exercise 2.23(b), which must also be a fixed point of $T_c^2(x)$ (indicated by x^* in Figure 2.44).

For the fourth piece, we seek the solution of

$$c^2(1 - x^*) = x^*,$$

which is

$$x^* = x_2^* = \frac{c^2}{c^2 + 1}$$

(indicated by x_2^* in Figure 2.44).

Of the four fixed points of $T_c^2(x)$, two are also fixed points of $T_c(x)$ (the origin and $x^* = c/(c + 1)$), so the other two, x_1^* and x_2^*, must form the period-2 orbit

$$\{x_1^*, x_2^*\} = \left\{\frac{c}{c^2 + 1}, \frac{c^2}{c^2 + 1}\right\}.$$

In order to verify explicitly that $\{x_1^*, x_2^*\}$ is a period-2 orbit, first note that $0 < x_1^* < \frac{1}{2}$ and $\frac{1}{2} < x_2^* < 1$ (this is clear from Figure 2.44). Therefore

$$T_c(x_1^*) = c x_1^* = \frac{c^2}{c^2 + 1} = x_2^*$$

and

$$T_c(x_2^*) = c(1 - x_2^*) = c\left(1 - \frac{c^2}{c^2 + 1}\right) = \frac{c}{c^2 + 1} = x_1^*,$$

thus showing explicitly that $\{x_1^*, x_2^*\}$ is a period-2 orbit.

Solution 2.30

(a) For both (i) and (ii), we use the definition of $T_2(x)$ given by Equation (2.43) for $c = 2$.

(i) $T_2(\frac{2}{7}) = \frac{4}{7}$ since $\frac{2}{7} < \frac{1}{2}$;

$\qquad T_2(\frac{4}{7}) = 2(1 - \frac{4}{7}) = \frac{6}{7}$ since $\frac{4}{7} > \frac{1}{2}$;

$\qquad T_2(\frac{6}{7}) = 2(1 - \frac{6}{7}) = \frac{2}{7}$ since $\frac{6}{7} > \frac{1}{2}$.

Thus $\{\frac{2}{7}, \frac{4}{7}, \frac{6}{7}\}$ satisfies the definition of a period-3 orbit under $T_2(x)$ as given by Equation (2.16) for general maps $f(x)$.

(ii) $T_2(\frac{2}{9}) = \frac{4}{9}$ since $\frac{2}{9} < \frac{1}{2}$;

$\qquad T_2(\frac{4}{9}) = \frac{8}{9}$ since $\frac{4}{9} < \frac{1}{2}$;

$\qquad T_2(\frac{8}{9}) = 2(1 - \frac{8}{9}) = \frac{2}{9}$ since $\frac{8}{9} > \frac{1}{2}$.

Thus $\{\frac{2}{9}, \frac{4}{9}, \frac{8}{9}\}$ satisfies the definition of a period-3 orbit under $T_2(x)$ as given by Equation (2.16) for general maps $f(x)$.

(b) Following the hint in the question:

$$
\begin{aligned}
\frac{1}{7} &= \frac{1}{8 - 1} \\
&= \frac{1}{8}\left(\frac{1}{1 - \frac{1}{8}}\right) \\
&= \frac{1}{8}\left(1 + \frac{1}{8} + \frac{1}{8^2} + \frac{1}{8^3} + \cdots\right) \\
&= \frac{1}{2^3} + \frac{1}{2^6} + \frac{1}{2^9} + \frac{1}{2^{12}} + \cdots \\
&= 0.001001001001\ldots,
\end{aligned}
$$

where the third equality followed from an expansion of a geometric series, and the last equality made use of Equation (2.45) to express the result in bicimal form. It then follows that

$$
\begin{aligned}
\frac{2}{7} &= 2\left(\frac{1}{2^3} + \frac{1}{2^6} + \frac{1}{2^9} + \frac{1}{2^{12}} + \cdots\right) \\
&= \frac{1}{2^2} + \frac{1}{2^5} + \frac{1}{2^8} + \frac{1}{2^{11}} + \cdots \\
&= 0.01001001001\ldots,
\end{aligned}
$$

where, again, the last equality made use of Equation (2.45) to express the result in bicimal form. The shifting operation on binary digits, as given by $T_2(x)$, is expressed in Equation (2.48). This is then applied successively to the bicimal representation of $\frac{2}{7}$ to give

$$
\begin{aligned}
T_2(0.010010010\ldots) &= 0.100100100\ldots, \\
T_2(0.100100100\ldots) &= 0.\overline{0}\overline{0}\overline{1}\overline{0}\overline{0}\overline{1}\overline{0}\overline{0}\overline{1}\ldots \\
&= 0.110110110\ldots, \\
T_2(0.110110110\ldots) &= 0.\overline{1}\overline{0}\overline{1}\overline{1}\overline{0}\overline{1}\overline{1}\overline{0}\overline{1}\ldots \\
&= 0.010010010\ldots,
\end{aligned}
$$

showing the required period-3 behaviour.

UNIT 3 Dynamics in two dimensions

Study guide

Sections 3.1, 3.3, 3.4 and 3.5 develop important new concepts and are essential to understanding the course. The experiment described in Section 3.2 is background reading.

It will be possible to understand this unit without having access to your computer, but at some stage you should work through the exercises which require use of Maple.

Introduction

Unit 2 discussed the surprisingly rich properties of a simple one-dimensional map. There are other interesting dynamical phenomena which occur in simple maps or flows, but which do not arise in one-dimensional problems. Most of these can be understood by considering two-dimensional systems. Two particularly significant examples are introduced in Section 3.1.

One very important difference from the one-dimensional case is that in two dimensions the dynamics can generate highly fragmented sets, which are referred to as *fractal sets*. The best-known example is a *strange attractor*, which arises in some two-dimensional maps. This unit will illustrate the strange attractor by means of an example in Subsection 3.1.1. The concepts required to understand fractal sets and their relation to dynamical systems will be discussed in *Unit 4*.

The other aspect which does not occur in one dimension is the existence of *area-preserving dynamics* in two dimensions. This important special case occurs in mechanical problems without friction and in problems involving the flow of incompressible fluids. These systems have properties which can only be understood using some very difficult techniques. In this course we can only point to some of the distinctive features of area-preserving dynamics.

In this unit it will be convenient to use a variety of different notations for two-dimensional maps. For example, sometimes the coordinates will be (x, y), sometimes (x_1, x_2), and vector notation will also be used, e.g. $\mathbf{x} = (x_1, x_2)$. Thus a two-dimensional map might be written as

$$\begin{pmatrix} x' \\ y' \end{pmatrix} = \begin{pmatrix} f(x, y) \\ g(x, y) \end{pmatrix}, \quad \begin{pmatrix} x_{n+1} \\ y_{n+1} \end{pmatrix} = \begin{pmatrix} f(x_n, y_n) \\ g(x_n, y_n) \end{pmatrix}, \tag{3.1}$$

or in vector notation as

$$\mathbf{x}' = \mathbf{f}(\mathbf{x}), \quad \mathbf{x}_{n+1} = \mathbf{f}(\mathbf{x}_n). \tag{3.2}$$

In some of these equations, primes are used distinguish the point after application of the map, for example, $\mathbf{x}'$ is the point reached by applying the map to $\mathbf{x}$: note that primes do not indicate differentiation in this context.

The properties of maps are explored using plots of the points visited by the map. The two-dimensional space spanned by the coordinates is called the *phase space* of the map, and the plots of sets of points visited will be referred to as *phase portraits*: these concepts were introduced in Section 1.4 of *Unit 1*, and examples are shown in Figures 3.1 and 3.8 below. These phase portraits are similar to the Poincaré and stroboscopic maps for continuous flows which were introduced in Subsection 1.3.4 of *Unit 1*. Information about the order in which the points are visited is lost when we make a phase portrait. For this reason, such plots might not give the most useful information for many real-world applications of dynamical systems, but we will see that they are very useful for illustrating and explaining how different dynamical behaviours arise.

The behaviour of two-dimensional dynamical systems encompasses a wide range of phenomena. In some cases computer experiments have produced phenomena which have not yet been satisfactorily analysed. This introductory unit can do no more than offer a glimpse of what the subject of two-dimensional dynamics contains. The current understanding has advanced rapidly since the 1970s because of the availability of electronic computers with good quality graphical output. Discoveries were made by using computer experiments to investigate the dynamics of maps, and analysis came later. In this unit we adopt the same approach, using the graphical features of Maple to experiment with maps. Because this is an introductory course, the analysis will not go far, and will emphasize useful ideas at the expense of rigour.

3.1 Two examples

This section discusses two examples of two-dimensional maps chosen to illustrate features which are not seen in one-dimensional maps. These are demonstrated with the help of simple Maple programs, which calculate the set of points generated by the map and plot them as a phase portrait. The section includes some exercises involving further experimentation with two-dimensional maps using Maple.

3.1.1 The Hénon map

The **Hénon map** is a map of the plane to itself. The coordinates (x, y) are mapped to (x', y') as follows:

$$\begin{pmatrix} x' \\ y' \end{pmatrix} = \begin{pmatrix} a - x^2 + by \\ x \end{pmatrix}. \tag{3.3}$$

The numbers a and b are parameters which may be varied to change the properties of the map. The map is named after Michel Hénon, a French astrophysicist, who introduced it in 1975. It is not a model for any physical process; rather, it is important because it is a very simple example of a two-dimensional map which allows many of the important properties of two-dimensional dynamics to be illustrated by varying the parameters a

and *b*. Hénon was motivated by a desire to find a system which shows similar chaotic behaviour to the Lorenz equations, but which is easier to analyse.

For many choices of *a* and *b*, the Hénon map will exhibit dynamical behaviour which has already been seen in the context of one-dimensional maps, such as orbits approaching a fixed point. Here we will concentrate on one distinctive new phenomenon, called a *strange attractor*, which exists for a limited region in the *ab*-plane, including the point $a = 1.2$, $b = 0.4$. The following piece of Maple code will generate the set of points (x_n, y_n) visited by the map starting from $(x_0, y_0) = (0, 0)$, for values of n satisfying $1 < n < 20\,000$. The program plots the points lying in a rectangle with corners at (x_a, y_a) and (x_b, y_b).

```
>  # Initializations:
>    N := 20000:                          # Number of iterates
>    xa := -2.5:  ya := -2.5:       # Coordinates of corners
     xb := 2.5:   yb := 2.5:        # of plotting region
>    x0 := 0:  y0 := 0:              # Initial values x0,y0
>    a := 1.2:  b := 0.4:             # Parameters of map
>  H := proc()
>    global x0,y0,x1,y1,a,b;
>    x1 := a-x0^2+b*y0;  y1 := x0;          # Henon map
>    x0 := x1;  y0 := y1;        # Replace initial values
>    [x0,y0]
>  end proc:
>  from 1 to 199 do H() end do:            # Iterate map
>  orbit := [seq(H(),k=200..N)]:
>  plots[pointplot](orbit,symbol=point,
   view=[xa..xb,ya..yb],colour=black,
   title=sprintf("Henon attractor: a = %a, b = %a",a,b));
```

This program declares some of the variables used in procedure H to be 'global'. This means that these variables can be referred to and used by the main program.

Running this program produces the plot shown in Figure 3.1.

The command `sprintf` is used to print a combination of text and numerical data. It is explained in the Maple help pages, but you do not need to know how to use it.

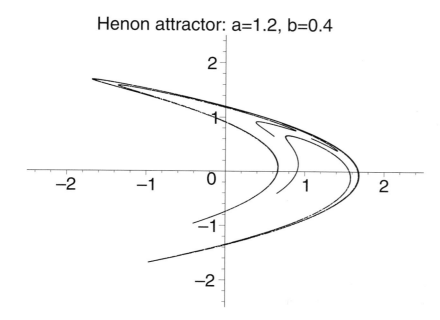

Figure 3.1   The Hénon attractor

121

Note that the first 200 iterations are not plotted, so that we can see the set that the iterations converge onto at large 'time' (large values of the iteration number), that is, the **attractor**. We discussed two types of attractor for two-dimensional dynamics in *Unit 1*: stable fixed points (Subsection 1.4.2) and limit cycles (Subsection 1.4.3). The set illustrated in Figure 3.1 is clearly not a fixed point, but neither does it appear to be a conventional limit cycle. The points appear at first sight to lie on a curve which folds back upon itself in a complicated fashion, but if we enlarge the boxed region of the curve shown in Figure 3.2 below, we see (in Figure 3.3) that each line appears to consist of a cluster of lines. Further magnification yields very similar images, as illustrated in Figure 3.4. Thus it is said that at least parts of the attractor are 'approximately self-similar under magnification'. This self-similarity is a characteristic feature of *fractal sets*, which will be explained later. This attractor with fractal properties is called a **strange attractor**. More precise definitions of both 'fractal' and 'strange attractor' will be given later, in *Unit 4* and in Subsection 3.4.4 of this unit, respectively. Note that the parameters a and b have different values from those in Figure 3.1: this illustrates the fact that the strange attractor exists for a range of parameter values.

The values of the parameters a, b and the choice of the magnified region for Figures 3.2 to 3.4 were taken from an illustration in K.T. Alligood, J.D. Sauer and J.A. Yorke (1996) *Chaos: an introduction to dynamical systems*, Springer, New York.

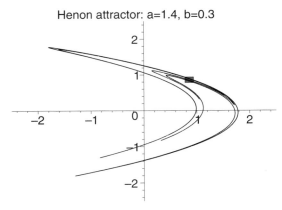

Figure 3.2   Strange attractor of the Hénon map, $a = 1.4$, $b = 0.3$. Figure 3.3 shows a magnification of the region in the small rectangle.

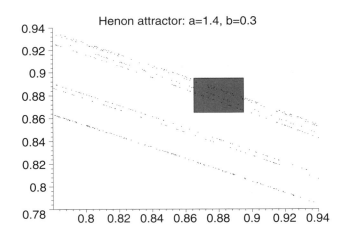

Figure 3.3   Magnification of the small rectangular region in Figure 3.2, showing that the line forming the attractor has a complex structure. The region in the rectangle is shown at higher magnification in Figure 3.4.

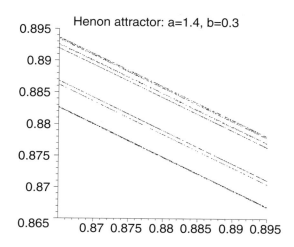

Figure 3.4 Further magnification of the strange attractor of the Hénon map, illustrating its self-similarity

The Maple code listed above allows you to select the rectangle within which the points are plotted. The following exercise gives instructions to enable you to demonstrate the self-similarity of the strange attractor for yourself.

Exercise 3.1

Edit the Maple code above to view the strange attractor in rectangles with opposite corners (x_a, y_a), (x_b, y_b) chosen as follows.

(a) $(-2.5, -2.5)$, $(2.5, 2.5)$

(b) $(0.78, 0.78)$, $(0.94, 0.94)$

(c) $(0.865, 0.865)$, $(0.895, 0.895)$

For this exercise reset the parameters of the map to $a = 1.4$, $b = 0.3$. Note that as the size of the rectangle decreases, the number of iterations must be increased so that you still see significant numbers of points in the region which is being plotted: try using a fivefold increase with each magnification. You should be able to reproduce Figures 3.2 to 3.4.

We have already seen two examples that have similarities to the Hénon attractor. In *Unit 1*, Subsection 1.2.3 showed an illustration of the dynamics of the Lorenz equations, and Subsection 1.5.2 showed chaotic behaviour of the Duffing oscillator. A careful investigation of these systems shows that they also exhibit strange attractors, having self-similar properties. One advantage of using the Hénon map to investigate strange attractors is that it is much easier to analyse two-dimensional maps than systems of differential equations such as the Lorenz equations.

The Hénon map can exhibit other types of behaviour, depending upon both the parameters a and b, and the initial point (x_0, y_0). For example, you may find that the points go to infinity, to a fixed point, or to a period-2 orbit, as well as a strange attractor.

Exercise 3.2

Use the Maple code to determine the long-time behaviour starting from the point $(x_0, y_0) = (0, 0)$ with the following parameter values.

(a) $a = 1.0$, $b = -0.3$ (b) $a = 1.28$, $b = -0.3$ (c) $a = 1.5$, $b = -0.4$

Also, with the parameter values $a = 1.28$ and $b = -0.3$, find the long-time behaviour for the following initial points.

(d) $(x_0, y_0) = (0.5, 0)$ (e) $(x_0, y_0) = (2.4, 2.4)$

We have stated that the attractor for the Hénon map can be a fractal set, having a complex fine-scale structure which appears similar to the original image when suitably magnified. Other fractal sets are found in the study of this and other two-dimensional maps. The following adaptation of the code on page 121 colours the initial points that do not escape to infinity (here we use the parameters $a = 1.4$, $b = -0.3$).

```
>  restart:                              # Initializations

>  x := NULL:

>  y := NULL:

>  N := 125:                 # Number of grid points is (2N+1)^2

>  M := 12:                    # Number of iterations to escape

>  a := 1.4:  b := -0.3:                     # Parameters of map

>  sx := 2.5:  sy := 12:      # Ranges of x,y: [-sx,sx],[-sy,sy]

>  nc := 0:

>  for i from -N to N do      # Double loop scans points on grid

>    for j from -N to N do

>      x0 := evalf(sx*i/N):

>      y0 := evalf(sy*j/N):

>      for k from 1 to M do       # Loop iterates map, starting

>        x1 := a-x0^2+b*y0:  y1 := x0:       # from grid point

>        x0 := x1:  y0 := y1:

>      end do:

>      d := sqrt(x0^2+y0^2):

>      if d<25 then            # If point has not escaped to large

>        x := x,evalf(sx*i/N):     # distance, add it to list

>        y := y,evalf(sy*j/N):

>        nc := nc+1:       # Increment number of points plotted

>      end if:

>    end do:

>  end do:

>  orbit := [seq([x[k],y[k]],k=1..nc)]:

>  plot(orbit,style=point,symbol=point,colour=red,
   view=[-sx..sx,-sy..sy],
   title="Henon basin: a=1.4, b=-0.3");
```

Running this code gives the picture shown in Figure 3.5.

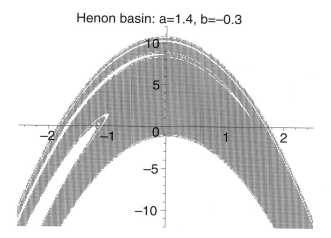

Figure 3.5 Fractal basin of attraction for the Hénon map

The set of points that do not escape is called the **basin of attraction**. This plot suggests that the boundary of the basin of attraction is a set with a rather complex structure. More detailed investigation shows that this set also has fractal properties, exhibiting approximate self-similarity under magnification. For other values of a and b, the Hénon map may not have a fractal basin of attraction.

Unit 4 will explain the definition of fractal sets and discuss the reasons why they occur in dynamical systems. But a property that is very important for producing chaotic behaviour and strange attractors will be mentioned at this stage. A characteristic feature of *chaotic* maps in two dimensions is that the dynamics involves **stretching and folding**. This fact is illustrated in Figure 3.6, which shows the image of a rectangular region under *one* iteration of the Hénon map, for parameter values $a = 1.4$, $b = 0.3$. The rectangle is stretched, folded and rotated by 90° by the action of the map.

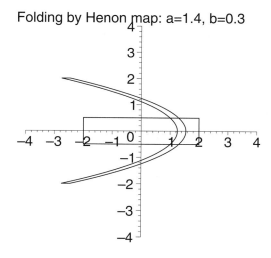

Figure 3.6 Illustrating the map of a rectangle under the Hénon map, showing that there is a stretching and folding action (and a rotation through 90°)

Later (in Subsection 3.4.4), after defining the largest Lyapunov exponent of a two-dimensional system in terms of an exponential separation of nearby trajectories, we will define a *chaotic* two-dimensional trajectory as one which has a positive largest Lyapunov exponent (and which remains bounded). By this definition, a chaotic system must have a 'stretching' action. If the chaotic map does not map points away to infinity (i.e. if the trajectory remains bounded), lines must fold back upon themselves, so that the action of chaotic maps involves both stretching and folding. In order for the map to have an 'attractor', points must be concentrated together by the action of the map. The area of the folded image of the rectangle in Figure 3.6 is less than that of the original rectangle. This area-contracting property is necessary to produce a strange attractor.

3.1.2 *The standard map*

The Hénon map was used to illustrate the phenomenon of the strange attractor, which does not occur in one-dimensional systems. Another situation which does not arise in one-dimensional models is area-preserving dynamics, where the area of any set is left unchanged under a map or a flow. Area-preserving flows arise naturally in two physical contexts, which will be explained below, but here we discuss one particular example, which is known as the **standard map**, in order to introduce some of the typical features of area-preserving maps. This map is called the 'standard map' because it arises as a model for the dynamics of a wide range of frictionless systems.

The standard map is a map where the coordinates (x, y) are mapped to (x', y') as follows:

$$\begin{pmatrix} x' \\ y' \end{pmatrix} = \begin{pmatrix} [x + y + K\sin(x)]\,\mathrm{mod}(2\pi) \\ y + K\sin(x) \end{pmatrix} \tag{3.4}$$

where $K > 0$ is a constant. Here the notation $X\,\mathrm{mod}(2\pi)$, read as 'X modulo 2π', means that integer multiples of 2π are added to X in order to keep its value in the interval $[0, 2\pi)$. This is natural if the variable X represents an angle in radians. The standard map satisfies a simple criterion for being area-preserving, which is presented here and will be explained later. To apply this criterion, we first evaluate the Jacobian matrix

$$\mathbf{J} = \begin{pmatrix} \frac{\partial x'}{\partial x} & \frac{\partial x'}{\partial y} \\ \frac{\partial y'}{\partial x} & \frac{\partial y'}{\partial y} \end{pmatrix}. \tag{3.5}$$

If the derivatives are defined at almost all points, and if $|\det(\mathbf{J})| = 1$ at all points where the derivatives are defined, then the map is area-preserving. (In saying 'almost all', we allow for the possibility that the derivatives are not defined on lines in (x, y)-space where the functions defining the map are discontinuous, such as the $\mathrm{mod}(2\pi)$ function in the definition of the standard map.)

Exercise 3.3

Calculate $\mathbf{J}$ for the standard map (ignoring points where derivatives are not defined because of discontinuities of the mod function). Using the above criterion, verify that the standard map is area-preserving.

[*Hint*: Note that for any differentiable function $F(x)$,

$$\frac{d}{dx}[F(x)\,\mathrm{mod}(2\pi)] = F'(x)$$

except at values of x where $F(x)$ is equal to an integer multiple of 2π.]

Exercise 3.4

Are there any combinations of a and b which make the Hénon map
area-preserving?

Exercise 3.5

Show that the standard map may be written in the form

$$y' = y + f(x),$$
$$x' = [x + y'] \bmod(2\pi),$$

for some choice of the function $f(x)$. Show that this map is area-preserving
for any differentiable function $f(x)$ which has period 2π.

Unlike the Hénon map, the standard map does describe a physical system.
Consider a wheel that is pivoted about the vertical axis (the z-axis), and
which rotates freely (like a roulette wheel, for example). On the wheel
there is a 'target', which makes an angle θ relative to the x-axis.
Periodically (at times $t_n = n\,\Delta t$, $n = 0, 1, 2, \ldots$) the target on the wheel is
'kicked' by an impulse, that is, a sharp jolt in which a very large force is
applied for a very short period of time. The impulse is applied in the
direction of the x-axis, as illustrated in Figure 3.7. You could think of the
impulse as resulting from the impact of a bullet hitting the target. It is
assumed that the impulse is applied to the target at equally-spaced time
intervals (like a machine gun): below we take the time interval to be unity
(that is, $\Delta t = 1$). This system is known as the **kicked rotor**, but we shall
see that its motion is described by the standard map.

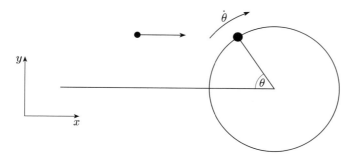

Figure 3.7   The kicked rotor: the target on the rotor makes an angle θ with the
x-axis. It is hit by a machine gun at regular time intervals (which we take to have
unit separation).

The impulse changes the rate of rotation of the wheel, which is denoted
by $\dot{\theta}$. The amount by which $\dot{\theta}$ changes depends upon the angle of the wheel
at the instant when the impulse is applied. If the target is aligned with the
x-axis, that is, if $\theta = 0$ or $\theta = \pi$, then the impulse will not change the
velocity at all, but if θ is close to $\pi/2$ or $3\pi/2$, the impulse will have a large
effect on the angular velocity $\dot{\theta}$. The change in angular velocity is
proportional to the component of the impulse force in the tangential
direction, implying that it is proportional to $\sin\theta$. The new angular
velocity is therefore $\dot{\theta}' = \dot{\theta} + K\sin\theta$, for some constant K. Let $\theta_n, \dot{\theta}_n$ be

the angle and angular velocity before the nth impulse (or 'kick'). Their values immediately before the next kick are

$$\dot{\theta}_{n+1} = \dot{\theta}_n + K\sin(\theta_n),$$
$$\theta_{n+1} = [\theta_n + \dot{\theta}_{n+1}]\,\mathrm{mod}(2\pi). \qquad (3.6)$$

Note that $\dot{\theta}_{n+1}$ appears in the right-hand side of the second of these equations, so that these equations are of the same form as (3.4) (as rewritten in Exercise 3.5: the variables θ and $\dot{\theta}$ correspond to x and y, respectively).

Although the 'kicked rotor' mechanical system seems rather contrived, the standard map turns up repeatedly as an approximation for the behaviour of frictionless mechanical systems which are subjected to a time-periodic force. For this reason, the standard map is known by various names, for example the **Chirikov–Taylor map** (named after two physicists who independently discovered its importance for understanding confinement of particles in fusion reactors and in particle accelerators).

Boris Valerianovich Chirikov (1928–) discovered the relevance of chaotic maps to magnetic confinement of particles in fusion reactors in 1959. Similar ideas were developed by J. Bryan Taylor in England in the 1960s.

This seemingly simple mechanical system behaves in different ways, depending on the values of K. The following Maple code can be used to investigate its behaviour.

```
>   restart:                              # Initializations
>   x := NULL:
>   y := NULL:
>   N := 400:                    # Number of iterations of map
>   M := 50:                     # Number of initial points
>   K := 1.0:
>   for j from 1 to M do         # This loop varies initial point
>      x0 := evalf(Pi):
>      y0 := 0.3*(j-25.5):
>      for k from 1 to N do               # This loop iterates map
>         x := x,x0:
>         y := y,y0:
>         y1 := evalf(y0+K*sin(x0)):
>         x1 := evalf(x0+y1):
         x1 := evalf(x1/(2*Pi)):
         x1 := evalf(2*Pi*(x1-floor(x1))):
>         x0 := x1:
>         y0 := y1:
>      end do:
>   end do:
>   orbit := [seq([x[k],y[k]],k=1..M*N)]:     # Plot pts visited
>   plot(orbit,style=point,symbol=point,colour=black,
       view=[0..2*Pi,-7.5..7.5],title="Standard map, K=1.0");
```

This code is a little more complex than the previous example. There are two loops: the loop in which the index k is varied is *nested* inside the loop which varies the index j. For each of the $M = 50$ values of j, the program starts iterating the standard map from the initial point $x = \pi$, $y = 0.3 \times (j - 25.5)$ (the choice of numbers here is rather arbitrary, but it is instructive to see the effect of changing the initial value of x to zero). For each value of j, the inner loop calculates $N = 400$ iterations of the map, and stores the results.

The value of x_1 must be replaced by $x_1 \bmod (2\pi)$, but there is no function in Maple which evaluates this directly. This is achieved in stages, using the function $\mathrm{floor}(X)$, which is equal to the largest integer which is less than or equal to X. In order to evaluate $x_1 \bmod (2\pi)$, first x_1 is divided by 2π, then we calculate $[x_1/2\pi] \bmod (1) = (x_1/2\pi) - \mathrm{floor}(x_1/2\pi)$. Finally, this is multiplied by 2π to give $x_1 \bmod (2\pi)$.

The code above produces Figure 3.8.

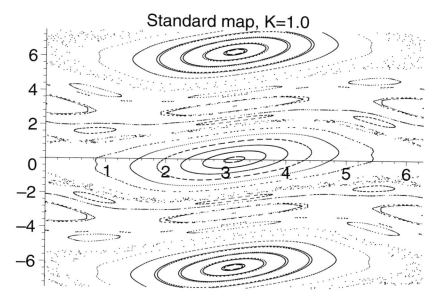

Standard map, K=1.0

Figure 3.8   Phase portraits of the standard map for $K = 1.0$, with 50 different initial positions

Try the following exercises, in which you insert different values of the kicking strength K and consider single trajectories with specified initial points.

Exercise 3.6

Use the code given above to investigate the effects of varying the kicking strength K in the standard map. Try using the values $K = 0.0$, $K = 0.25$, $K = 0.8$, $K = 1.2$ and $K = 5$.

Exercise 3.7

Modify the code given above to look at the behaviour of a single trajectory for the standard map with the specified initial point (x_0, y_0) and value of the parameter K.

(a) For $(x_0, y_0) = (0, 0.1)$, try setting K as follows.

   (i) $K = 0.1$ (ii) $K = 0.8$ (iii) $K = 1.2$ (iv) $K = 5.0$

(b) For $K = 0.9$, compare the following initial points.

   (i) $(x_0, y_0) = (0, 0.1)$ (ii) $(x_0, y_0) = (0, 1.8)$ (iii) $(x_0, y_0) = (0, 3.0)$

If you tried Exercise 3.6 you will have observed that the kicked rotor can exhibit many types of behaviour, even for a fixed value of K. For $K = 0.25$ we see (Figure 3.9) that the iterations remain confined to lines. This is consistent with the existence of a **constant of motion**, that is, a function $I(x, y)$ such that $I(x_n, y_n)$ is constant for all iterates (x_n, y_n) starting from a given initial point. The curves seen in the phase portraits of the kicked rotor are called **invariant curves** or **KAM curves**: KAM is an abbreviation for Kolmogorov, Arnold and Moser, the names of three mathematicians who proved the existence of these curves.

Andrey Nikolaevich Kolmogorov (1903–87) made outstanding contributions in many areas of mathematics (including probability theory, stochastic differential equations, turbulence, topology). His work on the existence of invariant curves was published in 1954. It was extended in different directions by Vladimir Igorevich Arnold (1937–) (who is known for many other contributions which involve the application of geometrical ideas to dynamical systems) and Jürgen Moser (1928–99); their papers were published in 1962 and 1963.

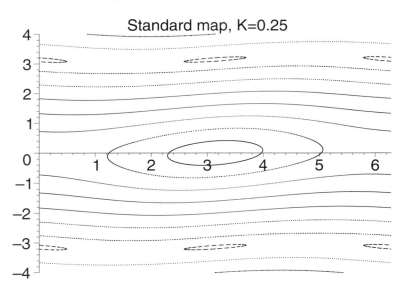

Figure 3.9   Phase portraits of the standard map for $K = 0.25$

For $K = 0.8$, the situation is more complicated (see Figure 3.10). For some initial points, the iterates lie on KAM curves similar to those for $K = 0.25$. However, there are other types of trajectory. Some trajectories fill out 'chains' of closed curves, and others cover two-dimensional regions with an apparently random scatter of points (in the sense that an iterate of the map (x_n, y_n) will eventually land arbitrarily close to any point in a two-dimensional region). There are KAM curves that form a continuous line from $x = 0$ to $x = 2\pi$. It is a fact (which will not be proved here) that trajectories do not cross from one side of a KAM curve to the other. These KAM curves therefore act as a barrier to the growth of the magnitude of the angular velocity $\dot{\theta}$ of the rotor.

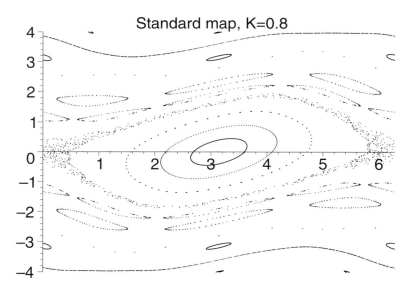

Figure 3.10   Phase portraits of the standard map for $K = 0.8$

For $K = 1.2$ there are no longer any curves joining $x = 0$ and $x = 2\pi$ without a break. Careful studies of the standard map show that the last KAM curve which joins $x = 0$ to $x = 2\pi$ disappears at $K = 0.9716\ldots$.

There is thus an abrupt transition in the behaviour of the map as K is increased. When K is less than the 'critical' value $K_c \simeq 0.97$, trajectories are confined between KAM curves, and the angular velocity of the kicked rotor remains bounded. However, when $K > K_c$ the angular velocity y of the rotor can become arbitrarily large or small, for many choices of the initial point (x_0, y_0).

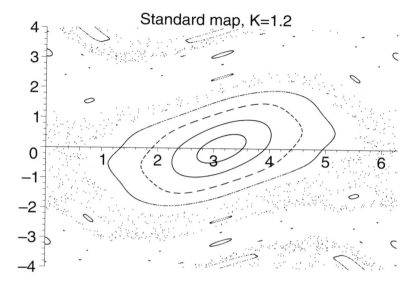

Figure 3.11   Phase portraits of the standard map for $K = 1.2$

For $K = 5.0$, the iterates form a random-looking pattern, and for most initial points the trajectory rapidly escapes to infinity. In fact, when K is large the behaviour of the standard map can be modelled successfully by a process called a *random walk*. This will be discussed further in *Unit 3* of Block C.

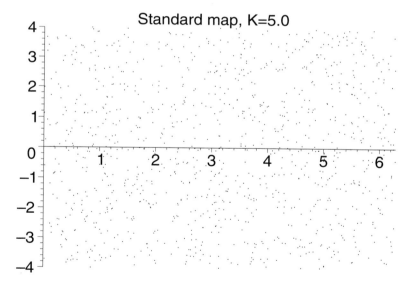

Figure 3.12   Phase portraits of the standard map for $K = 5.0$

3.2 An experimental demonstration: 'fractal scum'

Unit 1 has already discussed a variety of physical systems with chaotic dynamical behaviour. The two examples that we considered above were illustrated by plotting a 'phase portrait', that is, the set of points visited by the map as it is iterated. When we examine the motion of a physical system, the nature of the phase portrait is not usually readily apparent: we would have to record the coordinates of the system at a succession of times, and then make a plot in order to reveal patterns such as those in Figures 3.1 and 3.8.

Here we describe an experimental demonstration of chaotic behaviour which is of interest because it automatically generates patterns which are closely related to phase portraits.

The experiment is illustrated in outline in Figure 3.13. Some viscous liquid is held in a container, with the upper surface free. The bottom of the container is connected by tubes to a pump, which is turned on and off in a regular cycle. The upper surface of the liquid is sprinkled with a powder (the 'scum') consisting of particles of a material which is less dense than the liquid, which float on the surface.

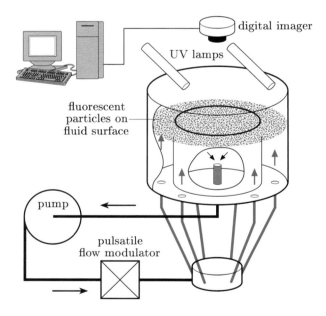

Figure 3.13 Experiment to demonstrate 'fractal scum'

After a long time has elapsed, the powder floating on the surface forms a very complex pattern, illustrated in Figure 3.14. The scientists who invented this experiment claim that this pattern is a fractal set, of the type which will be discussed in *Unit 4*.

Figure 3.14 'Fractal scum' pattern on the surface of a periodically stirred liquid.
Image courtesy of the American Association for the Advancement of Science (see below for full
reference).

It is important that the pump is turned on and off periodically, rather
than running continuously. If the pump were run continuously, the flow of
the fluid would be described by a system of two autonomous differential
equations, and the Poincaré–Bendixson theorem (discussed in *Unit 1*,
Subsection 1.4.4) would imply that the floating particles could not show
chaotic behaviour, only fixed points or limit cycles.

The first experiments of this type were reported by J.C. Sommerer and
E. Ott, in an article published in the journal *Science* in 1993. Although
the experiment is relatively simple for a laboratory scientist, there are
some complications. The article describes some of the technicalities of
getting the experiment to work nicely. For example, the choice of the
powder used to sprinkle on the surface is quite important, because
particles in many types of powder will stick together because of surface
tension effects: the experiment has been made to work with plastic
spheres, diameter 4×10^{-6} m, floating on a concentrated sugar solution.

Sommerer, J.C. and Ott E.
(1993) 'Particles floating on a
moving fluid: a dynamically
comprehensible physical
fractal', *Science*, **259**, pp.
335–9.

Although you will not be able to repeat the experiment yourself, you may
be able to see similar effects in a less carefully controlled situation. If you
sprinkle some flour onto the surface of water which is being gently heated
on a stove, you may be able to see patterns forming which have some
similarity to Figure 3.14.

The experiment has two features which are of some conceptual interest.
One of the nice features of this experiment is that you are able to see
patterns resembling phase portraits developing before your eyes, whereas
in most experiments the data must be collected and plotted to reveal the
phase portrait. But the pattern of dust particles is not a phase portrait; it
is the set of positions reached by a set of random initial points after a fixed
time. In this course we cannot consider the relation between these sets.

Another interesting aspect is that the experiment illustrates some points of similarity between fluid dynamics and other areas of nonlinear dynamics. It can be helpful to think of the velocity field of a dynamical system as carrying phase points, in the same manner as a moving fluid carries specks of dust. Here this conceptually valuable analogy becomes the physical reality of the experiment.

The experiment is also related to some practical problems, where fluid mechanics and dynamical systems theory meet. Raindrops are formed by collisions of microscopic water droplets in clouds, and the planets are thought to have been formed by collisions of interstellar dust particles surrounding the Sun in the early stages of its development. The question of whether these small droplets or particles can cluster onto fractal sets, such as those of Figure 3.14, is important in understanding the rate of collisions between particles.

3.3   Linear maps in two dimensions

The simplest type of two-dimensional map is a **linear map**. As well as it being of interest in its own right, it is important to analyse this special case for two reasons. First, when we study the separation of nearby trajectories of a general map in the next section, we will find that this is described by a linear map. Second, the examples of nonlinear maps which will be studied in detail in Section 4.3 of *Unit 4* are piecewise-linear, that is, linear maps which have discontinuities along lines in phase space.

A linear map in two dimensions is defined by a 2×2 matrix $\mathbf{A}$ acting on a vector $\mathbf{x} = (x_1, x_2)$,

$$\mathbf{x}' = \mathbf{A}\mathbf{x}, \tag{3.7}$$

or, explicitly in terms of the elements A_{ij} of $\mathbf{A}$,

$$\begin{aligned} x_1' &= A_{11}x_1 + A_{12}x_2, \\ x_2' &= A_{21}x_1 + A_{22}x_2. \end{aligned} \tag{3.8}$$

This linear map will act differently depending upon the direction of $\mathbf{x}$. It is instructive to consider how a linear map $\mathbf{x}' = \mathbf{A}\mathbf{x}$ transforms a small *region* of $\mathbf{x}$-space into a small region of $\mathbf{x}'$-space, as this gives a clearer understanding than just considering the map of points one at a time. By way of example, consider the images of both square and circular regions under a linear map. Mapping each point along a line produces another set of points forming a line, and because the map is linear, straight lines are mapped into straight lines, so squares are mapped into parallelograms. Also, circles are mapped into ellipses; see Figure 3.15.

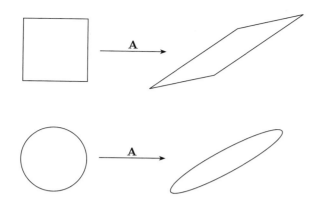

Figure 3.15   Application of a linear map to a circle and a square

Concerning the justification for these statements, it is easy to see that a square is mapped to a parallelogram. A linear transformation maps straight lines into straight lines. A linear transformation maps a pair of parallel lines to another pair of parallel lines. Because the transformation is continuous, a closed curve (the square) is mapped to another closed curve. Since we have seen that this image curve has parallel sides, it must be a parallelogram.

There are three interconnected approaches to understanding linear maps. We give a brief indication of their relationship before describing them in detail.

1. We can define three elementary linear transformations: **rotation**, **stretch** and **shear**. A general linear transformation can be written as a sequence (more technically, a composition) of these operations.

2. A linear transformation **A** can usually be reduced to a matrix in **diagonal form**, constructed from the **eigenvectors** and **eigenvalues** of the matrix **A**. This representation can be very convenient if we want to consider the effect of repeatedly applying the same transformation n times (where n is an integer), that is, the effect of $\mathbf{A}^n$. Using this representation, it is seen that the transformation $\mathbf{A}^n$ is closely related to applying an elementary 'stretching' operation n times.

3. Reduction to diagonal form is only really useful when the eigenvalues of **A** are real, because otherwise the 'stretching' operation involves complex numbers. In other cases, a more general reduction to *normal form* is useful: for example, when the eigenvalues are complex, the effect of $\mathbf{A}^n$ is closely related to applying a rotation operation n times.

3.3.1   Elementary linear transformations

We define three elementary types of linear transformation in two dimensions, described by simple 2×2 matrices **A**:

rotation $\mathbf{A}_{\mathrm{rot}}(\theta) = \begin{pmatrix} \cos\theta & \sin\theta \\ -\sin\theta & \cos\theta \end{pmatrix},$ (3.9)

stretch $\mathbf{A}_{\mathrm{str}}(\lambda_1, \lambda_2) = \begin{pmatrix} \lambda_1 & 0 \\ 0 & \lambda_2 \end{pmatrix},$ (3.10)

shear $\mathbf{A}_{\mathrm{sh}}(\tau) = \begin{pmatrix} 1 & \tau \\ 0 & 1 \end{pmatrix}.$ (3.11)

The effects of these elementary operations on a unit square are illustrated in Figure 3.16 (overleaf).

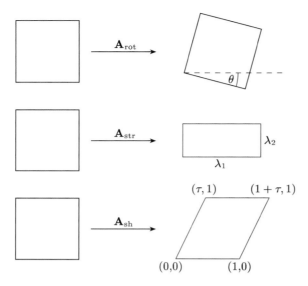

Figure 3.16 Application of three elementary linear transformations to a square

The matrix $\mathbf{A}_{\text{rot}}$ rotates objects clockwise about the origin by an angle θ. The matrix $\mathbf{A}_{\text{str}}$ stretches an object by a factor λ_1 in the x-direction and by a factor λ_2 in the y-direction. The shearing operation described by the matrix $\mathbf{A}_{\text{sh}}$ is less familiar. Points are shifted in the x-direction by an amount which is proportional to their y-coordinate. A physical example of a shearing operation is found in situations where oil lubricates two flat surfaces which have to slide over each other. The oil stays in contact with the surfaces that it touches. If the lower surface stays fixed, and the upper surface moves to the right, the motion of the oil trapped in between is a shearing motion, of the type described by the matrix $\mathbf{A}_{\text{sh}}$.

The rotation and the shear both map the square into a figure with the same area: they are therefore described as **area-preserving** linear transformations. The stretch is area-preserving only in the special case where $\lambda_1 \lambda_2 = 1$.

A general linear map in two dimensions is specified by the four elements of a 2×2 matrix. Note that the three elementary operations described in equations (3.9), (3.10) and (3.11) contain four numbers: a rotation angle θ, two stretching factors λ_1, λ_2, and a shearing parameter τ. This suggests that a general linear transformation $\mathbf{A}$ can be constructed by successive application of the three elementary operations, so that we may write

$$\mathbf{A} = \mathbf{A}_{\text{rot}}(\theta)\,\mathbf{A}_{\text{str}}(\lambda_1, \lambda_2)\,\mathbf{A}_{\text{sh}}(\tau). \tag{3.12}$$

In fact, a general linear transformation of a square, such as that in Figure 3.15, can be effected by applying first a shear, then a stretch and finally a rotation. There is nothing special about the order in which these operations are applied; for example, we could apply the stretch, then the rotation and finally the shear. But if the order is changed, different choices of the parameters λ_1, λ_2, θ, τ are required to produce the same transformation.

Exercise 3.8

Draw the image of the unit square with corners $(0,0)$, $(0,1)$, $(1,1)$ and $(1,0)$ under the linear transformations described by the following two matrices:

$$\mathbf{A} = \begin{pmatrix} 3 & 4 \\ 2 & 1 \end{pmatrix}, \quad \mathbf{A} = \begin{pmatrix} 0 & 2 \\ -2 & 0 \end{pmatrix}.$$

Exercise 3.9

(a) Draw the images of a square (use the same square as in Exercise 3.8) under the following sequence of operations: stretch with $\lambda_1 = 2$, $\lambda_2 = 1$, followed by shear with $\tau = 1$, followed by rotation by $\theta = \pi/4$.

(b) Calculate the product $\mathbf{A} = \mathbf{A}_{\mathrm{rot}}(\pi/4)\,\mathbf{A}_{\mathrm{sh}}(1)\,\mathbf{A}_{\mathrm{str}}(2,1)$.

(c) Calculate the effect of $\mathbf{A}$ on the unit square directly, and compare with the result of part (a).

An important property of the elementary transformations above is that their form is preserved under multiplication, as the following exercise shows.

Exercise 3.10

Show that the product of two rotation matrices is also a rotation matrix: $\mathbf{A}_{\mathrm{rot}}(\theta_1)\,\mathbf{A}_{\mathrm{rot}}(\theta_2) = \mathbf{A}_{\mathrm{rot}}(\theta_1 + \theta_2)$.

What are the corresponding relations for the products of stretching and shear matrices?

Exercise 3.11

Draw the effect on a unit square (again, use the same one as in Exercise 3.8) of a rotation by $\pi/4$ followed by a stretch with parameters $\lambda_1 = 3$, $\lambda_2 = \frac{1}{3}$.

Compare this with the effect of applying the stretch before the rotation.

On the basis of your sketches, would you expect that $\mathbf{A}_{\mathrm{str}}(\lambda_1, \lambda_2)\,\mathbf{A}_{\mathrm{rot}}(\theta) = \mathbf{A}_{\mathrm{rot}}(\theta)\,\mathbf{A}_{\mathrm{str}}(\lambda_1, \lambda_2)$ for general values of θ, λ_1 and λ_2? Calculate both of these products to check your guess.

3.3.2 Transformation to diagonal form

It is also useful to describe the action of a linear map by means of the **eigenvalues** λ and **eigenvectors** $\mathbf{u}$ of $\mathbf{A}$, which satisfy

$$\mathbf{A}\mathbf{u} = \lambda\mathbf{u}. \tag{3.13}$$

We see that if $\mathbf{x}$ is aligned with one of the eigenvectors (that is, $\mathbf{x} = a\mathbf{u}$ for some real constant a), then $\mathbf{x}' = \mathbf{A}\mathbf{u}$ is in the same direction as $\mathbf{x}$, multiplied by the scalar factor λ.

Provided that the matrix has distinct eigenvectors (which is usually the case), we can write the matrix $\mathbf{A}$ in the form

$$\mathbf{A} = \mathbf{T}\mathbf{\Lambda}\mathbf{T}^{-1} \tag{3.14}$$

where $\mathbf{\Lambda}$ is a **diagonal matrix**, with diagonal elements equal to the eigenvalues:

$$\mathbf{\Lambda} = \begin{pmatrix} \lambda_1 & 0 \\ 0 & \lambda_2 \end{pmatrix}. \tag{3.15}$$

The matrix $\mathbf{T}$ is constructed from the eigenvectors: the ith column of $\mathbf{T}$ is the eigenvector with eigenvalue λ_i.

More explicitly, let λ_j be an eigenvalue of $\mathbf{A}$, where j is an integer index which labels the eigenvalues (for two-dimensional matrices, j is either 1 or 2). Let $\mathbf{u}_j$ be the eigenvector with eigenvalue λ_j, and let u_{ij} be the ith component of the vector $\mathbf{u}_j$. The elements of the matrix $\mathbf{T}$ are $T_{ij} = u_{ij}$.

The matrix $\mathbf{T}^{-1}$ defines a transformation to a new coordinate system, $\mathbf{y} = \mathbf{T}^{-1}\mathbf{x}$, such that in the new coordinate system the action of the transformation is very simple: it is a stretching, of the type described by Equation (3.10):

$$\mathbf{y}' = \mathbf{\Lambda}\mathbf{y}. \tag{3.16}$$

If the same linear map is applied repeatedly, that is, if we replace $\mathbf{A}$ by $\mathbf{A}^n$, then we see that

$$
\begin{aligned}
\mathbf{A}^n &= \mathbf{T}\mathbf{\Lambda}\mathbf{T}^{-1}\mathbf{T}\mathbf{\Lambda}\cdots\mathbf{T}^{-1}\mathbf{T}\mathbf{\Lambda}\mathbf{T}^{-1} \\
&= \mathbf{T}\mathbf{\Lambda}^n\mathbf{T}^{-1} \\
&= \mathbf{T}\begin{pmatrix} \lambda_1^n & 0 \\ 0 & \lambda_2^n \end{pmatrix}\mathbf{T}^{-1}.
\end{aligned}
\tag{3.17}
$$

Thus, if λ_1 and λ_2 are real, the stretching effect is compounded on multiple application of the transformation.

The eigenvalues may be complex numbers, in which case the eigenvectors also have complex elements. In this case the transformation to diagonal form is less useful, and a more general approach, described in the next subsection, is more transparent.

3.3.3 Transformation to other normal forms

In the case where the eigenvalues are complex, the representation given by equations (3.14) and (3.15) is not very convenient. However, it is always possible to find a transformation matrix $\mathbf{T}$ which reduces the linear map to one of the three elementary real transformations considered in Subsection 3.3.1. We may write

$$\mathbf{A} = \mathbf{T}\mathbf{N}\mathbf{T}^{-1} \tag{3.18}$$

where $\mathbf{N}$ takes one of three **normal forms**, depending on the eigenvalues of $\mathbf{A}$. There are three cases.

1. If the matrix has two eigenvectors, with real eigenvalues λ_1 and λ_2, then the map is reduced to normal form by diagonalization, as discussed in Subsection 3.3.2, and the action of the map $\mathbf{x} \longmapsto \mathbf{A}\mathbf{x}$ is a stretching transformation in the coordinates $\mathbf{y} = \mathbf{T}^{-1}\mathbf{x}$:

$$\mathbf{N} = \begin{pmatrix} \lambda_1 & 0 \\ 0 & \lambda_2 \end{pmatrix}. \tag{3.19}$$

2. If one of the eigenvalues is complex, then the other must be too, and they must be complex conjugates of each other. We can write them in the polar form $\lambda = \alpha\exp(\pm i\theta)$ (with α real and positive). In this case the normal form is the product of a uniform stretch or **dilation** by a factor α and rotation through an angle θ:

$$\mathbf{N} = \alpha\begin{pmatrix} \cos\theta & \sin\theta \\ -\sin\theta & \cos\theta \end{pmatrix}. \tag{3.20}$$

3. In the special case where there is only one eigenvector of $\mathbf{A}$, the normal form is a shear: $\mathbf{N} = \mathbf{A}_{\mathrm{sh}}(\tau)$, for some value of the shear parameter τ.

Note that the effect of applying the linear transformation **A** repeatedly is very simple to calculate using the normal form: we have

$$\mathbf{A}^n = \mathbf{T}\mathbf{N}^n\mathbf{T}^{-1}, \tag{3.21}$$

and it is very easy to calculate $\mathbf{N}^n$, as indicated by the results of Exercise 3.10.

3.3.4 Calculating eigenvalues and reductions to normal form

In order to classify a given linear transformation **A**, we first determine its eigenvalues, and classify it as a stretch (real eigenvalues), a rotation/dilation (complex eigenvalues) or a shear (in the special case where there is only one eigenvector). We might then wish to determine the transformation to normal form, **T**.

In this course you will be asked to construct **T** only in cases where the eigenvalues are real, so that **T** is constructed from the eigenvectors of **A** as described in Subsection 3.3.2.

We are therefore concerned with calculating eigenvalues and eigenvectors of matrices. You have already seen that Maple can do this automatically. It is useful to know some formulae that help to determine eigenvalues by hand calculation.

We use two facts about the eigenvalues of a matrix. First, the **trace** t of a matrix (that is, the sum of its diagonal elements) is equal to the sum of its eigenvalues: for a 2×2 matrix **A** with elements A_{ij}, we have

$$t = \operatorname{tr} \mathbf{A} = A_{11} + A_{22} = \lambda_1 + \lambda_2. \tag{3.22}$$

Second, we use the fact that the **determinant** d is the product of the eigenvalues: for a 2×2 matrix **A**,

$$d = \det \mathbf{A} = A_{11}A_{22} - A_{12}A_{21} = \lambda_1\lambda_2. \tag{3.23}$$

Now, using Equation (3.22) we have $\lambda_2 = t - \lambda_1$, then using Equation (3.23) we find that λ_1 satisfies a quadratic equation of the form $\lambda_1^2 - t\lambda_1 + d = 0$, which is known as the **characteristic equation**. The eigenvalues are given by the solutions of this quadratic equation:

$$\lambda = \frac{t}{2} \pm \frac{1}{2}\sqrt{t^2 - 4d}. \tag{3.24}$$

Note that this equation works only for 2×2 matrices, where it gives both eigenvalues, by choosing different signs.

Exercise 3.12

Determine the eigenvalues of the matrix

$$\mathbf{A} = \begin{pmatrix} 4 & -1 \\ 5 & 1 \end{pmatrix},$$

and classify its normal form as a stretch, a rotation/dilation or a shear. If the normal form is a rotation/dilation or a shear, determine the values of the parameters α, θ or τ.

Exercise 3.13

Calculate the eigenvalues and eigenvectors of the matrix

$$\mathbf{A} = \begin{pmatrix} -1 & -4 \\ 2 & 5 \end{pmatrix},$$

and hence represent $\mathbf{A}$ in the form of Equation (3.14). Do the calculation by hand, and use Maple to check the result.

Exercise 3.14

Calculate $\mathbf{A}^{100}$ for the matrix in the previous exercise (without using Maple).

Exercise 3.15

For area-preserving maps, the determinant of the Jacobian matrix is $\det(\mathbf{J}) = \pm 1$ (see Subsection 3.1.2; a full discussion will be given in Subsection 3.5.1). It follows that for a linear area-preserving map we have $d = \pm 1$.

Consider the case where $d = 1$, so that the eigenvalues are determined from the trace t of the matrix. Show that if $|t| < 2$, then the normal form is a rotation with $\alpha = 1$, and show that the rotation angle satisfies $\cos(\theta) = t/2$. Also show that if $|t| > 2$, then the normal form is a stretch.

3.4 Quantifying instability

The previous section discussed the properties of linear systems. We now consider how to apply these results to general dynamical systems. One very useful approach for understanding the behaviour of dynamical systems is to study what happens to sets of orbits that are started at nearby points. If these orbits separate at an exponential rate (in the sense that the largest Lyapunov exponent, which will be defined shortly for the case of two-dimensional systems, is positive), the orbits are said to be chaotic.

Another motivation for considering the analysis of stability of dynamical systems is that it is one of rather few approaches which can be applied without modification to most dynamical systems.

In *Unit 2* we considered the stability of periodic points and the definition of Lyapunov exponents in one dimension. In this section the corresponding ideas are developed for two-dimensional systems.

In one dimension we analysed the stability of a map by studying the behaviour of two nearby trajectories, a reference trajectory and a slightly displaced test trajectory. Three ideas were introduced in *Unit 2*. We showed that the separation of the trajectories after one application of the map is determined by the derivative of the map. Also, the separation after several applications of the map is determined by a product of derivatives.

(See Subsection 2.2.3, Exercise 2.19 and the discussion in Subsection 2.3.2.) This idea was used to analyse the behaviour of the separation in the vicinity of fixed points and periodic points, leading to the concept of stable and unstable periodic orbits. Then this approach to quantifying the stability of orbits was extended (in Subsection 2.3.2) to a general trajectory by defining the Lyapunov exponent. Here we show how to extend these ideas to two-dimensional systems.

3.4.1 Mapping small displacements

In *Unit 2* we discussed the stability of a trajectory in one-dimensional systems. We compared the motion of a reference trajectory of a map specified by the function $f(x)$ (with starting value x_0) and a nearby trajectory (with starting value $x_0 + \delta x_0$, δx_0 being very small). We found that after one iteration of the map, the separation between $x_1 = f(x_0)$ and $x_1 + \delta x_1 = f(x_0 + \delta x_0)$ is $\delta x_1 = f'(x_0)\,\delta x_0 + \cdots$ (we will ignore terms of higher order in the small quantity δx_0). Let us consider how to extend this to a two-dimensional map, written in the form $\mathbf{x}' = \mathbf{f}(\mathbf{x})$ or in component form as

$$\begin{pmatrix} x_1' \\ x_2' \end{pmatrix} = \begin{pmatrix} f_1(x_1, x_2) \\ f_2(x_1, x_2) \end{pmatrix}. \tag{3.25}$$

We consider the difference between a reference trajectory which reaches $\mathbf{x}_n$ after n applications of the map, and a nearby trajectory starting at $\mathbf{x}_n + \delta\mathbf{x}_n$ (see Figure 3.17).

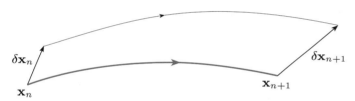

Figure 3.17   We consider a trajectory displaced by a small displacement $\delta\mathbf{x}_n$ from a point $\mathbf{x}_n$ on a reference trajectory. After one application of the map, the reference trajectory reaches $\mathbf{x}_{n+1}$ and the displacement is $\delta\mathbf{x}_{n+1}$.

Taylor expanding about $\mathbf{x}$, we have

$$\begin{aligned}
x_1' + \delta x_1' &= f_1(\mathbf{x}) + \frac{\partial f_1}{\partial x_1}(\mathbf{x})\,\delta x_1 + \frac{\partial f_1}{\partial x_2}(\mathbf{x})\,\delta x_2 + \cdots, \\
x_2' + \delta x_2' &= f_2(\mathbf{x}) + \frac{\partial f_2}{\partial x_1}(\mathbf{x})\,\delta x_1 + \frac{\partial f_2}{\partial x_2}(\mathbf{x})\,\delta x_2 + \cdots.
\end{aligned} \tag{3.26}$$

Thus we see that (ignoring terms of quadratic and higher order in $\delta\mathbf{x}$, which are assumed to be negligible when $|\delta\mathbf{x}|$ is sufficiently small) the small displacement from the reference trajectory is given by a linear transformation

$$\delta\mathbf{x}' = \mathbf{J}\,\delta\mathbf{x}, \tag{3.27}$$

where the Jacobian matrix $\mathbf{J}$ is given by

$$\mathbf{J}(\mathbf{x}) = \begin{pmatrix} \dfrac{\partial f_1}{\partial x_1} & \dfrac{\partial f_1}{\partial x_2} \\[2mm] \dfrac{\partial f_2}{\partial x_1} & \dfrac{\partial f_2}{\partial x_2} \end{pmatrix}, \tag{3.28}$$

and the partial derivatives are all evaluated at $\mathbf{x}$. Equation (3.27) is analogous to the one-dimensional case, where the stability of an orbit of the map $x_{n+1} = f(x_n)$ is determined by the derivative $f'(x)$ (see *Unit 2*, Subsections 2.2.3, 2.3.1 and 2.3.2).

Exercise 3.16

For the Hénon map with $a = 1$ and $b = \frac{1}{2}$, calculate the matrix $\mathbf{J}$ at positions $\mathbf{x}_0 = (0,0)$ and $\mathbf{x}_1 = (1,0)$.

In the case where $\mathbf{x} = (0.01, 0.01)$, calculate the action of this Hénon map on $\mathbf{x}$ directly from the definition (Equation (3.3)), and compare the result with that obtained using Equation (3.27), where $\delta\mathbf{x}$ is the small displacement from $\mathbf{x}_0$. Repeat this calculation for $\mathbf{x} = (1.005, 0.01)$, where this time the small displacement is relative to $\mathbf{x}_1$.

Consider what happens in the case where the map is applied several times. The displacement of the test trajectory from the reference trajectory, which starts at $\mathbf{x}_0$, is initially $\delta\mathbf{x}_0$. After one application of the map, the displacement is (approximately) $\delta\mathbf{x}_1 = \mathbf{J}(\mathbf{x}_0)\,\delta\mathbf{x}_0$, and the reference trajectory is at $\mathbf{x}_1 = \mathbf{f}(\mathbf{x}_0)$. Applying Equation (3.27) to the next application of the map, the displacement is $\delta\mathbf{x}_2 = \mathbf{J}(\mathbf{x}_1)\,\delta\mathbf{x}_1$. Using our expression for $\delta\mathbf{x}_1$, we find $\delta\mathbf{x}_2 = \mathbf{J}(\mathbf{x}_1)\,\mathbf{J}(\mathbf{x}_0)\,\delta\mathbf{x}_0$. If the map is applied n times, we have

$$\delta\mathbf{x}_n = \mathbf{J}_n(\mathbf{x}_0)\,\delta\mathbf{x}_0, \tag{3.29}$$

where the 2×2 matrix $\mathbf{J}_n$ is the product of matrices $\mathbf{J}$ at each application of the map:

$$\mathbf{J}_n(\mathbf{x}_0) = \mathbf{J}(\mathbf{x}_{n-1})\,\mathbf{J}(\mathbf{x}_{n-2})\cdots\mathbf{J}(\mathbf{x}_1)\,\mathbf{J}(\mathbf{x}_0). \tag{3.30}$$

Exercise 3.17

For the Hénon map with $a = 1$, $b = \frac{1}{2}$ and initial point $\mathbf{x}_0 = (0,0)$, calculate $\mathbf{J}(\mathbf{x}_0)$, $\mathbf{x}_1$ and $\mathbf{J}(\mathbf{x}_1)$. Hence calculate $\mathbf{J}_2(\mathbf{x}_0) = \mathbf{J}(\mathbf{x}_1)\,\mathbf{J}(\mathbf{x}_0)$. Use this to estimate the result of applying this Hénon map twice with initial value $(0.01, 0.01)$. Compare this with the analogous result in Exercise 3.16.

3.4.2   Fixed points of two-dimensional maps

In *Units 1* and *2* we considered fixed points of one-dimensional maps and flows, and also fixed points of two-dimensional flows (*Unit 1*, Subsection 1.4.2). We are now in a position to consider the remaining type of fixed point for one- or two-dimensional systems, namely fixed points of two-dimensional maps.

By analogy with the one-dimensional case, a fixed point of a map $\mathbf{x} \longmapsto \mathbf{x}' = \mathbf{f}(\mathbf{x})$ is defined as a point $\mathbf{x}^*$ such that $\mathbf{f}(\mathbf{x}^*) = \mathbf{x}^*$.

To describe the stability of the fixed point, we consider a nearby point $\mathbf{x} = \mathbf{x}^* + \delta\mathbf{x}$. The small separation $\delta\mathbf{x}$ is mapped linearly:

$$\delta\mathbf{x}' = \mathbf{J}(\mathbf{x}^*)\,\delta\mathbf{x}. \tag{3.31}$$

We will refer to the Jacobian matrix evaluated at the fixed point, $\mathbf{J}(\mathbf{x}^*)$, as the **stability matrix** of the fixed point.

Fixed points of general two-dimensional systems

The stability of the fixed points of maps can be classified in a similar way to the fixed points of two-dimensional flows, as considered in *Unit 1*, Subsection 1.4.2, but there are a few points of difference. Here we discuss the classification in terms of the normal form $\mathbf{N}$ of $\mathbf{J(x)}$: this is slightly easier because it avoids considering complex eigenvalues.

Given the 2×2 stability matrix $\mathbf{J}$ of a fixed point, we determine its reduction to normal form, $\mathbf{N} = \mathbf{T}^{-1}\mathbf{JT}$. There are then various cases, depending upon whether the normal form is a stretch, a rotation or a shear.

1. **Stretch**   If the normal form is a stretch, then it is described by specifying the real eigenvalues λ_1 and λ_2. In the following discussion we assume that $|\lambda_1| > |\lambda_2|$. If $|\lambda_2| > 1$, then every point (except the fixed point itself) is mapped away from the fixed point, which is a **repeller**. If $|\lambda_1| > 1$ but $|\lambda_2| < 1$, the fixed point is a **saddle**. If both $|\lambda_1| < 1$ and (consequently) $|\lambda_2| < 1$, then the fixed point is an **attractor**.

   There are various special cases, which are not typical because they require a 'coincidence' where two numbers happen to be equal. If the eigenvalues are equal, the direction of $\delta\mathbf{x}_n$ does not change, and the fixed point can be classified as a repelling or attracting **star** (for $|\lambda_1| > 1$ or $|\lambda_1| < 1$, respectively). Another special case is where the eigenvalues are equal in magnitude but opposite in sign. The classification of these special cases will not be considered in detail.

2. **Rotation**   If the normal form is a rotation, there are two parameters, the rotation angle θ and the dilation factor α (see Equation (3.20)). Here there are just two typical cases: if $\alpha < 1$ the fixed point is an **attracting spiral**, and if $\alpha > 1$ it is a **repelling spiral**.

   The special case $\alpha = 1$ is unusual for maps that are not area-preserving. For area-preserving maps, however, we must have $\alpha = 1$ if the fixed point has a normal form which is a rotation (see Exercise 3.15). These are referred to as **stable fixed points** of area-preserving maps.

3. **Shear**   For a typical dynamical system, you would be most unlikely to encounter a fixed point for which the normal form is a shear, because you have to 'tune' a parameter to produce a matrix which has only one eigenvector. This special case will not be discussed further.

Exercise 3.18

Show that the fixed points of the Hénon map must lie on the line $x = y$, and that the position of a fixed point must satisfy the equation $x = a - x^2 + bx$. Determine the positions of the fixed points.

For $b = 1$, determine the stability properties of the fixed points.

Fixed points of area-preserving maps

Consider the special case of a fixed point of an area-preserving map, described by a stability matrix $\mathbf{J}$. Because $\det(\mathbf{J}) = \pm 1$, the properties of the normal form are determined solely by the value of $t = \mathrm{tr}(\mathbf{J})$. In the following we consider only the case where $d = +1$.

1. **Unstable fixed points**: $|t| > 2$. Because $d = 1$, the eigenvalues are reciprocals, $\lambda_2 = 1/\lambda_1$, and unstable fixed points must be saddles, also called **hyperbolic fixed points**. Some texts distinguish between hyperbolic fixed points on the basis of the sign of the eigenvalues: if $\lambda_1 < -1$, the fixed point is described as being **hyperbolic with inversion**. This case occurs when $t < -2$.

2. **Stable fixed points**: $|t| < 2$. Because $d = 1$, the complex eigenvalues of $\mathbf{J}$ lie on the unit circle, and the orbit rotates about the fixed point on an ellipse. The parameter α is therefore unity. The eigenvalues may be written $\lambda = \exp(\pm i\theta)$, where θ is the rotation angle, so that the rotation angle is related to $t = \text{tr}(\mathbf{J})$ by the very simple relation $t = 2\cos\theta$, implying that $\theta = \arccos(t/2)$ (compare with the results of Exercise 3.15). The stable fixed points of an area-preserving map are sometimes referred to as **centres**.

3. **Marginally stable fixed points**. These occur when $t = \pm 2$. They are a special case.

Exercise 3.19

Show that the points $(0, 0)$ and $(\pi, 0)$ are fixed points of the standard map (Equation (3.4)) for all values of K. Classify these fixed points according to their stability. Does the nature of these fixed points change as K is varied?

3.4.3 Lyapunov exponents in two dimensions

Unit 2 introduced the Lyapunov exponent h for one-dimensional systems. Roughly speaking, the small separation $\delta x(t)$ for two nearby trajectories varies approximately exponentially as a function of time: $\delta x(t) \simeq \delta x(0) \exp(ht)$. The trajectory is said to be chaotic if $h > 0$.

The concept of the Lyapunov exponent can be extended to two dimensions. In two dimensions, there are two Lyapunov exponents, h_1 and h_2. The first Lyapunov exponent is defined in the same way as for a one-dimensional system: it gives the rate of exponential separation of two nearby orbits. The second Lyapunov exponent is harder to understand. Here we give a geometrical description, which makes connections with practical applications of Lyapunov exponents.

In order to define the two Lyapunov exponents, we consider a reference orbit of a map, which visits points $\mathbf{x}(n)$ (note that here we use a slightly different notation from Subsections 3.4.1 and 3.4.2). We also consider two orbits which are both very close to the reference orbit, separated by small displacements $\delta\mathbf{x}_1(n)$ and $\delta\mathbf{x}_2(n)$. These small separations are shown schematically in Figure 3.18.

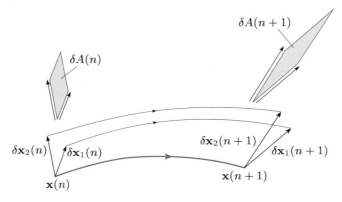

Figure 3.18 In two dimensions, the Lyapunov exponents contain information about the displacements of two trajectories from a reference trajectory. The second Lyapunov exponent contains information about the areas of the parallelograms spanned by the displacements of two trajectories from the reference trajectory.

Let δL_n be the distance between two nearby points after n iterations of the map, and let δA_n be the area of the parallelogram spanned by the separations $\delta \mathbf{x}_1(n)$ and $\delta \mathbf{x}_2(n)$:

$$\delta L_n = |\delta \mathbf{x}_1(n) - \delta \mathbf{x}_2(n)|, \quad \delta A_n = |\delta \mathbf{x}_1(n) \wedge \delta \mathbf{x}_2(n)|. \tag{3.32}$$

The notation $\mathbf{a} \times \mathbf{b}$ is also commonly used for the cross product of vectors $\mathbf{a}$ and $\mathbf{b}$.

(Although the cross product $\mathbf{a} \wedge \mathbf{b}$ is defined only in three dimensions, where $|\mathbf{a} \wedge \mathbf{b}|$ is interpreted as the area of the parallelogram spanned by the vectors $\mathbf{a}$ and $\mathbf{b}$, it is conventional to use a similar notation when working in two dimensions. Thus here we define $\mathbf{a} \wedge \mathbf{b}$ for vectors $\mathbf{a} = (a_1, a_2)$ and $\mathbf{b} = (b_1, b_2)$ to be the scalar quantity $a_1 b_2 - a_2 b_1$.)

We want to define h_1 as the rate of exponential growth of δL_n with n. We could consider writing the definition

$$h_1 = \lim_{n \to \infty} \frac{1}{n} \ln(\delta L_n), \tag{3.33}$$

but this would be unsatisfactory. A problem arises if h_1 is positive, because then eventually (for sufficiently large values of n) the separation of two nearby orbits ceases to be small. We therefore use a definition based on properties of the stability matrix of the map. The linearized equation describing small separations of two points is of the form $\delta \mathbf{x}(n) = \mathbf{J}_n \, \delta \mathbf{x}(0)$, where the stability matrix for n applications of the map is

$$\mathbf{J}_n = \mathbf{J}(\mathbf{x}_{n-1}) \, \mathbf{J}(\mathbf{x}_{n-2}) \cdots \mathbf{J}(\mathbf{x}_1) \, \mathbf{J}(\mathbf{x}_0). \tag{3.34}$$

We take $\delta \mathbf{x}(0) = \mathbf{e}_1$, where $\mathbf{e}_1$ is a unit vector in an arbitrarily chosen direction. It does not matter that this is not a small quantity, because the equation for $\delta \mathbf{x}(n)$ is linear. We define the **first Lyapunov exponent** in terms of the length of the vector $\delta \mathbf{x}(n) = \mathbf{J}_n \mathbf{e}_1$:

$$h_1 = \lim_{n \to \infty} \frac{1}{n} \ln(|\mathbf{J}_n \mathbf{e}_1|). \tag{3.35}$$

This sequence converges to the same limit for almost all choices of the direction of $\mathbf{e}_1$. We exclude any special choice of $\mathbf{e}_1$ for which the limit does not converge to its typical value.

Note that multiplying $\delta \mathbf{x}(n)$ by a constant number (K, say) does not alter the value of the limit of the sequence in Equation (3.35), because $\ln(K)/n \to 0$ as $n \to \infty$. Also, because we define $\delta \mathbf{x}(n)$ in terms of a linear map, $\delta \mathbf{x}(n) = \mathbf{J}_n \mathbf{e}_1$, the quantity $|\delta \mathbf{x}(n)|$ does not have to remain small.

We want to define the **second Lyapunov exponent** by saying that $h_1 + h_2$ is the rate of exponential growth of the area δA_n, and we could consider defining

$$h_1 + h_2 = \lim_{n \to \infty} \frac{1}{n} \ln \delta A_n. \tag{3.36}$$

Again, this would be unsatisfactory if the separations of trajectories do not remain small, and once again a satisfactory definition can be constructed using the stability matrix of the linearized equation of motion. We take the vectors $\delta \mathbf{x}_1(n)$ and $\delta \mathbf{x}_2(n)$ to be

$$\delta \mathbf{x}_1(n) = \mathbf{J}_n \mathbf{e}_1, \quad \delta \mathbf{x}_2(n) = \mathbf{J}_n \mathbf{e}_2 \tag{3.37}$$

(where $\mathbf{e}_2$ is another unit vector, perpendicular to $\mathbf{e}_1$). With this definition, the area $\delta A_n = |\delta \mathbf{x}_1(n) \wedge \delta \mathbf{x}_2(n)|$ may be written as $\delta A_n = |\det(\mathbf{J}_n)|$ (see Exercise 3.20 below). We may therefore write two equivalent definitions for $h_1 + h_2$:

$$h_1 + h_2 = \lim_{n \to \infty} \frac{1}{n} \ln |(\mathbf{J}_n \mathbf{e}_1) \wedge (\mathbf{J}_n \mathbf{e}_2)|$$

$$= \lim_{n \to \infty} \frac{1}{n} \ln |\det(\mathbf{J}_n)|. \tag{3.38}$$

Note that this equation defines $h_1 + h_2$: you must subtract the value of h_1, obtained via Equation (3.35), in order to obtain h_2. Both of the alternative forms in the right-hand side of Equation (3.38) are useful. The Maple program below uses the first form, whereas $h_1 + h_2$ can sometimes be calculated directly using the second form, as will be illustrated in Exercise 3.22.

Exercise 3.20

If $\delta\mathbf{x}_1 = \mathbf{J}_n\mathbf{e}_1$ and $\delta\mathbf{x}_2 = \mathbf{J}_n\mathbf{e}_2$, show that $\delta A_n = |\delta\mathbf{x}_1 \wedge \delta\mathbf{x}_2|$ is given by the expression $\delta A_n = |\det(\mathbf{J}_n)|$.

You may assume that $\mathbf{e}_1 \wedge \mathbf{e}_2 = -\mathbf{e}_2 \wedge \mathbf{e}_1 = 1$ and $\mathbf{e}_1 \wedge \mathbf{e}_1 = \mathbf{e}_2 \wedge \mathbf{e}_2 = 0$.

For many applications, the combination $h_1 + h_2$ is of more interest than h_2 alone. An example is the 'fractal scum' experiment discussed in Section 3.2. In this experiment, if the area δA_n decreases, then particles on the surface cluster together. Note that decreasing δA_n corresponds to $h_1 + h_2 < 0$, because $\delta A_n = |\det(\mathbf{J}_n)|$. Thus the sign of $h_1 + h_2$ determines whether the dust particles floating on the surface of the liquid cluster together. *Unit 4* will discuss other situations where the value of $h_1 + h_2$ is of more significance than h_2 alone.

The Maple code below can be used to estimate the two Lyapunov exponents of the strange attractor of the Hénon map. The program uses the definitions given by Equation (3.35) and the first version of Equation (3.38), by generating a sequence of vectors $\mathbf{v}_1(n) = \mathbf{J}(\mathbf{x}_{n-1})\,\mathbf{v}_1(n-1)$ and $\mathbf{v}_2(n) = \mathbf{J}(\mathbf{x}_{n-1})\,\mathbf{v}_2(n-1)$, starting from $\mathbf{v}_1(0) = \mathbf{e}_1 = (1,0)$ and $\mathbf{v}_2(0) = \mathbf{e}_2 = (0,1)$. Note that the operation of the program differs slightly from Equations (3.35) and (3.38) in that it repeatedly multiplies the vectors $\mathbf{v}_1, \mathbf{v}_2$ by $\mathbf{J}(\mathbf{x}_{n-1})$, rather than calculating the matrix product $\mathbf{J}_n$ (this is logically equivalent, but much more efficient because only two matrix multiplications are required at each step).

There is one further feature of this program which requires some explanation. After each application of the matrix $\mathbf{J}(\mathbf{x}_{n-1})$ to produce the vectors $\mathbf{v}_1(n)$ and $\mathbf{v}_2(n)$, a multiple of $\mathbf{v}_1(n)$ is added to $\mathbf{v}_2(n)$ to produce a vector which is orthogonal (at right angles) to $\mathbf{v}_1(n)$. If the arithmetic were carried out with perfect precision, this would make no difference to the value of the vector cross product in Equation (3.38). In practice this refinement does improve the accuracy, because otherwise the area is obtained by subtracting two very similar large numbers to give a small result.

```
>   restart:                              # Initializations
>   Digits := 20:                  # Note use of high precision
>   n := 1000:                         # Number of iterations
>   a := 1.2:  b := 0.4:            # Parameters of Henon map
>   x := 0.0:  y := 0.0:               # Initial conditions
>   v1 := <1.0,0.0>:  v2 := <0.0,1.0>:
>   J := <<0.0|b>,<1.0|0.0>>:          # Jacobian matrix
>   for i from 1 to n do               # Loop iterates map
>     xnew := a-x^2+b*y:  ynew := x:
>     x := xnew:  y := ynew:
```

```
>    J[1,1] := -2.0*x:          # Update Jacobian matrix
>    v1 := J.v1:                 # Update vectors by
>    v2 := J.v2:                 # matrix multiplication
>    p1 := v1.v1:              # The next three lines make
>    p2 := v1.v2:              # v2 orthogonal to v1
>    v2 := v2-(p2/p1)*v1:
>    d := sqrt(p1):              # Length of v1
>    s := abs(v1[1]*v2[2]-v1[2]*v2[1]):   # Area, v1 x v2
>    h1 := evalf(log(d)/i):       # Latest estimates of
>    `h1+h2` := evalf(log(s)/i):   # h1 and h1+h2
>    print(h1,`h1+h2`):
> end do:
> 'h[1]' = evalf[3](h1), 'h[2]' = evalf[3](`h1+h2`-h1);
```

This program prints out a sequence of numbers which are successive approximations to h_1 and $h_1 + h_2$, before finally printing the best estimates for h_1 and h_2 to three significant figures.

Exercise 3.21

Run the program above to determine approximate values of the Lyapunov exponents of the Hénon map. Notice that the values of $h_1 + h_2$ printed out after successive iterations do not fluctuate except in the last decimal place.

Exercise 3.22

Calculate the determinant $\det(\mathbf{J})$ for the Hénon map. Relate this to the value of $h_1 + h_2$ which is output by the Maple program above.

3.4.4 Chaos and strange attractors

Earlier, in *Unit 2*, we defined the criterion for chaotic behaviour of a one-dimensional system in terms of the Lyapunov exponent h. A trajectory is said to be chaotic if $h > 0$ and the motion is bounded.

Similarly, in two dimensions we define a trajectory to be chaotic if $h_1 > 0$ (where h_1 is the largest Lyapunov exponent). We have seen that two-dimensional systems can have trajectories which approach a structure which is called a 'strange attractor', but as yet we have not given a quantitative definition of this term. A definition will now be given in terms of the Lyapunov exponents h_1 and h_2. In order for an orbit to be attracting, we must require that points in phase space representing nearby orbits are drawn together so that their density increases. This is equivalent to saying that if we consider a set of points occupying a small area δA_n at the nth iteration of the map, then $\delta A_n \to 0$ as $n \to \infty$. Thus an orbit is considered to be an attractor if $h_1 + h_2 < 0$. The attractor is a strange attractor if $h_1 > 0$, so that the region is drawn out into a lengthening line as its area contracts. To summarize, we have the following.

1. An orbit is **chaotic** if $h_1 > 0$.
2. An orbit is an **attractor** if $h_1 + h_2 < 0$.
3. An orbit is a **strange attractor** if $h_1 + h_2 < 0$ but $h_1 > 0$. Note that strange attractors are (because of point 1 above) chaotic.

3.5 Area-preserving dynamics

We have already seen evidence that area-preserving maps have distinctive properties. The definitions of area-preserving dynamics are discussed in Subsection 3.5.1. Area-preserving flows arise in two physically important contexts, discussed in Subsections 3.5.2 and 3.5.6. We show that an autonomous area-preserving flow in two dimensions has a constant of motion, which implies that the flow explores lines in the two-dimensional phase space. In Subsection 3.5.3 we show how these lines, called *phase curves* or *phase trajectories*, provide useful information about the motion of the system.

In the case of area-preserving maps, discussed in Subsection 3.5.5, the situation is more complex, as we saw in our numerical investigation of the standard map.

3.5.1 Criteria for area-preserving dynamics

A flow in two dimensions is area-preserving if the area of any region remains unchanged as its constituent points move under the action of the dynamics. First we consider the criteria for maps and flows to be area-preserving, before discussing the physical contexts in which area-preserving flows arise. We have already mentioned the condition for a two-dimensional map to be area-preserving, in Subsection 3.1.2. We give a derivation below, before considering area-preserving flows.

Condition for an area-preserving map

Consider first the case of a map $\mathbf{x} \longmapsto \mathbf{x}' = \mathbf{f}(\mathbf{x})$. If a set consisting of points $\mathbf{x}$ has area A, then in general the set of points $\mathbf{x}' = \mathbf{f}(\mathbf{x})$ will have a different area, A'. We require that $A' = A$, for any set of points. To see how that condition can be imposed, we break an area up into very small squares of length ε (and area ε^2), and consider the area of the image of each square under the action of the map. By taking the limit as $\varepsilon \to 0$ we can approximate any area as a set of squares. If the map is differentiable, then in the vicinity of $\mathbf{x}$, small displacements are mapped linearly (as discussed in Subsection 3.4.1):

$$\delta\mathbf{x}' = \mathbf{J}(\mathbf{x})\,\delta\mathbf{x}, \tag{3.39}$$

where $\mathbf{J}(\mathbf{x})$ is the Jacobian matrix. The image of a small square under a linear map is a small parallelogram. If two edges of the square are represented by vectors $\delta\mathbf{x}_1 = \varepsilon\mathbf{e}_1$ and $\delta\mathbf{x}_2 = \varepsilon\mathbf{e}_2$ (where $\mathbf{e}_1$ and $\mathbf{e}_2$ are orthogonal unit vectors), these edges are mapped to the vectors

$$\begin{aligned}
\delta\mathbf{x}_1' &= \varepsilon(J_{11}\mathbf{e}_1 + J_{21}\mathbf{e}_2), \\
\delta\mathbf{x}_2' &= \varepsilon(J_{12}\mathbf{e}_1 + J_{22}\mathbf{e}_2).
\end{aligned} \tag{3.40}$$

The area $\delta A'$ of the parallelogram is the magnitude of the cross product:

$$\begin{aligned}
\delta A' &= |\delta\mathbf{x}_1' \wedge \delta\mathbf{x}_2'| \\
&= \varepsilon^2 |J_{11}J_{22} - J_{12}J_{21}| \\
&= \varepsilon^2 |\det(\mathbf{J})| \\
&= |\det(\mathbf{J})|\,\delta A
\end{aligned} \tag{3.41}$$

(compare Exercise 3.20). The condition for a two-dimensional map to be area-preserving is therefore

$$\det(\mathbf{J}) = \begin{vmatrix} J_{11} & J_{12} \\ J_{21} & J_{22} \end{vmatrix} = \pm 1. \tag{3.42}$$

Thus we can test whether a map is area-preserving by calculating $|\det(\mathbf{J})|$: if this quantity is unity for every point $\mathbf{x}$, then the map is area-preserving. In some cases the map might be defined in terms of discontinuous functions. In such cases we require only that the condition $|\det(\mathbf{J})| = 1$ should hold everywhere except for a set of lines and/or points.

Condition for an area-preserving flow

Having considered the condition for a two-dimensional map to be area-preserving, we now turn to giving the condition for a two-dimensional flow, $\dot{\mathbf{x}} = \mathbf{f}(\mathbf{x})$. The condition for a two-dimensional flow to be area-preserving is given by Equation (3.46) below. We sketch a derivation: you need not follow all of the details of the argument, but you should understand how to apply Equation (3.46).

In the following, $f_1(x_1, x_2)$ and $f_2(x_1, x_2)$ are the components of $\mathbf{f}(\mathbf{x})$, and $\mathbf{x}' = (x_1', x_2')$ is the position reached by the flow after a short time δt. From the Taylor series,

$$\begin{aligned} x_1' = x_1(t + \delta t) &= x_1(t) + \frac{dx_1}{dt}(t)\,\delta t + \cdots \\ &= x_1(t) + f_1(x_1, x_2)\,\delta t + \cdots, \end{aligned} \tag{3.43}$$

and similarly for $x_2' = x_2(t + \delta t)$. For sufficiently small δt, the flow may be approximated by a map:

$$\begin{aligned} x_1' &= x_1 + f_1(x_1, x_2)\,\delta t + \cdots, \\ x_2' &= x_2 + f_2(x_1, x_2)\,\delta t + \cdots. \end{aligned} \tag{3.44}$$

We consider the change in the area after a very short time δt, according to Equation (3.41). We linearize this map, writing $\delta \mathbf{x}' = \mathbf{J}(\mathbf{x})\,\delta \mathbf{x}$. The determinant of the linearized form of this map is determined from its Jacobian matrix $\mathbf{J}(\mathbf{x})$:

$$\begin{aligned} \det(\mathbf{J}) &= \begin{vmatrix} 1 + \frac{\partial f_1}{\partial x_1}\delta t & \frac{\partial f_1}{\partial x_2}\delta t \\ \frac{\partial f_2}{\partial x_1}\delta t & 1 + \frac{\partial f_2}{\partial x_2}\delta t \end{vmatrix} + \cdots \\ &= 1 + \left(\frac{\partial f_1}{\partial x_1} + \frac{\partial f_2}{\partial x_2} \right)\delta t + \cdots, \end{aligned} \tag{3.45}$$

where we have retained only terms up to first order in the small quantity δt. The action of the flow over a fixed time interval requires a large number of applications of the map: the required number is $N \propto 1/\delta t$. The change in the area is determined by the product of all of the N factors of $\det(\mathbf{J})$ for each time step. If $\det(\mathbf{J}) - 1$ is of second order in δt, then the product of all of the N factors of $\det(\mathbf{J})$ is equal to 1 plus an error which is of order $N\,\delta t^2$. This is of first order in δt because $N \propto 1/\delta t$. Taking the limit as $\delta t \to 0$, we then find that the flow is area-preserving. Comparing with Equation (3.45), we find the following condition for $\det(\mathbf{J}) - 1$ to be second order in δt, implying that the two-dimensional flow is area-preserving:

$$\frac{\partial f_1}{\partial x_1} + \frac{\partial f_2}{\partial x_2} = 0. \tag{3.46}$$

This condition can also be written in a vector calculus notation as

$$\boldsymbol{\nabla} \cdot \mathbf{f} = 0, \tag{3.47}$$

where $\boldsymbol{\nabla} \cdot \mathbf{f}$ is the **divergence** of the velocity $\mathbf{f}$. Those readers who have studied fluid mechanics will recognize the equation $\boldsymbol{\nabla} \cdot \mathbf{v} = 0$ as the condition for incompressible flow in a homogeneous fluid with velocity $\mathbf{v}$.

Exercise 3.23

Consider a differentiable function $\psi(x, y)$ and *define* a two-dimensional vector field (which is sometimes called the 'curl' of ψ) as

$$\mathbf{f} = \left(\frac{\partial \psi}{\partial y}, -\frac{\partial \psi}{\partial x} \right).$$

(For those readers who are familiar with vector calculus, this is the same as the curl of the vector field $\psi \mathbf{e}_3$, where $\mathbf{e}_3$ is a unit vector perpendicular to the xy-plane.) Show that this vector field satisfies $\nabla \cdot \mathbf{f} = 0$, and that it therefore generates an area-preserving flow.

Exercise 3.24

Let $\phi(x, y)$ be a twice-differentiable function, and define the vector field $\mathbf{f}$ as the gradient of ϕ, that is, $\mathbf{f} = \nabla \phi = (\partial \phi / \partial x, \partial \phi / \partial y)$. Show that this field generates an area-preserving flow if ϕ satisfies Laplace's equation:

$$\frac{\partial^2 \phi}{\partial x^2} + \frac{\partial^2 \phi}{\partial y^2} = 0.$$

3.5.2   Frictionless motion: Hamilton's equations

Consider the motion of a particle in one dimension, where the force $F(x)$ depends upon the position of the particle but not on the velocity $\dot{x}$. Here we consider only *autonomous* systems, in which the force on a particle at position x does not depend upon time. In one dimension this force can be written as the gradient of another function, which is called the **potential** (or **potential energy**), $V(x)$: it is conventional to include a minus sign, and to write $F = -dV/dx$. The exclusion of forces which depend upon velocity means that we cannot consider frictional forces. The **Newtonian equation of motion** (mass × acceleration = force) is $m\ddot{x} = -dV/dx$. This second-order equation can be rewritten as two first-order equations: writing the Newtonian equation in terms of the momentum $p = m\dot{x}$, we have

$$\dot{x} = \frac{p}{m}, \quad \dot{p} = -\frac{dV(x)}{dx}. \tag{3.48}$$

These equations can be written in the form

$$\dot{x} = \frac{\partial H}{\partial p}, \quad \dot{p} = -\frac{\partial H}{\partial x}, \tag{3.49}$$

which are called **Hamilton's equations**, where $H(x, p)$ is the **Hamiltonian function**, given by

$$H(x, p) = \frac{p^2}{2m} + V(x). \tag{3.50}$$

Hamilton's equations give the velocity for a flow in the two-dimensional phase space, with coordinates (x, p). We can use Equations (3.49) to show that this flow is area-preserving:

$$\frac{\partial \dot{x}}{\partial x} + \frac{\partial \dot{p}}{\partial p} = \frac{\partial}{\partial x} \left(\frac{\partial H}{\partial p} \right) - \frac{\partial}{\partial p} \left(\frac{\partial H}{\partial x} \right) = 0. \tag{3.51}$$

(This is the same calculation as in Exercise 3.23.) Equations (3.49) have a nearly symmetric form (note the minus in the second equation). They describe the motion of a particle along a line in one dimension with coordinate x, by means of a trajectory in a two-dimensional phase space, with coordinates x (position) and p (momentum).

Equations (3.49) were discovered by William Rowan Hamilton (1805–65). They are an elegant way of rewriting the standard second-order equation of motion $m\ddot{x} = F$ as two first-order equations, but you might ask whether this is more than just an exercise in notational elegance. In fact, there are several reasons why Hamilton's equations are of great importance, but we can do no more than hint at them in this course.

In fact, most advanced texts on mechanics without friction are based upon Hamilton's equations. One reason for this is that there are powerful techniques for treating problems by changing coordinates (from (x, p) to (x', p'), say) which transform the Hamiltonian function, but leave the equations of motion unchanged. (That is, the equations of motion are of the form $\dot{x}' = \partial H/\partial p'$, $\dot{p}' = -\partial H/\partial x'$.) Problems may be solved by transforming into a coordinate system where the Hamiltonian has a very simple form. Another reason for the importance of Hamilton's equations is that they can also occur in problems involving wave motion. As a consequence they give insights into the quantum theory of matter, which is based upon the assumption that the fundamental model for the motion of particles is the Schrödinger equation, which is a type of wave equation.

The Hamiltonian function (3.50) is the sum of the kinetic and potential energies for this system, but in more advanced applications (beyond the scope of this course) the Hamiltonian may not be the sum of a kinetic and a potential energy.

In one dimension, Hamilton's equations of motion can (in principle) be solved to give a trajectory $(x(t), p(t))$ (although in practice one may only be able to find a numerical approximation, and not an exact expression for the solution). Assuming that you have this solution (in the form of functions $x(t)$ and $p(t)$), how would the value of $H(x, p)$ change as you move along the trajectory? Using the chain rule of differentiation and Hamilton's equations of motion, we have

$$\frac{dH}{dt} = \frac{d}{dt}H(x(t), p(t)) = \frac{\partial H}{\partial x}\frac{dx}{dt} + \frac{\partial H}{\partial p}\frac{dp}{dt}$$
$$= \frac{\partial H}{\partial x}\frac{\partial H}{\partial p} - \frac{\partial H}{\partial p}\frac{\partial H}{\partial x} = 0. \tag{3.52}$$

Equation (3.52) then implies that the Hamiltonian function $H(x, p)$ remains equal to a constant, E say, along the trajectory of the particle:

$$H(x(t), p(t)) = E \qquad \text{(for trajectories of autonomous,}$$
$$\text{frictionless systems)}. \tag{3.53}$$

This last equation is just a statement of the law of conservation of the energy E. It shows that the trajectories follow contours of the Hamiltonian function such that $H(x, p)$ remains equal to the initial energy E. This falls short of determining the full solution in the form of the functions $x(t)$ and $p(t)$, but it does give useful information. For example, we know that when the particle is at position x, its momentum is determined by the condition that $H(x, p) = E$. In the cases where the Hamiltonian is of the form $H = p^2/2m + V(x)$, the momentum at position x takes one of two values:

$$p(x) = \pm\sqrt{2m[E - V(x)]}. \tag{3.54}$$

3.5.3   Trajectories of Hamiltonian flow

We have seen that the Hamiltonian equations of motion (3.49) imply that the trajectory of any particle follows a line of constant $H(x, p)$, that is, the trajectory follows a contour line of the function $H(x, p)$. Thus we can gain insight into the motion by plotting contour lines of $H(x, p)$.

The velocity of the point $(x(t), p(t))$ in phase space is $(\partial H/\partial p, -\partial H/\partial x)$ (see Equations (3.49)). This is obtained from the gradient of H, namely $(\partial H/\partial x, \partial H/\partial p)$, by rotating the gradient vector by $\pi/2$, so that it is aligned with a contour of $H(x, p)$. Note that the greater the gradient, the faster the phase point moves.

Exercise 3.25

Show that the velocity vector $\mathbf{f} = (\partial H/\partial p, -\partial H/\partial x)$ is obtained from the gradient of $H(x, p)$ by multiplication by a rotation matrix $\mathbf{A}_{\text{rot}}(\pi/2)$. Show that $|\mathbf{f}| = |\boldsymbol{\nabla} H|$.

These ideas will be illustrated below by considering two familiar physical systems. Before considering these examples, we first recall that Maple can plot contours of a function of two variables (this was discussed in *Unit 2* of Block A). For example, we show below that the Hamiltonian function for a simple pendulum (for certain choices of the mass, and other physical parameters) is $H(x, p) = p^2/2 - \cos(x)$. The contours of this function, which are the phase trajectories of the pendulum, can be generated by using the following code.

```
>   restart:
>   with(plots):
>   h := p^2/2-cos(x):
>   pi := evalf(Pi):
>   p1 := contourplot(h,x=-2*pi..2*pi,p=-4..4,contours=20):
>   p2 := implicitplot(h=1,x=-2*pi..2*pi,p=-4..4,
    grid=[100,100],thickness=2,colour=black):
>   display(p1,p2);
```

Note that implicitplot is used to highlight a special contour, the *separatrix* at $H(x, p) = 1$: the definition and significance of the separatrix will be discussed shortly. This code produces the output shown in Figure 3.19.

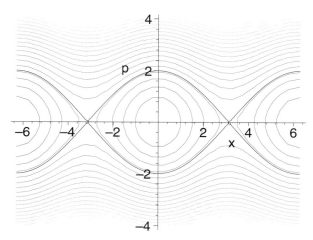

Figure 3.19 Contours of the Hamiltonian for a simple pendulum, $H(x, p) = \frac{1}{2}p^2 - \cos(x)$. The separatrix, which divides open and closed contours, is shown in black.

It is easy to adapt this code to produce contour plots for other choices of the Hamiltonian function.

Exercise 3.26

We show below that the Hamiltonian for a simple harmonic oscillator is $H = p^2/2m + Cx^2/2$, where m is the mass of the particle and C is the spring constant of the restoring force. Plot contours of the Hamiltonian function for $m = C = 1$, and for $m = 1$, $C = 1/4$. What are the forms of the curves?

Exercise 3.27

The potential energy function $V(x) = x^4 - 2x^2$ has two minima, of equal depth (in physics texts it is often referred to as a 'double-well potential'). Plot the contours of the corresponding Hamiltonian function, for a particle with $m = 1$.

In all of the examples that we have considered so far, the Hamiltonian function is of the form $H(x, p) = p^2/2m + V(x)$. A Hamiltonian of this form can have minima and saddle points, but never maxima. In advanced treatments of physics problems, other types of Hamiltonian function may appear; the following exercise considers one example.

Exercise 3.28

Write Maple code to plot the contours of the Hamiltonian function

$$H(x, p) = \cos(\sqrt{3}p/2 + x/2) + \cos(\sqrt{3}p/2 - x/2) + \cos(x).$$

(This Hamiltonian occurs in the analysis of the effect of a magnetic field on the motion of electrons in metals.) Note that this function has both maxima and minima. In which direction (clockwise or anticlockwise) do the phase trajectories circulate about minima and maxima?

Simple harmonic motion

An example of a **simple harmonic oscillator** is provided by a particle moving on a straight line, with displacement x. The mass of the particle is m, and it is attached to an immovable object by a spring of stiffness C. The kinetic energy is $m\dot{x}^2/2 = p^2/2m$, where $p = m\dot{x}$ is the momentum. The potential energy is $V = Cx^2/2$. The Hamiltonian is therefore

$$H(x, p) = \frac{p^2}{2m} + \frac{Cx^2}{2}. \tag{3.55}$$

The contours of the Hamiltonian function are therefore ellipses, as illustrated by working through Exercise 3.26.

Exercise 3.29

Consider a Hamiltonian function of the form $H(x,p) = (x^2 + p^2)^{\alpha/2}$, where $\alpha > 0$ is a constant. What is the form of the phase trajectories?

Show that the speed of the phase trajectory around a contour at energy $H(x,p) = E$ is constant. Calculate this speed, as a function of the energy E. What is the period of the orbit?

Explain how your answer agrees with standard results on the period of the harmonic oscillator when $\alpha = 2$.

The simple pendulum

The **simple pendulum** consists of a mass m attached to one end of a light rigid rod of length L, which has its other end free to rotate about a horizontal axis. (This system was also considered in *Unit 1*, Section 1.2, where we used θ for the angle.)

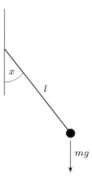

Figure 3.20   Simple pendulum

If the angle of the rod from the vertically downward position is x, then the kinetic energy is $ml^2\dot{x}^2/2$, and the potential energy is $V = -mgl\cos x$. The momentum is $p = ml\dot{x}$, and the Hamiltonian of this system is therefore

$$H(x,p) = \frac{p^2}{2m} - mgl\cos x. \tag{3.56}$$

Note that we specified a rod, rather than a string, so that we may consider situations where $|x| > \pi/2$, without the complication of a string becoming slack. The contours of this Hamiltonian function, satisfying $H(x,p) = E$ (where E is a constant, equal to the energy of the particle) were plotted in Figure 3.19 (for $m = l = g = 1$). Notice that in this case there are two different types of contour. For small values of the energy E, the contours are closed curves. This corresponds to an **oscillatory motion** of the particle, in which the pendulum swings back and forth between angles $\pm x_{\max}$ as the phase trajectory circulates about the contour. For sufficiently large energies, $E > 2mgl$, the particle still has kinetic energy when the rod is vertical (at $x = \pi$), and the pendulum rotates. When $E > 2mgl$, the particle always rotates in the same direction for a given choice of initial conditions: contours with $p > 0$ correspond to rotation with x always increasing, and for the open contours with $p < 0$, the angle is decreasing. The special contour which separates these different types of contour is called the **separatrix**.

Some general properties of Hamiltonian flows

We have seen that particle trajectories for autonomous area-preserving flows can be analysed by considering the contours of the Hamiltonian function $H(x, p)$: the phase trajectories are contours of the Hamiltonian. Now we discuss some general points concerning this relationship.

1. If $H(x, p)$ has maxima or minima, there will be phase trajectories which are closed curves. The motion on such a trajectory is a periodic oscillation. Typically, the period T will depend upon the energy, and $x(t)$ will not be sinusoidal. The maxima and minima are stable fixed points of the flow. The phase trajectories surrounding minima of $H(x, p)$ rotate clockwise.

2. As well as having maxima and minima, the Hamiltonian may have saddles, which are unstable fixed points of the flow.

3. The contours passing through saddles are called separatrices. They usually divide regions where the phase trajectories have different topologies. For example, they may separate closed phase trajectories (such as oscillatory motion of the pendulum) from open phase trajectories (such as the rotational motion of the pendulum).

3.5.4   The period of one-dimensional Hamiltonian flow

In the case where the phase trajectories are closed curves, the motion is periodic with some period T. Next we derive a simple formula which can be used to determine the period of motion on a closed phase trajectory at energy E. This formula gives the period in terms of the area of the closed trajectory. It gives a taste of the elegant geometrical ideas which make the use of Hamilton's equations so powerful for advanced treatments of frictionless mechanics. We will show that if a contour $H(x, p) = E$ encloses an area $A(E)$, then the period of motion around this contour is

$$T(E) = \frac{dA}{dE}. \tag{3.57}$$

To derive this relation, consider two closed contours, one defined by $H(x, p) = E$ and another nearby contour defined by $H(x, p) = E + \delta E$ (with δE small). Let the distance from a reference point on the contour at energy E be s, and let the width of the region between the two contours at position s be $w(s)$ (see Figure 3.21).

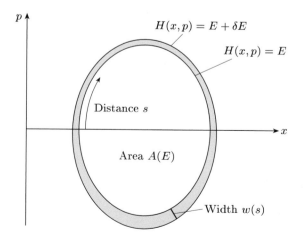

Figure 3.21   Two contours of the Hamiltonian, $H(x, p) = E$ enclosing an area $A(E)$, and $H(x, p) = E + \delta E$ enclosing $A(E + \delta E) = A(E) + \delta A$. The distance along the inner contour is s, and the difference in area is approximated by the integral of $w(s)$ along the length of the contour.

The width $w(s)$ is related to the gradient of the Hamiltonian function:

$$|\boldsymbol{\nabla} H| \, w(s) = \delta E. \tag{3.58}$$

In the solution to Exercise 3.25 it is shown that the speed of the phase point along the contour of the Hamiltonian function is equal to the magnitude of the gradient of the Hamiltonian. Using Equation (3.58), the speed $v(s)$ of the phase point at distance s along the contour therefore satisfies

$$v(s) = \frac{\delta E}{w(s)}. \tag{3.59}$$

The period of motion around the orbit is

$$T = \int_0^L \frac{1}{v(s)} \, ds = \frac{1}{\delta E} \int_0^L w(s) \, ds, \tag{3.60}$$

where L is the length of the contour $H(x, p) = E$. Note that the area between the contours at energies E and $E + \delta E$ is (to leading order in the small quantity δE)

$$\delta A = \int_0^L w(s) \, ds, \tag{3.61}$$

so (comparing with Equation (3.60)) we find

$$T = \frac{\delta A}{\delta E}. \tag{3.62}$$

Taking the limit as $\delta E \to 0$ gives the desired result, Equation (3.57).

Thus we see that there is a very simple method to calculate the period of a periodic trajectory of one-dimensional Hamiltonian flow at energy E: calculate the area $A(E)$ enclosed by the contour of $H(x, p)$ at energy E, then the period is $T = dA/dE$.

Exercise 3.30

Calculate $A(E)$ for the harmonic oscillator of Equation (3.56), and determine the period. Check that the result agrees with the standard formula for the period of a simple harmonic oscillator.

Exercise 3.31

Sketch the phase trajectories for a particle moving in a potential $V = \alpha|x|$. Calculate the area $A(E)$, and hence determine the period T as a function of its energy E.

3.5.5   A comment on area-preserving maps

Thus far in this section we have considered area-preserving *flows*. However, in Subsection 3.1.2 we discussed an area-preserving *map*, the kicked rotor. Its behaviour was far more complicated than the area-preserving flows, and the complexity of pictures such as Figure 3.8 suggests that understanding the properties of typical area-preserving maps would be very difficult. It is far beyond what can be covered in this introductory account.

Some features are common to both area-preserving maps in two dimensions and area-preserving flows of the type considered above. In the case of area-preserving flows, the trajectories are always confined to lines (contours of the Hamiltonian). This suggests that in autonomous area-preserving maps, the trajectories might always be confined to lines (which were called KAM curves in Subsection 3.1.2). These lines would correspond to the existence of a constant of motion, $I(x, y)$, analogous to the Hamiltonian function.

The illustrations in Subsection 3.1.2 show that this expectation is only partially correct. In the case of the standard map, we see that the KAM curves disappear as the value of the parameter K is increased. The KAM curves can be constructed by using **perturbation theory**, an elaborate sequence of successive approximations which converges only for sufficiently small K, and then only if the KAM curve is sufficiently far removed from periodic points of the map. Since periodic points of large period can be shown to occur arbitrarily close to any point in the phase space of the map, the construction of KAM curves is a very subtle problem.

When $K \gg 1$, the evolution of the value of y can be modelled as a *random walk*. This will be discussed in *Unit 3* of Block C, after random walks have been introduced in *Unit 2* of that block.

3.5.6 Flow of incompressible fluids

Besides frictionless motion, there is another, perhaps more obvious, context in which area-preserving flows arise. Liquids are very resistant to being compressed. In a two-dimensional model for the flow of a liquid, the volume (in two dimensions, the area) of any small element remains constant. Such fluid flows are therefore modelled by area-preserving flows or area-preserving maps. It can be useful to keep this idea in mind, because intuition about how a liquid can flow might help to understand the properties of area-preserving dynamics. It is also useful to be aware of limitations of this analogy.

An area-preserving flow can be generated from a function $\psi(x, y)$ as follows:

$$\dot{x} = \frac{\partial \psi}{\partial y}, \quad \dot{y} = -\frac{\partial \psi}{\partial x} \tag{3.63}$$

(this was demonstrated in Exercise 3.23). The function $\psi(x, y)$ is called the **stream function** in texts on fluid mechanics. Equations (3.63) are identical in form to Hamilton's equations (3.49). In two-dimensional fluid flow, the stream function is equivalent to the Hamiltonian function of a frictionless one-dimensional mechanical system. In the previous subsection we also showed that the value of ψ remains constant along a trajectory. Thus, for each element of the fluid, $\psi(x, y)$ remains constant. This means that the contours of $\psi(x, y)$ are the streamlines of the flow.

Many practical fluid-mechanical problems in which the z-component of the fluid velocity is zero are solved by constructing stream functions (with the stream function chosen so that the boundary of the region is a contour line of $\psi(x, y)$). These methods will not be developed here: we simply remark upon this connection because it can be helpful to visualize Hamiltonian flow as a fluid flow.

We end with two remarks on the limitations of this analogy. First, the precise analogy between Hamiltonian motion and incompressible flow does not carry over to fully three-dimensional flows. For example, in more than one dimension, Hamilton's equations take the form

$$\frac{dx_i}{dt} = \frac{\partial H}{\partial p_i}, \quad \frac{dp_i}{dt} = -\frac{\partial H}{\partial x_i}, \quad i = 1, \ldots, N, \tag{3.64}$$

where $H(x_1, \ldots, x_N, p_1, \ldots, p_N)$ is the Hamiltonian function. Thus Hamiltonian dynamics always occurs in a space with an even number of dimensions, because every coordinate x_i is paired with a momentum p_i. It is therefore immediately clear that the motion of an incompressible fluid in three dimensions cannot be a Hamiltonian flow.

A second remark concerns the 'fractal scum' experiment considered in Section 3.2. The flow of the particles on the surface of the fluid is not a Hamiltonian flow. The fluid motion in three dimensions can be treated as incompressible, but motion on the surface is not incompressible because there are regions where fluid is welling up to the surface or else sinking back down. More technically, the equation for an incompressible flow in three dimensions is of the form

$$\boldsymbol{\nabla} \cdot \mathbf{v} = \frac{\partial v_x}{\partial x} + \frac{\partial v_y}{\partial y} + \frac{\partial v_z}{\partial z} = 0. \tag{3.65}$$

Although the fluid velocity at the surface has no vertical component, so that $v_z = 0$ at the surface, there is no reason why $\partial v_z / \partial z$ should be equal to zero at the surface. The divergence of the two-dimensional velocity field is therefore

$$\frac{\partial v_x}{\partial x} + \frac{\partial v_y}{\partial y} = -\frac{\partial v_z}{\partial z}, \tag{3.66}$$

which is typically non-zero. The fractal scum experiment is not, therefore, an illustration of an area-preserving dynamical system.

Learning outcomes

After studying this unit you should be able to:

- appreciate the behaviour of two-dimensional maps as seen in phase portraits, including strange attractors and the distinctive features of area-preserving maps such as invariant (KAM) curves;
- use Maple to investigate the phase portrait of a map;
- understand the classification of two-dimensional linear maps, using diagonalization and normal forms;
- understand the action of elementary linear transformations (rotation, stretch and shear) and their composition;
- determine eigenvalues of 2×2 matrices;
- understand the behaviour of the small separation of two trajectories using a linear approximation (the Jacobian matrix);
- classify properties of the fixed points of a two-dimensional map using their stability matrices;
- understand the Lyapunov exponents of a trajectory of a two-dimensional map, and estimate their values by adapting a Maple program;
- apply the criterion to determine whether a map or flow is area-preserving;
- sketch contours of a Hamiltonian function (using Maple, or otherwise), and relate the contours to trajectories;
- calculate the period of periodic motion of a Hamiltonian system.

Solutions to Exercises

Solution 3.1

You should produce plots which resemble those in Figures 3.2 to 3.4.

You may find that the program becomes very slow as you increase the number of iterations. You can speed it up by testing whether the data points are within the plotting rectangle, and storing only points that lie inside this rectangle.

Solution 3.2

In parts (a) and (b), you were not asked to determine the coordinates of the fixed point or limit cycle, but the information is given here so that you can confirm that you have found the correct points.

(a) This gives convergence to a fixed point at $x = y = 0.542\,686\,044\,2$.

(b) This gives convergence to a period-2 orbit, which alternately visits $(0.761\,803\,401\,0, 0.538\,196\,598\,6)$ and $(0.538\,196\,598\,6, 0.761\,803\,401\,0)$.

(c) This gives a trajectory which escapes to infinity.

(d) Starting at $(0.5, 0)$ converges to the same period-2 orbit as in part (b).

(e) Starting at $(2.4, 2.4)$ gives a trajectory which escapes to infinity.

Solution 3.3

Ignoring points at which the modulus function is discontinuous, the Jacobian matrix is
$$\mathbf{J} = \begin{pmatrix} 1 + K\cos(x) & 1 \\ K\cos(x) & 1 \end{pmatrix}.$$
The determinant of this matrix is
$$\det(\mathbf{J}) = (1 + K\cos(x)) \times 1 - 1 \times K\cos(x) = 1.$$
The standard map is therefore area-preserving.

Solution 3.4

The Jacobian matrix for the Hénon map is
$$\mathbf{J} = \begin{pmatrix} -2x & b \\ 1 & 0 \end{pmatrix},$$
so $\det(\mathbf{J}) = -b$. Thus the Hénon map is area-preserving when $b = \pm 1$, whatever the value of a.

Solution 3.5

The second equation is written in a form where y', the new value of y, appears on the right-hand side. Substituting for $y' = y + f(x)$, the second equation reads $x' = [x + y + f(x)] \bmod (2\pi)$. This is identical to the equations for the standard map when $f(x) = K\sin(x)$. The Jacobian matrix is
$$\mathbf{J} = \begin{pmatrix} 1 + f'(x) & 1 \\ f'(x) & 1 \end{pmatrix},$$
so $\det(\mathbf{J}) = 1$.

Solution 3.6

If you try this exercise you should generate pictures that are similar to Figures 3.9 to 3.12. You can speed up the program by reducing N and M. The pictures in the text are not identical to the ones that you will produce by simply changing the value of K in the Maple program: they used different initial positions. Also note that the figures do not include a picture for $K = 0.0$.

Solution 3.7

The code is modified by changing the initial point and removing the outer loop with index j. (Alternatively, you can set $M = 1$.)

(a) (i) The points lie along a line in (x, y)-space, connecting $x = 0$ to $x = 2\pi$.

(ii) The points are scattered in a finite region, which lies between the lines $y = \pm 2.5$.

(iii) The points eventually spread to very large and very small values of y, but some regions remain empty.

(iv) The points resemble a random scatter, and the trajectory quickly reaches large values of y.

(b) (i) The points are scattered around two curves.

(ii) The points lie close to two curves which connect $x = 0$ to $x = 2\pi$ and which cross each other.

(iii) The points lie on two closed curves which are centred around $x = 0$ and $x = \pi$, respectively (the former curve appears in two pieces, because we break the range of the angle variable at $x = 0$).

Solution 3.8

In each case you should calculate the positions of the corners of the square after applying the map, that is, the points $\mathbf{x}' = \mathbf{A}\mathbf{x}$, for $\mathbf{x} = (0, 0)^T$, $\mathbf{x} = (0, 1)^T$, $\mathbf{x} = (1, 1)^T$ and $\mathbf{x} = (1, 0)^T$.

For the first matrix, the transformed positions of the corners are $(0, 0)$, $(4, 1)$, $(7, 3)$ and $(3, 2)$. Plotting these points and joining them in sequence gives the parallelogram in Figure 3.22.

For the second matrix, the transformed vertices are $(0, 0)$, $(2, 0)$, $(2, -2)$ and $(0, -2)$. Plotting these gives the square in the figure.

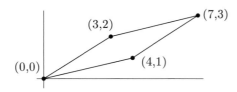

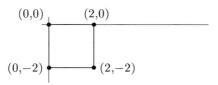

Figure 3.22   Results of applying a linear map to a square

Solution 3.9

(a) By inspection, the stretch, shear and rotation transform the square as shown in the sequence (1)–(4) in Figure 3.23.

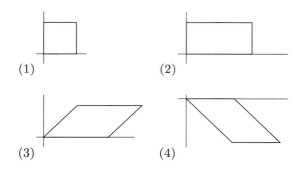

Figure 3.23   Application of a stretch, shear and rotation in sequence to a square

(b) The matrix describing the compound transformation is

$$\mathbf{A} = \begin{pmatrix} \cos(\pi/4) & \sin(\pi/4) \\ -\sin(\pi/4) & \cos(\pi/4) \end{pmatrix} \begin{pmatrix} 1 & 1 \\ 0 & 1 \end{pmatrix} \begin{pmatrix} 2 & 0 \\ 0 & 1 \end{pmatrix}$$

$$= \frac{1}{\sqrt{2}} \begin{pmatrix} 1 & 1 \\ -1 & 1 \end{pmatrix} \begin{pmatrix} 2 & 1 \\ 0 & 1 \end{pmatrix}$$

$$= \frac{1}{\sqrt{2}} \begin{pmatrix} 2 & 2 \\ -2 & 0 \end{pmatrix}$$

$$= \sqrt{2} \begin{pmatrix} 1 & 1 \\ -1 & 0 \end{pmatrix}.$$

(c) Applying $\mathbf{A}$ to the coordinates of each vertex of the square in turn gives positions $(0,0)$, $(\sqrt{2},0)$, $(2\sqrt{2}, -\sqrt{2})$ and $(\sqrt{2}, -\sqrt{2})$. Plotting these points and connecting them by lines gives the final figure in the sequence shown in part (a) above.

Solution 3.10

For rotations, the product law is

$$\mathbf{A}_{\text{rot}}(\theta_1)\,\mathbf{A}_{\text{rot}}(\theta_2)$$

$$= \begin{pmatrix} \cos\theta_1 & \sin\theta_1 \\ -\sin\theta_1 & \cos\theta_1 \end{pmatrix} \begin{pmatrix} \cos\theta_2 & \sin\theta_2 \\ -\sin\theta_2 & \cos\theta_2 \end{pmatrix}$$

$$= \begin{pmatrix} \cos\theta_1 \cos\theta_2 - \sin\theta_1 \sin\theta_2 & \sin\theta_1 \cos\theta_2 + \sin\theta_2 \cos\theta_1 \\ -\cos\theta_1 \sin\theta_2 - \cos\theta_2 \sin\theta_1 & \cos\theta_1 \cos\theta_2 - \sin\theta_1 \sin\theta_2 \end{pmatrix}$$

$$= \begin{pmatrix} \cos(\theta_1 + \theta_2) & \sin(\theta_1 + \theta_2) \\ -\sin(\theta_1 + \theta_2) & \cos(\theta_1 + \theta_2) \end{pmatrix}$$

$$= \mathbf{A}_{\text{rot}}(\theta_1 + \theta_2),$$

where we have simplified using the standard formulae for $\cos(a + b)$ and $\sin(a + b)$. Thus rotations are compounded by adding the rotation angles.

For compounding stretching transformations, the stretching factors are multiplied:

$$\mathbf{A}_{\text{str}}(A_1, A_2)\,\mathbf{A}_{\text{str}}(B_1, B_2) = \begin{pmatrix} A_1 & 0 \\ 0 & A_2 \end{pmatrix} \begin{pmatrix} B_1 & 0 \\ 0 & B_2 \end{pmatrix}$$

$$= \begin{pmatrix} A_1 B_1 & 0 \\ 0 & A_2 B_2 \end{pmatrix}$$

$$= \mathbf{A}_{\text{str}}(A_1 B_1, A_2 B_2).$$

For shearing transformations, the product law is

$$\mathbf{A}_{\text{sh}}(\tau_1)\,\mathbf{A}_{\text{sh}}(\tau_2) = \begin{pmatrix} 1 & \tau_1 \\ 0 & 1 \end{pmatrix} \begin{pmatrix} 1 & \tau_2 \\ 0 & 1 \end{pmatrix}$$

$$= \begin{pmatrix} 1 & \tau_1 + \tau_2 \\ 0 & 1 \end{pmatrix}$$

$$= \mathbf{A}_{\text{sh}}(\tau_1 + \tau_2),$$

so the shearing parameters are added.

Solution 3.11

By inspection, the effect of a rotation and then a stretch to the square is shown in Figure 3.24(a). Applying the stretch and then the rotation produces a different result, shown in Figure 3.24(b).

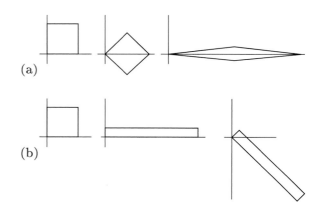

Figure 3.24   Rotation and stretching do not commute

On the basis of this construction, we should not expect stretching and rotation matrices to commute (except for some special cases). To confirm this:

$$\mathbf{A}_{\text{rot}}(\theta)\,\mathbf{A}_{\text{str}}(\lambda_1, \lambda_2) = \begin{pmatrix} \cos\theta & \sin\theta \\ -\sin\theta & \cos\theta \end{pmatrix} \begin{pmatrix} \lambda_1 & 0 \\ 0 & \lambda_2 \end{pmatrix}$$

$$= \begin{pmatrix} \lambda_1 \cos\theta & \lambda_2 \sin\theta \\ -\lambda_1 \sin\theta & \lambda_2 \cos\theta \end{pmatrix},$$

$$\mathbf{A}_{\text{str}}(\lambda_1, \lambda_2)\,\mathbf{A}_{\text{rot}}(\theta) = \begin{pmatrix} \lambda_1 & 0 \\ 0 & \lambda_2 \end{pmatrix} \begin{pmatrix} \cos\theta & \sin\theta \\ -\sin\theta & \cos\theta \end{pmatrix}$$

$$= \begin{pmatrix} \lambda_1 \cos\theta & \lambda_1 \sin\theta \\ -\lambda_2 \sin\theta & \lambda_2 \cos\theta \end{pmatrix}.$$

Solution 3.12

The trace and determinant of $\mathbf{A}$ are $t = 5$, $d = 9$. Using Equation (3.24), the eigenvalues are therefore $\lambda = \frac{5}{2} \pm \frac{1}{2}\sqrt{25 - 36} = \frac{5}{2} \pm \sqrt{11}i/2$. Because the eigenvalues are complex, the normal form is the product of a uniform stretch and a rotation. Writing the eigenvalues in the polar form $\lambda = \alpha \exp(\pm i\theta)$, we have

$$\alpha = \sqrt{(5/2)^2 + 11/4} = \sqrt{36/4} = 3,$$

$$\theta = \arctan\left(\frac{\sqrt{11}}{5}\right).$$

Solution 3.13

The trace and determinant of $\mathbf{A}$ are $t = 4$ and $d = 3$. Using Equation (3.24), the eigenvalues are therefore $\lambda = 2 \pm \frac{1}{2}\sqrt{16 - 12} = 2 \pm 1$, i.e. $\lambda_1 = 1$ and $\lambda_2 = 3$. Writing down the eigenvalue equation $\mathbf{A}\mathbf{u} = \lambda\mathbf{u}$, setting $\mathbf{u} = (1, a)^T$ and solving the resulting equation for a, we find that the eigenvalue $\lambda_1 = 1$ has eigenvector $\mathbf{u}_1 = (1, -\frac{1}{2})^T$, and the eigenvalue $\lambda_2 = 3$ has eigenvector $\mathbf{u}_2 = (1, -1)^T$. The matrix $\mathbf{T}$ and its inverse $\mathbf{T}^{-1}$ may therefore be written

$$\mathbf{T} = \begin{pmatrix} 2 & 1 \\ -1 & -1 \end{pmatrix}, \quad \mathbf{T}^{-1} = \begin{pmatrix} 1 & 1 \\ -1 & -2 \end{pmatrix}.$$

We can therefore write

$$\mathbf{A} = \begin{pmatrix} 2 & 1 \\ -1 & -1 \end{pmatrix} \begin{pmatrix} 1 & 0 \\ 0 & 3 \end{pmatrix} \begin{pmatrix} 1 & 1 \\ -1 & -2 \end{pmatrix}$$

$$= \begin{pmatrix} 2 & 1 \\ -1 & -1 \end{pmatrix} \begin{pmatrix} 1 & 1 \\ -3 & -6 \end{pmatrix}$$

$$= \begin{pmatrix} -1 & -4 \\ 2 & 5 \end{pmatrix}.$$

Solution 3.14

Applying Equation (3.17), we have

$$\mathbf{A}^{100} = \begin{pmatrix} 2 & 1 \\ -1 & -1 \end{pmatrix} \begin{pmatrix} 1^{100} & 0 \\ 0 & 3^{100} \end{pmatrix} \begin{pmatrix} 1 & 1 \\ -1 & -2 \end{pmatrix}$$

$$= \begin{pmatrix} 2 & 1 \\ -1 & -1 \end{pmatrix} \begin{pmatrix} 1 & 1 \\ -3^{100} & -2 \times 3^{100} \end{pmatrix}$$

$$= \begin{pmatrix} 2 - 3^{100} & 2 - 2 \times 3^{100} \\ 3^{100} - 1 & 2 \times 3^{100} - 1 \end{pmatrix}.$$

Solution 3.15

If the determinant is $d = 1$, Equation (3.24) gives $\lambda = \frac{1}{2}t \pm \frac{1}{2}\sqrt{t^2 - 4}$.

If $|t| < 2$, the eigenvalues are complex, so the normal form is the product of a rotation and a dilation. In this case let us write $t = 2\cos\theta$ for some angle θ, so that $\sqrt{4 - t^2} = 2\sin\theta$, and the eigenvalues are $\lambda = \exp(\pm i\theta)$. Thus, if $|t| < 2$, the normal form is the product of a rotation with angle $\theta = \arccos(t/2)$ and dilation with factor $\alpha = 1$ (thus is just a rotation).

In the case where $|t| > 2$, the eigenvalues are real and the normal form is a stretch.

Solution 3.16

The Jacobian is

$$\mathbf{J}(x, y) = \begin{pmatrix} -2x & b \\ 1 & 0 \end{pmatrix}.$$

For $a = 1$, $b = \frac{1}{2}$, we find the Jacobian at $\mathbf{x}_0 = (0, 0)$ and $\mathbf{x}_1 = (1, 0)$:

$$\mathbf{J}(\mathbf{x}_0) = \begin{pmatrix} 0 & \frac{1}{2} \\ 1 & 0 \end{pmatrix}, \quad \mathbf{J}(\mathbf{x}_1) = \begin{pmatrix} -2 & \frac{1}{2} \\ 1 & 0 \end{pmatrix}.$$

For the initial point $\mathbf{x}_0' = (0.01, 0.01)$, we find that the first point visited is

$$\mathbf{x}_1' = (1 - 10^{-4} + 0.01/2, 0.01) = (1.0049, 0.01).$$

The value of $\mathbf{x}_1'$ predicted by the linear approximation is

$$\mathbf{x}_1' = \mathbf{x}_1 + \mathbf{J}(\mathbf{x}_0)\,\delta\mathbf{x}_0$$

$$= \begin{pmatrix} 1 \\ 0 \end{pmatrix} + \begin{pmatrix} 0 & \frac{1}{2} \\ 1 & 0 \end{pmatrix} \begin{pmatrix} 0.01 \\ 0.01 \end{pmatrix}$$

$$= (1, 0) + (0.005, 0.01)$$

$$= (1.005, 0.01).$$

This is in good agreement with the exact value.

For $\mathbf{x}_1 = (1, 0)$, the next point visited is $\mathbf{x}_2 = (0, 1)$. For the initial point $\mathbf{x}_1' = (1.005, 0.01)$, we find that the first point visited is

$$\mathbf{x}_2' = (1 - (1.005)^2 + 0.005, 1.005)$$

$$= (-0.004\overset{5025}{\cancel{975}}, 1.005).$$

The value of $\mathbf{x}_2'$ predicted by the linear approximation is

$$\mathbf{x}_2' = \mathbf{x}_2 + \mathbf{J}(\mathbf{x}_1)\,\delta\mathbf{x}_1$$

$$= \begin{pmatrix} 0 \\ 1 \end{pmatrix} + \begin{pmatrix} -2 & \frac{1}{2} \\ 1 & 0 \end{pmatrix} \begin{pmatrix} 0.005 \\ 0.01 \end{pmatrix}$$

$$= (0, 1) + (-0.005, 0.005)$$

$$= (-0.005, 1.005).$$

Again, this is in good agreement with the exact value.

Solution 3.17

The first iterate of the Hénon map is $\mathbf{x}_1 = (1, 0)$. The parameters a, b and the points $\mathbf{x}_0, \mathbf{x}_1$ are the same as for the previous exercise, along with the values of the Jacobian obtained there. The Jacobian matrix for two successive applications of the map is therefore

$$\mathbf{J}_2(\mathbf{x}_0) = \mathbf{J}(\mathbf{x}_1)\,\mathbf{J}(\mathbf{x}_0)$$

$$= \begin{pmatrix} -2 & \frac{1}{2} \\ 1 & 0 \end{pmatrix} \begin{pmatrix} 0 & \frac{1}{2} \\ 1 & 0 \end{pmatrix}$$

$$= \begin{pmatrix} \frac{1}{2} & -1 \\ 0 & \frac{1}{2} \end{pmatrix}.$$

The result of applying the Hénon map to $\mathbf{x}_1 = (1, 0)$ is $\mathbf{x}_2 = (0, 1)$. We therefore predict that the point reached by two applications of the Hénon map starting from $(0.01, 0.01)$ is

$$\mathbf{x}_2' = \mathbf{x}_2 + \mathbf{J}_2(\mathbf{x}_0)\,\delta\mathbf{x}_0$$

$$= \begin{pmatrix} 0 \\ 1 \end{pmatrix} + \mathbf{J}_2(\mathbf{x}_0) \begin{pmatrix} 0.01 \\ 0.01 \end{pmatrix}$$

$$= (-0.005, 1.005).$$

This agrees with the result in Exercise 3.16.

Solution 3.18

We seek a fixed point of the Hénon map (with $a > 0$) by setting $x' = x$, $y' = y$ in Equation (3.3). The second equation of the Hénon map gives $y' = x$, so the fixed points satisfy $y' = y = x$. Thus any fixed point lies on the line $x = y$. From Equation (3.3), its x-coordinate then satisfies

$$x = a - x^2 + bx,$$

which has solution

$$x = \frac{b-1}{2} \pm \frac{1}{2}\sqrt{(1-b)^2 + 4a}.$$

We consider the case where $b = 1$, so that there are two fixed points on the line $x = y$, at $x = +\sqrt{a}$ and $x = -\sqrt{a}$. The Jacobian matrix at each of these fixed points is

$$\mathbf{J} = \begin{pmatrix} \mp 2\sqrt{a} & 1 \\ 1 & 0 \end{pmatrix},$$

so for the fixed point at $x = \sqrt{a}$, the eigenvalues are given by $\lambda = -\sqrt{a} \pm \sqrt{1+a}$, and for the fixed point at $x = -\sqrt{a}$, the eigenvalues are given by $\lambda = +\sqrt{a} \pm \sqrt{1+a}$.

It follows that both of the fixed points are unstable, because one eigenvalue has magnitude greater than unity. The fact that $d = -1$ implies that the other eigenvalue has magnitude less than unity, so the fixed points are saddles.

Solution 3.19

By inspection, substituting $(x, y) = (0, 0)$ into the standard map gives $(x', y') = (0, 0)$, so $(0, 0)$ is a fixed point. Similarly, $(\pi, 0)$ is a fixed point.

The Jacobian of the standard map is

$$\mathbf{J} = \begin{pmatrix} 1 + K\cos(x) & 1 \\ K\cos(x) & 1 \end{pmatrix}.$$

Because this is an area-preserving map, the nature of the fixed point is determined by $t = \mathrm{tr}(\mathbf{J})$. This matrix has trace $t = 2 + K\cos(x)$, so for the fixed points at $x = 0$ and $x = \pi$, we have $t = 2 + K$ and $t = 2 - K$, respectively. The fixed point at $x = 0$ is therefore unstable for all $K > 0$, but the fixed point at $x = \pi$ is stable for $0 < K < 4$ and unstable for $K > 4$.

Solution 3.20

If the elements of $\mathbf{J}_n$ are J_{ij}, then

$$\delta\mathbf{x}_1 = J_{11}\mathbf{e}_1 + J_{21}\mathbf{e}_2, \quad \delta\mathbf{x}_2 = J_{12}\mathbf{e}_1 + J_{22}\mathbf{e}_2,$$

so

$$\delta\mathbf{x}_1 \wedge \delta\mathbf{x}_2 = J_{11}J_{22} - J_{12}J_{21} = \det(\mathbf{J}_n).$$

Solution 3.21

The program prints out a succession of approximations for h_1 and $h_1 + h_2$. The final values are expected to be the most accurate: these are
0.358 731 546 368 248 213 74 and
$-0.916\,290\,731\,874\,155\,065\,18$, respectively. The values of h_1 are fluctuating considerably, so it is not meaningful to quote the estimate with high precision. From this experiment we can conclude that the values

are $h_1 \simeq 0.359$ and $h_2 \simeq -1.28$. If you have the patience to run this program for a larger number of iterations, you will (in all likelihood) obtain a more precise value for the Lyapunov exponents. Using 10^4 iterations of the map gives $h_1 \simeq 0.34$, $h_2 \simeq -1.26$.

Solution 3.22

The reason why the program prints out the same estimate for $h_1 + h_2$ is that the area of the parallelogram spanned by the vectors $\mathbf{v}_1$ and $\mathbf{v}_2$ decreases by the same factor, independent of the point (x_n, y_n) which the map has reached. This factor is $|\det(\mathbf{J})| = b$. Thus, for the Hénon map, we have $h_1 + h_2 = \ln(b)$, so $h_1 + h_2 = -0.916\ldots$ when $b = 0.4$.

Solution 3.23

The components of the velocity field are $f_1 = \partial\psi/\partial y$ and $f_2 = -\partial\psi/\partial x$. The condition for this velocity field to give an area-preserving flow, Equation (3.46), therefore gives

$$\frac{\partial f_1}{\partial x} + \frac{\partial f_2}{\partial y} = \frac{\partial}{\partial x}\left(\frac{\partial\psi}{\partial y}\right) - \frac{\partial}{\partial y}\left(\frac{\partial\psi}{\partial x}\right) = 0.$$

The flow is therefore area-preserving.

Solution 3.24

The condition for the velocity field $\mathbf{f}$ to give an area-preserving flow is $\boldsymbol{\nabla} \cdot \mathbf{f} = 0$. If $\mathbf{f} = (\partial\phi/\partial x, \partial\phi/\partial y)$, then the condition for area-preserving flow is

$$\frac{\partial}{\partial x}\left(\frac{\partial\phi}{\partial x}\right) + \frac{\partial}{\partial y}\left(\frac{\partial\phi}{\partial y}\right) = 0.$$

Thus ϕ must satisfy Laplace's equation.

Solution 3.25

We have

$$\mathbf{A}_{\mathrm{rot}}(\pi/2)\boldsymbol{\nabla}H = \begin{pmatrix} \cos(\pi/2) & \sin(\pi/2) \\ -\sin(\pi/2) & \cos(\pi/2) \end{pmatrix}\begin{pmatrix} \frac{\partial H}{\partial x} \\ \frac{\partial H}{\partial p} \end{pmatrix}$$

$$= \begin{pmatrix} 0 & 1 \\ -1 & 0 \end{pmatrix}\begin{pmatrix} \frac{\partial H}{\partial x} \\ \frac{\partial H}{\partial p} \end{pmatrix}$$

$$= \left(\frac{\partial H}{\partial p}, -\frac{\partial H}{\partial x}\right).$$

The modulus of the gradient of H and that of $\mathbf{f}$ are therefore equal:

$$|\mathbf{f}|^2 = |\boldsymbol{\nabla}H|^2 = \left(\frac{\partial H}{\partial x}\right)^2 + \left(\frac{\partial H}{\partial p}\right)^2.$$

Solution 3.26

You should find that the contours are circles when $m = C = 1$, and elliptical in the other case.

When $m = C = 1$, the equation of the contour is $x^2 + p^2 = 2E$, so the contour at $H(x, p) = E$ is a circle of radius $\sqrt{2E}$. In general, the equation is transformed into that of a circle by making the linear transformation $x \longmapsto x' = \sqrt{Cm}\,x$, so for general choices of C and m the contour is an ellipse.

Solution 3.27

You should see the pattern shown in Figure 3.25.

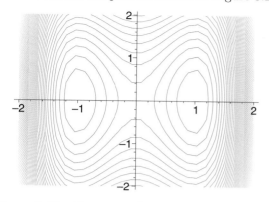

Figure 3.25 Contours of the Hamiltonian for a double-well potential

Solution 3.28

You should see the pattern shown in Figure 3.26.

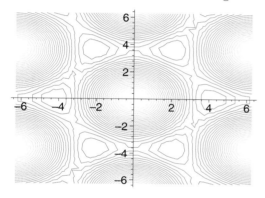

Figure 3.26 Contours of a Hamiltonian with periodic structure

By changing the range of the contours being plotted, you can confirm that the curves with sixfold symmetry surround maxima.

To determine the direction of flow, consider a trajectory moving on an orbit surrounding a minimum. If the Hamiltonian function has no singular point at its minimum, it may be expanded as a Taylor series about the minimum, and this Taylor series has no linear term. If the point lies above the minimum (that is, displaced in the positive p-direction from the minimum), then $\partial H/\partial p$ is positive, so $\dot{x}$ is positive. The phase point therefore rotates clockwise about contours surrounding minima of $H(x,p)$. Similarly, orbits about maxima circulate anticlockwise.

Solution 3.29

Because $x^2 + p^2 = R^2$ is the equation of a circle of radius R in the phase plane, the phase trajectory of this Hamiltonian at energy E is a circle with $R^\alpha = E$, so the radius is $R = E^{1/\alpha}$. The gradient of the Hamiltonian is inwards towards the centre of the circle, and has magnitude $|\nabla H| = \alpha R^{\alpha-1}$, which is independent of the position on the circle. Because the speed is equal to the magnitude of the gradient (see Exercise 3.25), the speed is $v = \alpha R^{\alpha-1} = \alpha E^{(\alpha-1)/\alpha}$.

The length of the orbit is $2\pi R$, so the period is

$$T = 2\pi R/v = \frac{2\pi}{\alpha} E^{\frac{1}{\alpha} - \frac{\alpha-1}{\alpha}} = \frac{2\pi}{\alpha} E^{\frac{2-\alpha}{\alpha}}.$$

The case $\alpha = 2$ coincides with the Hamiltonian for a harmonic oscillator with $m = \frac{1}{2}$, $C = 2$. This system executes simple harmonic motion with angular frequency $\omega = \sqrt{C/m} = 2$, with corresponding period $T = 2\pi/\omega = \pi$. This agrees with the general result above for the special case $\alpha = 2$.

Solution 3.30

The contours of the Hamiltonian are ellipses, centred at $x = p = 0$ and with their axes aligned with the x- and p-axes, and crossing these axes at $\pm x_0$ and at $\pm p_0$. The area is given by $A = \pi x_0 p_0$. From Equation (3.56), the values of the intersection points are $x_0 = \sqrt{2E/C}$ and $p_0 = \sqrt{2mE}$. The area is therefore

$$A(E) = 2\pi \sqrt{\frac{m}{C}} E.$$

The period is therefore $dA/dE = 2\pi\sqrt{m/C}$, independent of the energy E. This is in agreement with the well-known result that a simple harmonic oscillator has angular frequency $\omega = \sqrt{C/m}$, corresponding to a period $T = 2\pi/\omega = 2\pi\sqrt{m/C}$.

Solution 3.31

The Hamiltonian is $H(x,p) = p^2/2m + \alpha|x|$. The contours of this function consist of sections of parabolas, as you can verify by using Maple, as illustrated in Figure 3.27.

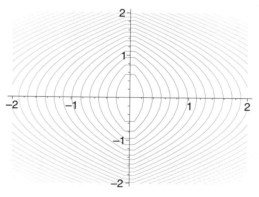

Figure 3.27 Contours of the Hamiltonian $H = p^2/2m + \alpha|x|$, for $m = \alpha = 1$

If the contour intersects the x-axis at $\pm x_0$, then the area enclosed by the contour is

$$
\begin{aligned}
A(E) &= 4 \int_0^{x_0} p(x, E)\, dx \\
&= 4 \int_0^{x_0} \sqrt{2m(E - \alpha x)}\, dx \\
&= 4\sqrt{2mE}\, \frac{E}{\alpha} \int_0^1 \sqrt{1 - u}\, du \\
&= \frac{8\sqrt{2}}{3} \frac{m^{1/2} E^{3/2}}{\alpha}.
\end{aligned}
$$

The period is

$$T(E) = \frac{dA}{dE} = \frac{4\sqrt{2mE}}{\alpha}.$$

UNIT 4 Fractals and dynamics

Study guide

This unit discusses some rather difficult concepts, but (at the introductory level of this text) their application requires only simple calculations. The unit therefore has rather few exercises: you should attempt all of them. Sections 4.1 to 4.5 all contain topics that may be assessed. Most of the unit can be studied without using Maple on your computer.

Introduction

In *Unit 3* we discussed the attracting set of the Hénon map. We showed evidence that for a suitable choice of the parameters, the attracting set is neither a fixed point nor a limit cycle. We showed that this *strange attractor*, illustrated in Figure 4.1, contains structure which looks nearly identical under different degrees of magnification, as illustrated in Figures 4.2 and 4.3.

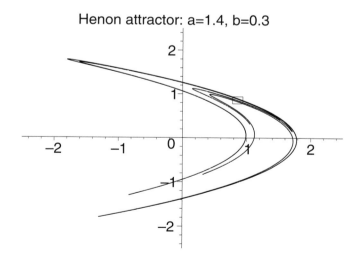

Figure 4.1 Strange attractor of the Hénon map: the region in the small box is shown magnified in Figure 4.2

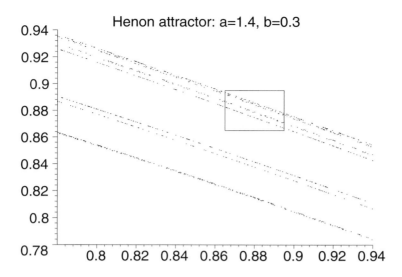

Figure 4.2 A magnification of a small region of Figure 4.1: the region in the box is shown at higher magnification in Figure 4.3

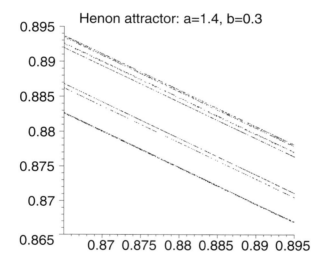

Figure 4.3 Further magnification of the box in Figure 4.2, showing self-similarity

We mentioned that self-similarity under magnification is a characteristic of *fractal sets*, and showed that the basin of attraction can also have a highly fragmented structure. The objectives of this unit are as follows.

1. To give some further examples of fractal sets, including fractals constructed by a simple iteration, which can be analysed in detail.

2. To explain the properties that define fractal sets, including the idea that they may be described by a *fractal dimension*, which need not take integer values. There are in fact a variety of ways to assign a 'fractal dimension' to a set. The one we adopt here is called the *box-counting dimension*.

3. To illustrate how fractal sets can arise in dynamics, using exact calculations for some simple piecewise-linear models, which are introduced in Section 4.3.

4. To explain the *Kaplan–Yorke formula*, which gives a relation between the *Lyapunov exponents* of a system and the fractal dimension.

4.1 Fractal sets

The term 'fractal' was introduced quite recently, in a book by Benoit Mandelbrot (1924–), a mathematician who was employed by IBM. His book *Fractals: form, chance and dimension*, published in 1977, was significant in that it suggested that the natural world has abundant examples of objects which have a fragmented form, with similar structures appearing on a range of different length scales. Mandelbrot suggested that these structures are analogous to sets which had been invented by mathematicians, and which were known to have non-integer dimension (in a sense which will be explained in Subsection 4.1.1 below).

Mandelbrot's book was first published in 1975 in French under the title *Les objets fractals: forme, hasard et dimension*. This appears to be the first published mention of the word 'fractal'.

Mandelbrot's book did not provide any theory to explain why the examples from the natural world should have fractal structures. Neither did it contain significant new mathematical ideas. But his book did open up a new way for physical scientists to look at phenomena. The word 'fractal' is now found in the abstracts of thousands of scientific papers every year. There are now numerous examples where the mechanism for forming fractal sets is understood, and where understanding that a physical phenomenon gives rise to a fractal structure is seen to have important consequences. Understanding the concept of a fractal set is now part of scientific culture.

It is much harder to understand why fractal sets arise than to describe them. There is no single mechanism. Here we give an indication of how fractal sets arise in simple dynamical systems, such as the strange attractor illustrated above. Other mechanisms may determine the structure of other natural fractals, such as the examples in Subsection 4.1.3 below.

The term 'fractal' is used for a large variety of unusual sets, and it is better to present some examples before discussing a definition. First we describe what is perhaps the simplest fractal set, the *middle-third Cantor set*, in some detail. Then we consider some other examples of 'regular' fractal sets, called *fractal curves*, *fractal gaskets* and *fractal dusts*, which are also generated by simple recursive procedures. We then discuss some other examples from the natural world and from physical sciences which seem to have something in common with these mathematical constructs. Finally, we end this section with a discussion of the common features of these sets. There is no agreed strict definition of the term 'fractal', but we list a set of properties which a fractal set is expected to possess.

4.1.1 The middle-third Cantor set

The **middle-third Cantor set** is the most widely discussed elementary example of a fractal. It is a subset of the set of real numbers between 0 and 1, that is, a subset of the interval $[0, 1]$. The Cantor set itself cannot be specified in a finite list of its components. Rather, it is defined by specifying a sequence of sets $\mathcal{S}_n$, $n = 0, 1, 2, \ldots$, which approach the middle-third Cantor set in the limit as $n \to \infty$.

The set $\mathcal{S}_0$ is the unit interval from 0 to 1 (that is, $\mathcal{S}_0 = [0, 1]$). We then remove the middle third of this set to give $\mathcal{S}_1$ (which is therefore the union of two intervals: $\mathcal{S}_1 = [0, \frac{1}{3}] \cup [\frac{2}{3}, 1]$). The set $\mathcal{S}_2$ is obtained by removing the middle third of both components of $\mathcal{S}_1$, giving the four intervals of the set $\mathcal{S}_2$, and so on. The sequence of sets is illustrated in Figure 4.4 (where the intervals are drawn as a set of bars, rather than lines, to make them more visible).

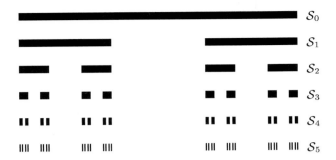

Figure 4.4 Construction of the middle-third Cantor set as a limit of a sequence of sets

Note that at the nth stage the set $\mathcal{S}_n$ has 2^n intervals, each of length $\frac{1}{3^n}$. Thus the total length of the intervals approaches zero, whilst their number approaches infinity.

The limit of this process, the Cantor set, is quite hard to comprehend. It has no length, but every point of the set has other elements of the set which are arbitrarily close. This Cantor set is a type of highly fragmented set which is reminiscent of some of the examples introduced in Subsection 3.1.1 of *Unit 3*.

Exercise 4.1

Calculate the total length L_n of each of the sets $\mathcal{S}_n$ in Figure 4.4. Also determine the shortest distance d_n between the intervals forming the set $\mathcal{S}_n$. Show that both L_n and d_n approach zero as $n \to \infty$.

One aspect of the middle-third Cantor set which is particularly noteworthy is that it contains miniature images of itself. For example, if we take the subset of the Cantor set in the interval $[0, \frac{1}{3}]$ and stretch it by multiplying each number in this subset by a factor of 3, we end up with a set which is identical to the original Cantor set. This property is explored in detail in Exercise 4.4 below.

The construction of the middle-third Cantor set has an interesting relation to the *ternary representation* of numbers, which gives useful insights into the structure of the set. We are used to the decimal representation of numbers; for example, if we write $X = 23.572$, we mean that

$$X = 2 \times 10 + 3 \times 1 + 5 \times \tfrac{1}{10} + 7 \times \tfrac{1}{100} + 2 \times \tfrac{1}{1000}. \qquad (4.1)$$

In general, we are used to representing numbers in the range $0 \leq X < 1$ in the form

$$X = c_1 \times \tfrac{1}{10} + c_2 \times \tfrac{1}{100} + c_3 \times \tfrac{1}{1000} + \cdots = \sum_{n=1}^{\infty} c_n 10^{-n}, \qquad (4.2)$$

where $c_1, c_2, c_3, \ldots$ are all integers in the range 0–9. There is nothing special about using powers of 10; for example, a general number $0 \leq X < 1$ can also be written

$$X = a_1 \times \tfrac{1}{3} + a_2 \times \tfrac{1}{9} + \cdots + a_j \times \frac{1}{3^j} + \cdots = \sum_{j=1}^{\infty} a_j 3^{-j}. \qquad (4.3)$$

Here the a_j all take values 0, 1 or 2, which is the **ternary representation** of X, and we can denote the number X by giving its list of coefficients:

$$X = (a_1, a_2, a_3, \dots). \tag{4.4}$$

In general, we can replace 3 by any positive integer $n \geq 2$, and allow coefficients in the range $0, 1, \dots, n-1$, in which case we have the **base-n representation**.

There is an interesting relation between the ternary representation of numbers and the middle-third Cantor set. The set of numbers between $\frac{1}{3}$ and $\frac{2}{3}$ have ternary expansions which begin with $a_1 = 1$. Thus the set $\mathcal{S}_1$ consists of numbers with ternary expansions which begin with $a_1 = 0$ or $a_1 = 2$. The set $\mathcal{S}_2$ consists of numbers with ternary expansions for which neither a_1 nor a_2 is equal to 1.

In general, we can show that $\mathcal{S}_n$ consists of the set of numbers for which each of the first n coefficients a_j is not equal to 1. In view of the observations in the preceding paragraph, this should not be surprising. To show this, we proceed in stages as follows (but you need not study this in detail, because the methods will not be required later).

1. First note that by making a free choice of any of the coefficients, we can generate any number in the interval $[0, 1]$. Also, by taking all of the coefficients $a_j = 0$ for $j \leq n$, but making a free choice of the remaining coefficients, we can generate any number in the interval $[0, 3^{-n}]$. Call this set of numbers $\mathcal{A}_n = [0, 3^{-n}]$.

2. Next consider the set of numbers which are generated by allowing a free choice of the a_j for $j \leq n$, but setting $a_j = 0$ for $j > n$. This set consists of all of the rational numbers $k/3^n$, with $k = 0, 1, 2, \dots, 3^n - 1$. Call this set $\mathcal{B}_n = \{k3^{-n} : k = 0, 1, 2, \dots, 3^n\}$.

3. Now consider the set $\mathcal{C}_n$ of numbers $x = 3^{-n} + x_{\mathcal{A}_n} + x_{\mathcal{B}_{n-1}}$, where $x_{\mathcal{A}_n}$ and $x_{\mathcal{B}_{n-1}}$ are elements of the sets $\mathcal{A}_n$ and $\mathcal{B}_{n-1}$. The set $\mathcal{C}_n$ consists of a set of intervals of length 3^{-n}, with their lower limits at positions $k3^{-(n-1)} + 3^{-n}$, where $k = 0, 1, 2, \dots, 3^{n-1}$, that is, $\mathcal{C}_n = \{3^{-n} + x + y : x \in \mathcal{A}_n, y \in \mathcal{B}_{n-1}\}$.

    Note that the set $\mathcal{C}_n$ is also the set of numbers for which the ternary representation has $a_n = 1$, but for which there are no other constraints on the values of the ternary coefficients. We define the set $\overline{\mathcal{C}}_n = [0, 1] \setminus \mathcal{C}_n$, that is, $\overline{\mathcal{C}}_n$ is the set of numbers in the interval $[0, 1]$ which are not elements of $\mathcal{C}_n$. This set is illustrated in Figure 4.5 for $n = 0, 1, 2, 3$. It consists of the set of numbers for which the ternary representation has $a_n = 0$ or $a_n = 2$, but there are no other constraints on the coefficients.

4. Now note that the set $\mathcal{S}_n$ is the intersection

    $$\mathcal{S}_n = \overline{\mathcal{C}}_n \cap \overline{\mathcal{C}}_{n-1} \cap \dots \cap \overline{\mathcal{C}}_1. \tag{4.5}$$

    To determine this intersection of sets, every condition on the numbers forming the component sets must be applied. The elements of the set $\mathcal{S}_n$ may be selected by the condition that none of the a_j are equal to 1 for $j = 1, \dots, n$.

5. Taking the limit as $n \to \infty$, we see that the middle-third Cantor set is the set of numbers for which none of the ternary coefficients a_n are equal to unity.

Other examples have been seen in *Units A3* and *B2*, which discussed the hexadecimal and bicimal representations of numbers, respectively.

Figure 4.5   The sets $\bar{C}_n$ for $n = 0, 1, 2, 3$

Exercise 4.2

The number X with a ternary expansion
$(a_1, a_2, a_3, \ldots) = (0, 2, 0, 2, 0, 2, \ldots)$ is an element of the middle-third
Cantor set. Show that this number is $X = \frac{1}{4}$. What are the ternary
coefficients of $\frac{3}{4}$?

[*Hint*: Note that X can be written as the sum of a number with ternary
expansion $(0, 2)$ and a multiple of X.]

Exercise 4.3

Other Cantor sets can be constructed by deleting different numbers of
intervals of different sizes; for example, we could do either of the following.

1. At each stage remove the middle two quarters of every interval, so that
    $\mathcal{S}_1 = [0, \frac{1}{4}] \cup [\frac{3}{4}, 1]$.

2. At each stage remove the second and fourth fifth of every interval, so
    that $\mathcal{S}_1 = [0, \frac{1}{5}] \cup [\frac{2}{5}, \frac{3}{5}] \cup [\frac{4}{5}, 1]$.

How would the Cantor sets produced by iterating each of these deletion
schemes relate to base-4 and base-5 expansions of numbers?

Exercise 4.4

Show that if $(a_1, a_2, a_3, \ldots)$ is a set of coefficients for the ternary
representation of a number which is an element of the Cantor set, then
$(a_2, a_3, a_4, \ldots)$ is also a ternary representation of another element of this
set.

Hence show that for every number X which is an element of the
middle-third Cantor set, $3X - \text{floor}(3X)$ (where $\text{floor}(x)$ is the largest
integer which is less than or equal to x) is also an element of the Cantor
set.

The function introduced in Exercise 4.4 is an example of a piecewise-linear
mapping. The fact that the Cantor set was shown to be mapped into itself
under this transformation is a first indication of the fact that it is possible
to make clear connections between fractals and mappings. These
connections will be considered in Sections 4.3 and 4.4.

4.1.2 Fractal curves, gaskets and dusts

We stated that the middle-third Cantor set is an example of a fractal set, but the term fractal has not yet been defined. It will be useful to introduce a few more examples of fractal sets before discussing what they have in common, and trying to refine these observations into a definition. These further examples will not be restricted to subsets of the unit interval; they will include curves and other sets constructed in the plane.

Our first example is a construction called the **Koch curve**, which is illustrated in Figure 4.6. Here we take a straight-line segment (a) of unit length, and replace it by a segment (b) with a 'kink', consisting of four segments of length $\frac{1}{3}$. Each segment of this curve is then recursively replaced with a kinked segment, as in Figure 4.6 parts (c) to (e).

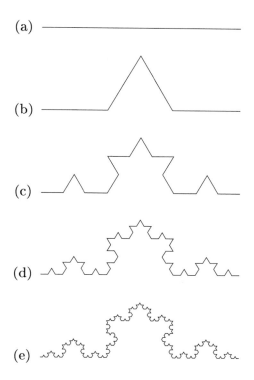

Figure 4.6   The Koch curve is the limit of this sequence of curves

The limiting set produced by repeating this procedure indefinitely is called the Koch curve. The feature that it shares with the Cantor set is that if you 'magnify' certain fragments of the set, you generate the original set. This feature is described as being **self-similar under magnification**; it is one of the characteristic features of fractal sets. In the case of the Koch curve, some segments have to be rotated by 60° as well as magnified. (It is complications like this that make it difficult to write a rigid definition of what constitutes a 'fractal' set.)

Figures 4.7 and 4.8 illustrate two other fractals generated by indefinite recursive subdivision of a simple set, namely the **Sierpinski gasket** and the **Sierpinski carpet**. The Sierpinski carpet is often referred to as a fractal 'dust' because it can be divided into isolated components of arbitrarily small size.

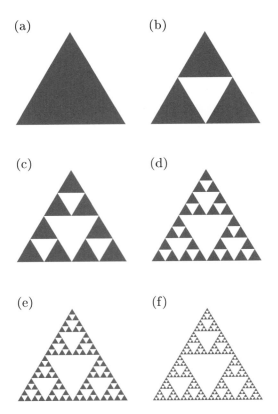

Figure 4.7   Illustrating the successive stages in the construction of the Sierpinski gasket as the limit of a sequence of sets

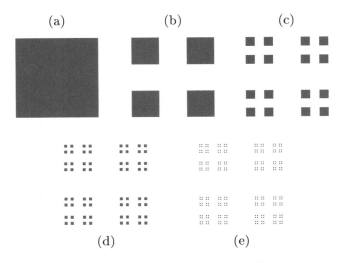

Figure 4.8   Illustrating the construction of the Sierpinski carpet

All of the four examples of fractals illustrated so far have their origin in pure mathematics. Georg Cantor (1845–1918) invented his Cantor set in the course of work on distinguishing different classes of infinite sets, during the period 1874–84. The Koch curve was invented by Helge von Koch (1870–1924), a Swedish mathematician. The title of his paper of 1906 (translated into English from the original French) is 'On a continuous curve without tangent, obtained by an elementary geometrical construction'. Waclaw Sierpinski (1882–1969) was a Polish mathematician who made extensive contributions to set theory and number theory. His fractal constructions date from approximately 1915.

4.1.3 *Irregular fractals in the natural world*

All of the examples of fractals which have been discussed so far in this section are constructed by a simple recursive procedure, and are relatively easy to analyse. The motivation for introducing fractals in a course on dynamics is that fractal sets tend to appear in dynamical processes, and some examples of such sets have been seen already (such as Figures 3.1 and 3.5 of *Unit 3*). These examples are less regular in their structure; for example, they do not exhibit *exact* self-similarity under magnification.

It turns out that many objects in the natural world also have an irregular structure which looks approximately the same when viewed on different length scales. We shall discuss a few more examples of objects which might be termed 'fractal', before discussing the defining properties of fractals.

Figure 4.9 shows a picture of a piece of copper metal which was grown by passing a small electric current through an electrode in a copper sulphate solution. The metal has a delicate tree-like structure.

Figure 4.9   This object is a piece of copper produced by passing an electric current through a solution of copper sulphate under controlled conditions.
Image courtesy of Kevin R. Johnson, http://en.wikipedia.org/wiki/Fractal.

Figure 4.10 shows a plastic block which has been damaged by the heating effect of an electrical current which resulted from applying a very high electrical potential. The current flows along a path that repeatedly divides, until the smallest filaments are so fine that they can be seen clearly only with a microscope. This type of pattern is called a **Lichtenberg figure**. Lightning discharges in the atmosphere have a similar structure (but they are harder to study because they are transitory).

Georg Christoph Lichtenberg (1742–99) was the first professor of experimental physics in Germany, appointed at Göttingen. The figures that now bear his name were produced in experiments during 1777, which were also prescient of the development of xerographic printing in the twentieth century.

Figure 4.10   This pattern is produced by a high-voltage electrical discharge through a block of acrylic plastic.
Image courtesy of Bert Hickman, http://en.wikipedia.org/wiki/Image:Square1.jpg.

Fractal sets can be produced by random processes, and both of the examples above are quite closely related to a mathematical model called **diffusion-limited aggregation**, illustrated in Figure 4.11.

Figure 4.11 A diffusion-limited aggregation cluster is a fractal structure which is generated by a simple random process.

Image courtesy of The American Physical Society, from Kaufman, H. et al. (1995) 'Parallel diffusion-limited aggregation', *Physical Review E*, **52**, no. 5, pp. 5602–5609.

In diffusion-limited aggregation, particles move around erratically, following a type of trajectory called a *random walk*, which will be studied in *Unit 3* of Block C. We assume that there is a small 'seed' cluster of particles at the origin. When a particle collides with part of the cluster, it stops moving and becomes part of the cluster itself. This process tends to accumulate new particles on the tips of any protruding points, producing a tree-like structure.

We have seen that there are various physical processes that lead to fractal structures. Many of these physical fractals are quite well understood. In other cases the most we can say is that a set appears to have fractal properties; for example, Mandelbrot famously suggested that the coastline of Britain is a fractal set, but there is no clear model to support this suggestion.

The illustrations in this section were intended to demonstrate the wide variety of sets which have been called 'fractal'. Now we consider what all of these examples have in common.

4.1.4 Defining properties of fractal sets

By now you are probably asking 'what is the precise definition of a fractal?' This turns out to be a case where it is more constructive to be vague rather than making a precise definition, because the set of examples that have 'fractal' properties is so diverse that a satisfactory definition is difficult. As we mentioned above, the term **fractal** was coined by Mandelbrot, who noted that many physical phenomena generate sets with the properties listed below.

Mandelbrot gave a definition of the term fractal, which is not universally accepted and is too technical to discuss here. In this course, we say that a set is fractal if it has *all* of the following properties.

1. Fractals have fine structure on all length scales below an upper size scale. For example, the middle-third Cantor set has empty intervals of size $1/3^k$ for all positive integers k.

In the material world, there is always a lower size limit (typically set by atomic size scales) where the self-similarity breaks down. Material objects can therefore only approximate ideal, mathematical fractal sets.

2. Magnification of a region of a fractal set gives a set which is 'similar' (in some sense) to the entire set.

    In some examples, this self-similarity might be exact; for example, the middle-third Cantor set contains subsets which, upon magnifying them and shifting the origin, reproduce the original set.

    In other cases, the self-similarity is not exact. Approximate self-similarity is hard to define, but a practical test is to take two images of a supposed fractal at different magnifications, and ask whether you can distinguish them. For example, if the axes were removed from Figures 4.2 and 4.3, would you be able to tell them apart?

3. It is possible to define a **generalized dimension**, such as the box-counting dimension which is discussed below. Except for some special cases (which we cannot consider here), this has a non-integer value for fractal sets. Non-fractal sets always have an integer box-counting dimension.

Sets with *all* of the above properties will be referred to as fractal sets.

4.2   The box-counting fractal dimension

One interesting question about fractals is whether there are means to quantify them; for example, is there a well-defined number which distinguishes between two fractals? This can be achieved by introducing a generalized dimension, often loosely referred to as the 'fractal dimension'.

There are a variety of definitions of the 'fractal dimension'. The box-counting dimension, which we describe here, is the easiest to understand. Most advanced texts on fractals prefer the *Hausdorff dimension*, for a variety of technical reasons. For the fractal sets we consider, however, different definitions of the dimension will give very similar (in many cases identical) results.

Felix Hausdorff (1868–1942) was a German pioneer of point set topology.

Consider some subsets of the plane, illustrated in Figure 4.12. The region (a) is easily recognized as being two-dimensional (two continuously variable numbers, such as Cartesian coordinates (x, y), are required to label each point within this set). The line (b) is one-dimensional, because only one continuously variable number, such as the length from one end, is needed to specify a point on this line. The set of points (c) is a zero-dimensional set, because no continuously variable quantity labels different points in this set (a discrete set of numbers, such as a set of integers, will suffice). The Sierpinski gasket (illustrated in (d) by means of an element in its defining sequence) appears to be problematic: it is 'more' than a set of lines, but 'less' than a two-dimensional region of the plane. In the next subsection we describe how a generalized dimension, which need not have integer values, can be assigned to sets.

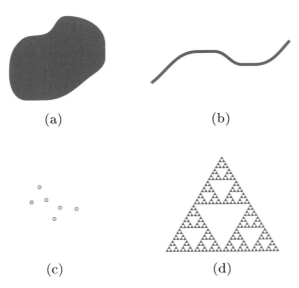

Figure 4.12   Various subsets of the plane. The area (a), line (b) and set of points (c) are respectively two-dimensional, one-dimensional and zero-dimensional sets, but what is the dimension of the Sierpinski gasket (d)?

4.2.1 Definition of box-counting dimension

We start by giving the definition of the box-counting dimension D, so that you can see what ideas are required. We will then explain the components of the definition by means of simple examples, and discuss how the definition relates to more familiar concepts of dimension.

Let us consider a set S which is a subset of a d-dimensional space. We pick a value for a positive number, denoted by ε, and divide the d-dimensional space into d-dimensional cubes of side length ε. In each of these cubes we determine whether there is an element of S contained within the cube, in which case we say that the cube belongs to the **ε-covering set** of S. (This is illustrated in Figure 4.13 for the case where $d = 2$, so that the 'cubes' are squares.) Let the number of cubes ('boxes') of side ε forming the ε-covering set of S be $N(\varepsilon)$. Then the **box-counting dimension** D of the set S is defined as

$$D = -\lim_{\varepsilon \to 0} \frac{\ln N(\varepsilon)}{\ln \varepsilon}. \tag{4.6}$$

Note that the definition involves taking a limit as the size ε of the boxes approaches zero.

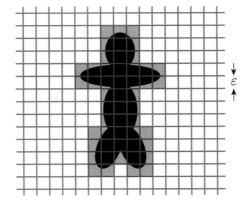

Figure 4.13   Illustrating the ε-covering set (shaded pink and black) for an area in the plane (shaded black)

This definition at first sight appears rather different from familiar notions of the dimension of a set. In order to make the connections clearer, we shall now discuss the definition in more detail, taking as an example the case where we want to determine the dimension of a subset of the plane, so that $d = 2$. In this case the d-dimensional cubes are squares of edge length ε. An example of a covering set for a given value of ε is shown in Figure 4.13. Consider what happens as ε is reduced. This is illustrated for covering an ellipse and a line in Figure 4.14. As ε is reduced, we need more and more boxes to cover the set. In the case where the set is a two-dimensional region such as the ellipse in Figure 4.14(a), the number of boxes is increased by (approximately) a factor of four when the edge length of the box is halved. In the case of covering a line in Figure 4.14(b), when you halve the edge length of each square, you need (approximately) twice as many squares to cover the set.

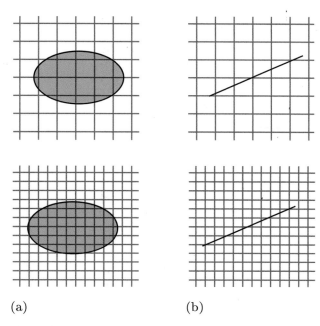

(a)   (b)

Figure 4.14   Effect of reducing the ε of the ε-covering set, for (a) a two-dimensional set and (b) a one-dimensional set

More generally, we can argue that the number of tiles of side length ε required to cover a two-dimensional region is inversely proportional to the square of the length of each box (that is, $N(\varepsilon) \propto 1/\varepsilon^2$), whereas the number required to cover a line is inversely proportional to ε (that is, $N(\varepsilon) \propto 1/\varepsilon$). Fractal sets have the property that $N(\varepsilon)$ has a power-law dependence on ε, with an exponent α which is not an integer. For a fractal set, $N(\varepsilon)$ is proportional to $1/\varepsilon^\alpha$, for some positive constant α. To summarize:

$$\text{line} \qquad N(\varepsilon) \propto \frac{1}{\varepsilon},$$

$$\text{area} \qquad N(\varepsilon) \propto \frac{1}{\varepsilon^2}, \qquad\qquad (4.7)$$

$$\text{fractal} \quad N(\varepsilon) \propto \frac{1}{\varepsilon^\alpha}.$$

If $N = C/\varepsilon^\alpha$ (for some constant C), then $\ln N = \ln C - \alpha \ln \varepsilon$ and the definition (4.6) implies that the dimension is $D = \alpha$. Now applying the definition of the box-counting dimension, Equation (4.6), to (4.7), you will see that it gives $D = 1$ as the box-counting dimension of a line, and $D = 2$ as the box-counting dimension of an area. These are in agreement with the

Of course, $N(\varepsilon)$ is an integer, whereas $\varepsilon^{-\alpha}$ varies continuously as a function of ε, so these proportional relationships are only approximate. To be more precise, we can replace (4.7) with the assumption that $N(\varepsilon) = C/\varepsilon^\alpha + \delta N(\varepsilon)$, where C is some constant, and where $|\delta N(\varepsilon)|/N(\varepsilon)$ is bounded by a function which decreases as $\varepsilon \to 0$.

idea that a line is a one-dimensional object, and an area is a two-dimensional object. For the fractal object, the definition gives $D = \alpha$ for the box-counting dimension. Note that D need not be an integer, or even a rational number: it can take any value in the range $0 \leq D \leq d$.

It is possible to conceive of highly fragmented sets for which the function $N(\varepsilon)$ might have something other than a power-law behaviour, for example $N(\varepsilon) \propto \ln(1/\varepsilon)$. In order for a set to be considered as a fractal, it is usually required that its box-counting dimension (Equation (4.6)) is not an integer.

4.2.2 Evaluation of box-counting dimension

For some simple fractal sets, such as the middle-third Cantor set, which are constructed by a recursive procedure, the value of the box-counting dimension can be determined exactly. Other fractal sets, including those which typically arise from dynamical systems, do not have a regular structure. Their box-counting dimension can only be estimated by using a computer program to count $N(\varepsilon)$ for a sequence of values of ε which approach zero. The dimension cannot be determined exactly by this approach, because for very small values of ε the computer program will take a very long time to count $N(\varepsilon)$, but the accuracy of the result increases as the program is run for a longer time period. In this subsection we discuss the exact evaluation of the box-counting dimension for some regular fractal sets which are constructed by simple iterative schemes.

We start by considering how to calculate the box-counting dimension of the middle-third Cantor set, which turns out to be a number between zero and one. We then see how the approach generalizes.

One aspect that is common to most of these examples is that $N(\varepsilon)$ is calculated not for all values of ε, but only for a sequence of values ε_n, $n = 0, 1, 2, \ldots$, such that $\lim_{n \to \infty} \varepsilon_n = 0$.

To determine the dimension of the middle-third Cantor set, it will be convenient to consider such a sequence of values of ε: we use the sequence of values $\varepsilon_n = 1/3^n$, because these correspond to the sizes of the intervals used in the construction of the set. For each ε_n, the ε-covering set consists of 2^n boxes, so $N(\varepsilon_n) = 2^n$ for $\varepsilon_n = 1/3^n$. The box-counting dimension can be written as a limit as $n \to \infty$ (because $\lim_{n \to \infty} \varepsilon_n = 0$). The box-counting dimension is therefore

$$
\begin{aligned}
D &= -\lim_{n \to \infty} \frac{\ln N(\varepsilon_n)}{\ln \varepsilon_n} \\
&= -\lim_{n \to \infty} \frac{\ln(2^n)}{\ln(1/3^n)} \\
&= \lim_{n \to \infty} -\frac{n \ln(2)}{n \ln(1/3)} \\
&= \frac{\ln(2)}{\ln(3)}.
\end{aligned}
\tag{4.8}
$$

Thus we conclude that the box-counting dimension of the middle-third Cantor set is $\ln(2)/\ln(3) = 0.6309 \ldots$.

Exercise 4.5

What is the dimension of a Cantor set produced by successively deleting the middle two quarters of each interval in the set? (This Cantor set is the limit of the sequence $\mathcal{S}_0 = [0, 1]$, $\mathcal{S}_1 = [0, \frac{1}{4}] \cup [\frac{3}{4}, 1]$, $\mathcal{S}_2 = [0, \frac{1}{16}] \cup [\frac{3}{16}, \frac{1}{4}] \cup [\frac{3}{4}, \frac{13}{16}] \cup [\frac{15}{16}, 1]$, ...)

Exercise 4.6

A Cantor set is constructed by taking the unit interval and retaining M equally spaced intervals of length a (with $Ma < 1$, and with the start of the first interval at 0, and the end of the last interval at 1). Each interval of length a is then itself subdivided according to the same pattern. What is the box-counting dimension of the resulting Cantor set? Check your result by applying the formula to the middle-third Cantor set.

Exercise 4.7

Show that the box-counting dimension of the Sierpinski carpet (see page 172) is $D = \ln(4)/\ln(3)$.

In the examples above it was easy to find a sequence of values of ε to neatly cover the set. Is it possible to change the shape of the covering boxes? For example, it might be more convenient to cover a subset of the plane with (say) equilateral triangles with sides of length ε. In the following we show how this type of change may be justified. (You need not study this in detail, because the method will not be required in later sections.)

Let us compare the number of triangles of side length ε that are required to cover a set with the number of squares of side lengths ε and $\varepsilon/3$. Let these numbers be $N_t(\varepsilon)$, $N(\varepsilon)$ and $N(\varepsilon/3)$, respectively. Note that we can cover the triangle with the larger square, but that the triangle can cover the smaller square (see Figure 4.15).

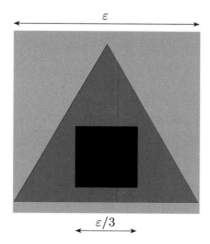

Figure 4.15 A triangle is covered by a large square, but covers a smaller square

It follows that

$$N(\varepsilon) \le N_{\mathrm{t}}(\varepsilon) \le N(\varepsilon/3). \tag{4.9}$$

Now note that

$$\lim_{\varepsilon \to 0} \frac{\ln(N(\varepsilon/3))}{\ln(\varepsilon)} = \lim_{\varepsilon' \to 0} \frac{\ln(N(\varepsilon'))}{\ln(3\varepsilon')} = \lim_{\varepsilon' \to 0} \frac{\ln(N(\varepsilon'))}{\ln(\varepsilon') + \ln(3)} = -D, \tag{4.10}$$

where we changed the variable in the limit from ε to $\varepsilon' = \varepsilon/3$. The final equality holds because as $\varepsilon' \to 0$, the term $\ln(\varepsilon')$ becomes arbitrarily large in magnitude and the term $\ln(3)$ can therefore be ignored. Applying the definition of the box-counting dimension, Equation (4.6), to each term in (4.9), and taking note of (4.10), we find

$$D \le -\lim_{\varepsilon \to 0} \frac{\ln(N_{\mathrm{t}}(\varepsilon))}{\ln(\varepsilon)} \le D, \tag{4.11}$$

so

$$-\lim_{\varepsilon \to 0} \frac{\ln(N_{\mathrm{t}}(\varepsilon))}{\ln(\varepsilon)} = D. \tag{4.12}$$

This means that the box-counting dimension can be obtained from the number of covering triangles, $N_{\mathrm{t}}(\varepsilon)$, using the standard expression, Equation (4.6).

Exercise 4.8

What is the box-counting dimension of the Sierpinski gasket?

[*Hint*: Use triangles as the covering objects.]

The argument above can be adapted to show that other shapes can be used as the covering objects.

4.2.3   Numerical determination of the dimension

The box-counting dimension can always be estimated using a computer program. There are many ways of doing this, which make use of alternative approaches to covering the set. Here we describe the simplest approach, which is just a direct implementation of the definition of the box-counting dimension.

The following code can be used to estimate the box-counting dimension of the attractor of a two-dimensional map (we use the Hénon map, discussed in *Unit B3*, Subsection 3.1.1, as our example). The program prints out a sequence of values of ε, which differ by a factor of two at each step, and the corresponding values of $N(\varepsilon)$.

```
>  restart:
>  n := 50000:                        # Number of iterates
>  m := 7:                          # Number of epsilon values
>  epsilon0 := 0.5:                 # Ratio of epsilon values
>  a := 1.4:  b := 0.3:             # Parameters of Henon map
```

```
>  H := proc()
>    local x1,y1;
>    global x0,y0,a,b,epsilon;
>    x1 := a-x0^2+b*y0;  y1 := x0;
>    x0 := x1;  y0 := y1;
>    [floor(x1/epsilon),floor(y1/epsilon)]
>  end proc:
>  XYvalues := NULL:
>  # Loop varies epsilon:
>  for j from 1 to m do
>    epsilon := epsilon0^j:
>    x0 := 0.0:  y0 := 0.0:
>    # Iterate map and construct set of squares visited:
>    pts := {seq(H(),i=0..n)}:
>    N := nops(pts):                 # Number of squares visited
>    print('N'=N, 'epsilon'=epsilon):
>    # Data for least-squares fit:
>    XYvalues := XYvalues,[evalf(-log(epsilon)),evalf(log(N))]
>  end do:
>  XYvalues := [XYvalues]:
>  plot(XYvalues,labels=["-log(epsilon)","log(N)"]);
>  # Perform least-squares fit:
>  CurveFitting:-LeastSquares(XYvalues,'x'):       # Returns
                                                   # "m*x+c"
>  Dim := evalf[3](coeff(%,'x')):
>  print('D' = Dim):
```

This program requires a little explanation. (It is not necessary to understand every detail of its operation, but you should be able to adapt it to calculate the fractal dimension of the attractor of another map.) There is a loop (index j) which simply varies the value of ε, and an iteration (index i) which iterates the map, producing a set of points (x_i, y_i) which are visited by the map. Each point is assigned to a square of side length ε by calculating the integer pair $(\mathrm{floor}(x_i/\varepsilon), \mathrm{floor}(y_i/\varepsilon))$, which labels the square in which the point has landed. These integer labels are added to a sequence. The number of squares visited, $N(\varepsilon)$, is evaluated by taking the number of elements in this set. The program prints out pairs of values $(N(\varepsilon), \varepsilon)$. To determine the box-counting dimension D, we plot a graph of $\ln(N(\varepsilon))$ versus $\ln(1/\varepsilon)$: in the limit as $\varepsilon \to 0$, the curve should approach a straight line of slope D. Ideally, we should make a careful analysis of how to extract the best possible estimate of the limiting value of the slope as $\varepsilon \to 0$. In the simple program above, however, we make use of a least-squares fitting facility which is built into the Maple package in order to estimate D.

Exercise 4.9

Run this code and produce an estimate for the box-counting dimension of the Hénon attractor for $a = 1.4$, $b = 0.3$.

4.3 Piecewise-linear systems

We have seen that fractal sets, such as the Hénon attractor, can arise in dynamical systems. In Section 4.4 we shall discuss two examples of dynamical systems where the reasons for the occurrence of a fractal set can be understood precisely. These examples are both members of a class called **piecewise-linear** dynamical systems, which we consider in this section.

Linear equations are usually far easier to analyse than nonlinear ones. For this reason it is useful to introduce some model dynamical systems which are described by maps which are linear, except along some lines where they are discontinuous. Many properties of typical nonlinear chaotic systems can be analysed exactly for the case of piecewise-linear maps, without recourse to computer calculations.

We have already mentioned that maps with chaotic behaviour typically have a 'stretch and fold' action, such as that illustrated in *Unit 3*, Figure 3.6. It is useful to introduce a piecewise-linear map that has similar characteristics. We first introduce an area-preserving map of this type called the *baker's map*, and then give a generalization in which the dynamical system is contracting, called the *skinny baker's map*. The baker's map is an important model because it is the simplest model for chaotic behaviour in Hamiltonian (frictionless) systems. The skinny baker's map is important because it is a model having a fractal attractor which is sufficiently simple that the Lyapunov exponents and fractal dimension of the attractor can be calculated exactly.

4.3.1 The baker's map

The **baker's map** is a map of the unit square to itself. It is defined by the following mapping:

$$(x, y) \longmapsto (x', y') = \begin{cases} (\frac{1}{2}x, 2y) & \text{if } 0 \le y \le \frac{1}{2}, \\ (\frac{1}{2}x + \frac{1}{2}, 2y - 1) & \text{if } \frac{1}{2} < y \le 1. \end{cases} \qquad (4.13)$$

This can be understood as the result of applying two operations in succession. First the unit square is subjected to a linear transformation where it is squeezed by a factor of $\frac{1}{2}$ in the x-direction, then it is stretched by a factor of 2 in the y-direction. This is followed by cutting the stretched image of the square, and stacking the two parts side-by-side; see Figure 4.16.

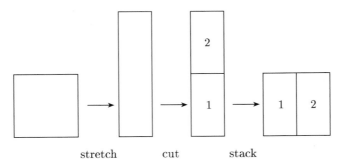

Figure 4.16   Definition of the baker's map

The baker's map interleaves stretched fragments of the square, as illustrated in Figure 4.17.

  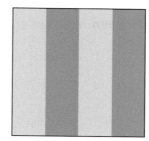

Figure 4.17   Layering action of the baker's map

The name of this mapping arises from its similarity to the process of rolling dough.

The baker's map has chaotic properties. A map is regarded as chaotic if its largest Lyapunov exponent is positive. The following example considers the Lyapunov exponents of the baker's map.

Example 4.1

What is the Jacobian matrix for the baker's map at a point (x, y)? Deduce the values of the two Lyapunov exponents.

Solution

The Jacobian matrix is

$$\mathbf{J} = \begin{pmatrix} \frac{1}{2} & 0 \\ 0 & 2 \end{pmatrix}$$

for any point except upon those lines where the matrix is discontinuous.

This is independent of the point reached by the mapping. The Jacobian matrix for n applications of the mapping is therefore $\mathbf{J}_n = \mathbf{J}^n$. Writing any initial vector as $\mathbf{v} = v_1 \mathbf{e}_1 + v_2 \mathbf{e}_2$, the vector $\mathbf{v}_n = \mathbf{J}_n \mathbf{v}$ has components $v_1'(n) = v_1/2^n$ and $v_2'(n) = v_2 \times 2^n$. The length of the vector increases with every application of the map by a factor which approaches 2 as $n \to \infty$. In the limit, the length of the vector $\mathbf{v}_n$ therefore approaches $2^n v_2$. The first Lyapunov exponent is therefore

$$h_1 = \lim_{n \to \infty} \frac{1}{n} \ln(2^n v_2) = \ln(2).$$

Also, note that $\det(\mathbf{J}) = 1$ at every point (x, y) (except for the lines where the map is discontinuous), so $\det(\mathbf{J}_n) = [\det(\mathbf{J})]^n = 1$. This implies that $h_1 + h_2 = 0$: it is a consequence of the fact that the baker's map is an area-preserving mapping. Thus

$$h_1 = \ln(2), \quad h_2 = -\ln(2). \quad \blacklozenge$$

In Subsection 3.4.3 of *Unit 3* it was observed that the definition of h_1 (Equation (3.35)) works for almost any choice of the unit vector $\mathbf{e}_1$. In this example, however, it is clear that any choice of $\mathbf{e}_1$ alone would be a bad one, and hence it is necessary to use a more general linear combination $v_1 \mathbf{e}_1 + v_2 \mathbf{e}_2$.

In Subsection 4.1.1 we showed how the construction of the middle-third Cantor set is related to the ternary representation of numbers. There are often connections between the dynamics of piecewise-linear maps and the representation of numbers in some suitable base. The following example explores a connection between the dynamics of the baker's map and the binary representation of numbers.

Example 4.2

The pair of numbers representing the initial condition of the baker's map, (x_0, y_0), corresponds to a sequence of numbers a_n and b_n which form their binary representation, such that

$$x_0 = \tfrac{1}{2}a_1 + \tfrac{1}{4}a_2 + \tfrac{1}{8}a_3 + \cdots + \tfrac{1}{2^n}a_n + \cdots,$$
$$y_0 = \tfrac{1}{2}b_1 + \tfrac{1}{4}b_2 + \tfrac{1}{8}b_3 + \cdots + \tfrac{1}{2^n}b_n + \cdots,$$

where the numbers a_n and b_n are all either 0 or 1.

Show that the baker's map effects the following transformation on these binary coefficients:

$$\begin{pmatrix} a_1 & a_2 & a_3 & \ldots & a_n \\ b_1 & b_2 & b_3 & \ldots & b_n \end{pmatrix} \longmapsto \begin{pmatrix} b_1 & a_1 & a_2 & \ldots & a_{n-1} \\ b_2 & b_3 & b_4 & \ldots & b_{n+1} \end{pmatrix}.$$

Note that the a_n are shifted to the right, the b_n to the left, and that one of the b coefficients is transferred to the a set. (It is often the case that you can relate properties of simple piecewise-linear maps to shift operations in the representation of numbers.)

Solution

If $0 \leq y < \tfrac{1}{2}$, then $x' = (0, a_1, a_2, \ldots)$ and $y' = (b_2, b_3, b_4, \ldots)$. In this case $b_1 = 0$, so the expressions for x' and y' fit the specified pattern.

If $\tfrac{1}{2} \leq y < 1$, then $x' = (1, a_1, a_2, \ldots)$ and $y' = (b_2, b_3, b_4, \ldots)$. In this case $b_1 = 1$, so again the expressions for x' and y' fit the specified pattern. ◆

4.3.2   The skinny baker's map

The baker's map as defined above is an area-preserving map. It is also of interest to define an area-contracting map, which can be used to understand properties of systems such as the Hénon map which have stretch and fold dynamics. The **skinny baker's map** is defined by

$$(x, y) \longmapsto (x', y') = \begin{cases} (\tfrac{1}{3}x, 2y) & \text{if } 0 \leq y \leq \tfrac{1}{2}, \\ (\tfrac{1}{3}x + \tfrac{2}{3}, 2y - 1) & \text{if } \tfrac{1}{2} < y \leq 1. \end{cases} \qquad (4.14)$$

This map results from stretching and cutting as for the standard baker's map, but in this case there is a region of the unit square which is inaccessible; see Figure 4.18.

Figure 4.18   Construction of the skinny baker's map

As the skinny baker's map is further iterated, less and less of the unit square is accessible. The map differs from the action of the Hénon map in that it is 'stretching and cutting' rather than 'stretching and folding', but for our purposes it captures the essential features.

Exercise 4.10

What is the Jacobian matrix for the skinny baker's map at a point (x, y)?
Deduce the values of the two Lyapunov exponents.

4.4   Cantor sets and dynamical systems

In *Unit 3*, we saw two examples of apparently fractal sets appearing in the
Hénon map: the strange attractor and the fractal boundary of the basin of
the attractor. In this section the relevance of fractal sets to dynamics will
be demonstrated using two simple piecewise-linear systems. First we
consider a simple one-dimensional example in which the *stable set* of a tent
map is shown to have a fractal structure: this has some similarity to the
fractal basin of attraction. Then we discuss a piecewise-linear map in two
dimensions which has an attractor which is a simple fractal set.

4.4.1   The stable set of a tent map

First we show how a fractal set can arise in the dynamics of a very simple
one-dimensional map. We consider the tent map defined by

$$f(x) = \begin{cases} 3x & \text{if } x \leq \frac{1}{2}, \\ 3(1-x) & \text{if } x > \frac{1}{2}. \end{cases} \tag{4.15}$$

Figure 4.19 shows a graph of the function defining this mapping.

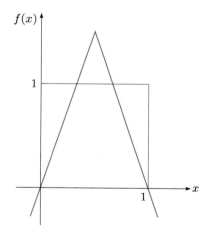

Figure 4.19   Function defining a tent map; note that the middle third of the
interval $[0, 1]$ is mapped out of this interval

Let us consider the set of points that remain inside the interval $[0, 1]$. Note
that any points outside this interval are mapped further away from the
interval with each application of the mapping. Also, points which were in
the interval $(\frac{1}{3}, \frac{2}{3})$ are mapped outside the interval on the first application
of the mapping, and therefore never return. After one application of the
map, only points in the set $\mathcal{S}_1 = [0, \frac{1}{3}] \cup [\frac{2}{3}, 1]$ remain inside the interval
$[0, 1]$. Note that $\mathcal{S}_1$ is the first in the sequence of sets discussed in
Subsection 4.1.1, which have the middle-third Cantor set as their limit.

There is another way of looking at the set of points that remain inside the interval $[0, 1]$ after one iteration of this tent map. Any point $x' = f(x)$ in the interval $[0, 1]$ was reached either from $x = x'/3$ or from $x = 1 - x'/3$. If we know that x' lies in a certain set $\mathcal{S}_n$, we know that its preceding point x lies in a set $\mathcal{S}_{n+1}$ which has two components, both of which are images of $\mathcal{S}_n$ reduced in size by a factor of three, as illustrated in Figure 4.20.

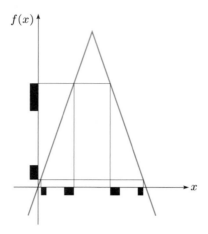

Figure 4.20   If $x' = f(x)$ lies in the set $\mathcal{S}_n$ (here consisting of two intervals shown against the vertical axis), it must have originated in a set $\mathcal{S}_{n+1}$ (shown as four intervals against the horizontal axis). The set $\mathcal{S}_{n+1}$ consists of two images of $\mathcal{S}_n$, which are obtained by a linear transformation of $\mathcal{S}_n$, each reducing its length by a factor of three.

Next consider which points remain inside the interval $\mathcal{S}_0 = [0, 1]$ after two applications of the mapping. We have already seen that after one iteration the set of points which are not mapped outside the interval is $\mathcal{S}_1 = [0, \frac{1}{3}] \cup [\frac{2}{3}, 1]$, the same as the first set in the sequence defining the middle-third Cantor set. We then apply the construction described in the preceding paragraph to obtain the set of points which do not escape from the unit interval after two applications of the map. This construction produces a set $\mathcal{S}_2$ containing two images of $\mathcal{S}_1$, which are reduced in size by a factor of three. This set is also one of the sequence of sets introduced in Subsection 4.1.1, which have the middle-third Cantor set as their limit.

In general, when we apply the construction of Figure 4.20 to any of the sets $\mathcal{S}_n$ in the sequence which generates the middle-third Cantor set, we produce its successor in the sequence. The set of points which have not escaped from the interval after n iterations therefore approaches the middle-third Cantor set as $n \to \infty$. We say that the middle-third Cantor set is the **stable set** of the tent map (4.15).

Exercise 4.11

Consider the piecewise-linear map

$$f(x) = \begin{cases} 3x & \text{if } x < \frac{2}{3}, \\ 3x - 2 & \text{if } x \geq \frac{2}{3}. \end{cases} \tag{4.16}$$

Draw a graph of $f(x)$. From which values of x does the map reach $x' = f(x)$? Show that the stable set of this map is also the middle-third Cantor set.

This example shows that Cantor sets can appear in dynamical systems. It is, however, a little contrived because this non-escaping set has zero length, and in a real-world application you would be very unlikely to have an initial condition which lies in this set. The next example is more complex because it discusses a two-dimensional mapping, but in this case we will see that the attracting set is a fractal set.

4.4.2 The attractor of the skinny baker's map

Here we take a further look at the skinny baker's map, introduced in Subsection 4.3.2.

After n iterations of the map, only those points with values of x that lie within the set S_n in the sequence for constructing the middle-third Cantor set are accessible to the map. The variable y may lie anywhere in the interval $[0, 1]$. The attracting set is therefore the Cartesian product of the middle-third Cantor set and the interval $[0, 1]$.

This Cantor set is analogous to that of the strange attractor of the Hénon map and other nonlinear maps. The strange attractors of nonlinear maps do not have the simple regular structure and precise self-similarity of the attractor of the skinny baker's map because the stretching action of the map is not the same at all positions. This suggests that in order to understand the fractal dimension of the attractor of a general nonlinear map, we may wish to relate the fractal dimension to an average of the stretching behaviour of the map. The Lyapunov exponents give such an average over the trajectory of the map.

Exercise 4.12

Show that the box-counting dimension of the attractor set of the skinny baker's map is $D = 1 + \ln(2)/\ln(3)$.

4.5   The Lyapunov dimension

In *Unit 3*, we saw that the trajectories of some dynamical systems can approach a fragmented set which is called a 'strange attractor'. We have seen in Subsection 4.2.3 that this set is a fractal set, with a box-counting dimension D. The box-counting dimension D is a means of quantifying the self-similar clustering of elements of a fractal set. We have seen examples of calculating D for fractal sets which are generated by simple recursive procedures. In the case of a fractal strange attractor, it is possible to estimate the fractal dimension numerically, using a program such as that in Subsection 4.2.3. It is, however, usually very hard to calculate the fractal dimension from first principles.

The **Kaplan–Yorke dimension** or **Lyapunov dimension** D_L is a quantity which is often a very good approximation to the box-counting dimension D. It was first described by J.L. Kaplan and J.D. Yorke in a paper published in 1979, but it is often called the Lyapunov dimension because it uses the *Lyapunov exponents*, h_1 and h_2, which we introduced in *Unit 3*, Subsection 3.4.3.

An advantage of the Lyapunov dimension is that it is often possible to calculate Lyapunov exponents directly from the definition of the map, without recourse to using a numerical evaluation such as that discussed in *Unit 3*, Subsection 3.4.3. We cannot go into methods for calculating Lyapunov exponents in this course, but we remark that we have seen examples where precise information can be obtained about Lyapunov exponents (see, for example, Exercise 4.10 above or Exercise 3.22 in *Unit 3*).

First we discuss the arguments which motivate the definition of the Lyapunov dimension. These arguments are loosely stated. This is not because they are being oversimplified for this course, but rather because in general there is no precise relation between the Lyapunov dimension and other quantities. Later, however, we show that $D_L = D$ exactly for a strange attractor of a piecewise-linear flow.

In the following we only consider the case of two-dimensional maps (although the Lyapunov dimension can be defined for higher-dimensional systems). We assume that the Lyapunov exponents h_1 and h_2 are known. We first consider the case where $h_1 > 0$ while $h_1 + h_2 < 0$ (other cases are discussed later). Consider how a small square region of side length ε evolves under a map with stretch-and-fold dynamics. We expect that the square will be stretched in one direction into a parallelogram, while its area contracts. Eventually, it is stretched out into a region which is no longer small enough for the linear approximation of the map to remain valid. The image of the square will be so stretched out that it appears as a narrow line, which will fold back upon itself (see Figure 4.21(a)). From the definition of the Lyapunov exponent (discussed in *Unit 3*, Subsection 3.4.3), after many applications of the map we expect that the length of this line is approximately $L = \varepsilon \exp(nh_1)$. We also expect that the area of the image of the original square is approximately $A = \varepsilon^2 \exp[n(h_1 + h_2)]$.

In order to estimate the box-counting dimension, we model the transformed region, illustrated schematically in Figure 4.21(a), by a rectangle of length $L = \varepsilon \exp(nh_1)$ and area $A = \varepsilon^2 \exp[n(h_1 + h_2)]$. This crude approximation is justified by arguing that the folds of the stretched region in Figure 4.21(a) have little effect on how many squares are required to cover it.

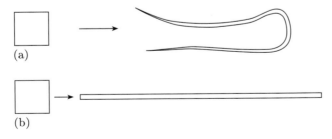

(a)

(b)

Figure 4.21 Schematic illustration of the mapping of a small square: (a) the square is stretched and folded; (b) in a simplified model the image of the square is a rectangle, which can be covered by $N(\varepsilon_n)$ squares of side ε_n

Now consider how the box-counting dimension might be estimated. The rectangular region in Figure 4.21(b) has width $w = A/L$, where A is its area and L is its length, so we estimate

$$w = \frac{\varepsilon^2 \exp[n(h_1 + h_2)]}{\varepsilon \exp(nh_1)} = \varepsilon \exp(nh_2). \qquad (4.17)$$

We may cover this rectangle by squares of side $\varepsilon_n = w$, and the number of squares required is $N(\varepsilon_n) = L/w = \exp[n(h_1 - h_2)]$. This leads to the following estimate for the box-counting dimension:

$$
\begin{aligned}
D_{\mathrm{L}} &= -\lim_{n \to \infty} \frac{\ln[N(\varepsilon_n)]}{\ln(\varepsilon_n)} \\
&\simeq -\lim_{n \to \infty} \frac{\ln[\exp(nh_1 - nh_2)]}{\ln[\varepsilon \exp(nh_2)]} \\
&= \lim_{n \to \infty} \frac{h_2 - h_1}{h_2 + \frac{1}{n} \ln(\varepsilon)} = \frac{h_2 - h_1}{h_2}.
\end{aligned}
\qquad (4.18)
$$

This expression was obtained under the assumption that $h_1 > 0$ (so that the square is stretched under the action of the map) and $h_1 + h_2 < 0$ (so that its area decreases under the action of the map), implying that $h_2 < 0$. It may therefore also be written in the alternative forms

$$D_{\mathrm{L}} = 1 + \frac{h_1}{|h_2|} = 2 + \frac{h_1 + h_2}{|h_2|}. \qquad (4.19)$$

The latter expression is of some interest, as it states that the amount by which the dimension of the attracting set falls short of the dimension of space (that is, $d = 2$) is proportional to the exponent $-(h_1 + h_2)$, which describes the rate at which areas contract under the action of the map.

In the discussion leading to (4.18) it was assumed that $h_1 > 0$ (so that the original square region is stretched) and that $h_1 + h_2 < 0$ (so that areas contract). In order to give a generally applicable expression for the Lyapunov dimension, we must consider other possible combinations of signs.

1. If the largest Lyapunov exponent h_1 is negative, any short line segment contracts to a point under the action of the mapping. The attractor has dimension zero in this case, and we therefore define $D_{\mathrm{L}} = 0$ when $h_1 < 0$.

2. If $h_1 > 0$ but $h_1 + h_2 < 0$, then line segments are stretched, but small areas contract. It is therefore reasonable for the dimension to be greater than one but less than two in this case. This is the case considered above, and D_{L} is given by Equation (4.19).

3. If $h_1 > 0$ and $h_1 + h_2 > 0$, then areas expand under the action of the map: there is no attractor, and the points reached by iteration of the map fill out a two-dimensional region. In this case we therefore set $D_{\mathrm{L}} = 2$.

To summarize: the formula for the Lyapunov dimension of a two-dimensional map is

$$
D_{\mathrm{L}} = \begin{cases}
0 & \text{if } h_1 < 0, \\
1 + \frac{h_1}{|h_2|} & \text{if } h_1 > 0,\ h_1 + h_2 < 0, \\
2 & \text{if } h_1 + h_2 > 0.
\end{cases}
\qquad (4.20)
$$

The Lyapunov dimension D_{L} is often a very good approximation to the box-counting dimension D. (It is actually an even better approximation to another type of fractal dimension, called the information dimension, which we cannot describe in this introductory course.) In some cases D_{L} and D are exactly equal; an example is given below. It is a valuable insight that the fractal properties of the attractor are related to the Lyapunov exponents. In some cases the Lyapunov exponents can be calculated from first principles, so that Equation (4.20) provides an estimate for the box-counting dimension which does not rely upon a numerical calculation.

We conclude by discussing two examples where the Lyapunov dimension is evaluated.

Lyapunov dimension of the skinny baker's map

In Exercise 4.12 we considered the box-counting dimension of the attractor of the skinny baker's map, which is $D = 1 + \ln(2)/\ln(3)$ exactly. Also, in Exercise 4.10 we showed that the Lyapunov exponents for this system are $h_1 = \ln(2)$ and $h_2 = -\ln(3)$ exactly. The Lyapunov dimension is therefore $D_{\mathrm{L}} = 1 + \ln(2)/\ln(3)$, which is exactly equal to the box-counting dimension.

Lyapunov dimension of the Hénon attractor

Now let us examine whether the Lyapunov dimension D_{L} is close to the box-counting dimension D for the strange attractor of the Hénon map. All of the required data were obtained (approximately) from Maple programs, for the parameter values $a = 1.4$, $b = 0.3$. In *Unit 3*, Exercise 3.21, we found $h_1 \simeq 0.36$, $h_2 \simeq -1.27$. Using these values, we obtain the Lyapunov dimension $D_{\mathrm{L}} = 1 + 0.34/1.26 \simeq 1.27$. Earlier in this unit (Exercise 4.9), we determined the box-counting dimension to be $D \simeq 1.22$. These results are in reasonable agreement, but a more sophisticated numerical method gives $D_{\mathrm{L}} = 1.264 \pm 0.002$ and $D = 1.261 \pm 0.003$.

These results are quoted in Russell, D.A., Hanson, J.D. and Ott, E.(1980) 'Dimension of strange attractors', *Physical Review Letters*, **45**, pp. 1175–8.

Learning outcomes

After studying this unit you should be able to:
- define a Cantor set in terms of a limit of a sequence of sets, and relate its properties to the representation of numbers in an appropriate base;
- appreciate the properties defining a fractal set, and be able to distinguish fractal and non-fractal sets;
- understand the definition of the box-counting dimension, and be able to calculate this dimension analytically or numerically (as appropriate) for certain types of set;
- understand the fractal nature of the stable set for certain piecewise-linear maps;
- use the Lyapunov dimension formula as an approximation to the box-counting dimension of the attracting set of a two-dimensional dynamical system.

Solutions to Exercises

Solution 4.1

There are 2^n intervals of length $1/3^n$, so $L_n = (2/3)^n$. The separation of the closest pairs of intervals is $d_n = 1/3^n$. Both L_n and d_n approach zero as $n \to \infty$.

Solution 4.2

Write
$$
\begin{aligned}
X &= (0, 2, 0, 2, \ldots) \\
&= (0, 2) + (0, 0, 0, 2, 0, 2, \ldots) \\
&= (0, 2) + \tfrac{1}{9}(0, 2, 0, 2, \ldots) \\
&= \tfrac{2}{9} + \tfrac{1}{9}X,
\end{aligned}
$$
so $\tfrac{8}{9}X = \tfrac{2}{9}$. Hence $X = \tfrac{1}{4}$.

Noting that $1 = (2, 2, 2, \ldots)$, we have
$$
\tfrac{3}{4} = (2, 2, 2, \ldots) - (0, 2, 0, 2, \ldots) = (2, 0, 2, 0, \ldots).
$$

Solution 4.3

By analogy with the method for constructing the middle-third Cantor set, the elements of the first set would be represented by a number expressed in the base-4 representation, with coefficients $0, 3$ allowed and $1, 2$ forbidden.

Similarly, elements of the second set correspond to a base-5 representation, where none of the coefficients is either 1 or 3.

Solution 4.4

The test for a number being an element of the middle-third Cantor set is simply the condition that none of the ternary coefficients is unity. If the given set passes this test, it will still pass if one coefficient is deleted from the list.

If $X = (a_1, a_2, a_3, \ldots)$, then $3X = 3a_1 + (a_2, a_3, a_4, \ldots)$, and $\mathrm{floor}(3X) = 3a_1$. Hence $3X - \mathrm{floor}(3X) = (a_2, a_3, a_4, \ldots)$. Thus, by means of the observation above, we see that the function $X \longmapsto 3X - \mathrm{floor}(3X)$ maps elements of the middle-third Cantor set to other elements of the same set.

Solution 4.5

The set $\mathcal{S}_n$ is covered by 2^n intervals of length $1/4^n$. Setting $\varepsilon_n = 1/4^n$ and $N(\varepsilon_n) = 2^n$, we find
$$
D = -\lim_{n \to \infty} \frac{\ln(2^n)}{\ln(4^{-n})} = \frac{\ln(2)}{\ln(4)} = \frac{1}{2}.
$$

Solution 4.6

The set is constructed as a limit of a sequence of sets $\mathcal{S}_n$, analogous to those for the middle-third Cantor set. The set $\mathcal{S}_n$ is covered by M^n intervals of length a^n. The fractal dimension is therefore
$$
D = -\frac{\ln(M)}{\ln(a)}.
$$

For the middle-third Cantor set, $M = 2$, $a = \tfrac{1}{3}$. Substituting these values into the above equation for D gives $D = \ln(2)/\ln(3)$, as expected.

Solution 4.7

The nth member of the sequence of approximating sets shown in Figure 4.8 is covered by 4^n squares of length $1/3^n$. Thus $\varepsilon_n = 1/3^n$, $N(\varepsilon_n) = 4^n$, and we find
$$
D = \frac{\ln(4)}{\ln(3)}.
$$

Solution 4.8

Consider the sets shown in Figure 4.7, where we assume that the figure is constructed inside a triangle with side length unity. The limit of this sequence is the Sierpinski gasket. The nth set in this sequence can be covered by 3^n equilateral triangles of side length $1/2^n$. Setting $\varepsilon_n = 2^{-n}$ and $N(\varepsilon_n) = 3^n$, we find
$$
D = -\lim_{n \to \infty} \frac{\ln(3^n)}{\ln(2^{-n})} = \frac{\ln(3)}{\ln(2)}.
$$

Solution 4.9

The program should output the following values for $N(\varepsilon), \varepsilon$:

$$
\begin{aligned}
&29, 0.5 \\
&73, 0.25 \\
&161, 0.125 \\
&384, 0.0625 \\
&898, 0.03125 \\
&2084, 0.015625 \\
&4628, 0.0078125
\end{aligned}
$$

It should also print out an estimate for the box-counting dimension, $D = 1.22$. We can estimate that the dimension is close to 1.22, but the error in this estimate is uncertain. A more sophisticated approach leads to an estimate $D \simeq 1.264$, quoted in the following paper: D.A. Russell, J.D. Hanson and E. Ott (1980) 'Dimension of strange attractors', *Physical Review Letters*, **45**, 1175–8.

Solution 4.10

In this case the Jacobian matrix is
$$
\mathbf{J} = \begin{pmatrix} \frac{1}{3} & 0 \\ 0 & 2 \end{pmatrix}.
$$

Using the same argument as for Example 4.1, we find that $h_1 = \ln(2)$. What differs in the case of the skinny baker's map is that the area of the allowed region decreases by the factor $\frac{2}{3}$ at each iteration of the map. An equivalent statement is that the determinant of the Jacobian is $\det(\mathbf{J}) = \frac{2}{3}$, independent of the position (x_n, y_n). The sum of the first two Lyapunov exponents is therefore $h_1 + h_2 = \ln(\frac{2}{3})$. Thus we find
$$
h_1 = \ln(2), \quad h_2 = -\ln(3).
$$

Solution 4.11

The graph of the mapping function $f(x)$ is shown in Figure 4.22.

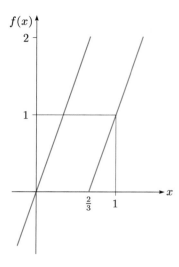

Figure 4.22   Graph of $f(x)$ for the map in Equation 4.16

As for the tent map, Equation (4.15), the set S_{n+1} consists of two linearly scaled images of the set S_n. The only difference between this example and the tent map is that in the former case the image in the interval $[\frac{2}{3}, 1]$ is 'inverted' so that 0 maps to 1, and 1 maps to $\frac{2}{3}$, whereas in this example the image in the interval $[\frac{2}{3}, 1]$ is not inverted so 0 maps to $\frac{2}{3}$, and 1 maps to 1.

The sequence of sets S_n which are generated starting from $S_0 = [0, 1]$ is identical to that for the tent map, so the stable set is also the middle-third Cantor set.

Solution 4.12

As noted in the text, after n iterations of the skinny baker's map, the accessible region is the Cartesian product of the set S_n defined in Subsection 4.1.1, and the interval $[0, 1]$. This set may be covered by squares of length $\varepsilon_n = 3^{-n}$. Each of the 2^n intervals forming S_n corresponds to a rectangular region which is covered by 3^n squares of length 3^{-n}. The total number of squares is therefore $N(\varepsilon_n) = 3^n \times 2^n$. The box-counting dimension is therefore

$$D = -\lim_{n\to\infty} \frac{\ln(6^n)}{\ln(1/3^n)} = \frac{\ln(6)}{\ln(3)} = 1 + \frac{\ln(2)}{\ln(3)}.$$

Index